S0-AZC-303

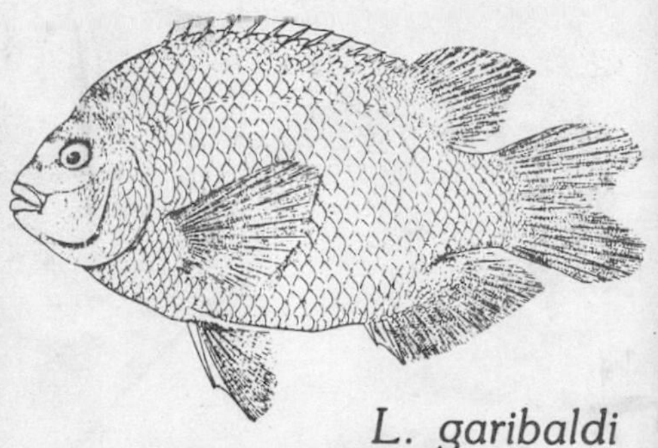
EX LIBRIS
L. garibaldi

The Atlantic Salmon

By the same author

Water, Land and People (*with Bernard Frank*)

Salmon of the Pacific Northwest: Fish versus Dams

THE Atlantic Salmon

A Vanishing Species?

ANTHONY NETBOY

Illustrated with Photographs and Maps

Houghton Mifflin Company

Boston 1968

First Printing R

Library of Congress Catalog Card Number: 68-23214

Printed in the United States of America

To Elizabeth
who shared the problems and pleasures
of writing this book

Contents

Illustrations

Plates

Maps, charts and drawings

Tables

Preface

This book is the result of a project undertaken partly with the financial assistance of the Conservation Foundation of Washington, D.C. It involved a journey to almost all the countries in Europe where the Atlantic salmon has been or is still an important resource, and discussions and correspondence with many persons both in Europe and the United States. The substance of the book is derived from all of these contacts and from numerous works in several languages listed in the Bibliography.

It is impossible to list by name all the persons who assisted in some way. I am especially grateful, however, to the late F. T. K. Pentelow, Ian Wood, W. J. M. Menzies, K. A. Pyefinch, J. S. Barclay, and Major-General R. N. Stewart for their invaluable assistance in supplying information and advice on the complex problems of maintaining the salmon resources of Great Britain. Dr. Arthur E. J. Went, R. L. Williams and C. J. McGrath were immensely helpful in a similar fashion in Ireland.

The assistance and co-operation of many persons in Continental countries made possible much of the research embodied in this volume. I am in great debt to Dr. Arne Lindroth and Dr. Erik Montén in Sweden; Magnus Berg in Norway; M. Roger Bachelier, George Beall and Dr. Richard Vibert in France; and to the International Council for the Exploration of the Sea, and especially to Mrs. Lise Sode-Mogensen of the headquarters staff. Leiv Rosseland sent me vital data on the Norwegian Fishery.

Mr. Andrew W. Anderson, formerly Fishery Attaché (Europe) at the American Embassy in Copenhagen, facilitated contacts in the Scandinavian countries and kept me informed of developments in the Baltic and Greenland fisheries. His successor, Arthur M. Sandburg, was equally helpful.

The chapter on Spain could not have been written without the co-operation of Max R. Borrell of the office of Under-secretary of Tourism, one of the keenest sportsmen I know, and supreme *aficionado* of the salmon. I was aided in seeing the salmon rivers of Spain by Maximiliano Elegido, director of the Servicio Nacional de Pesca Fluvial y Caza. Viktor Olsen made it possible for me to visit the salmon rivers of the Trondheim district in Norway, and Tore Hytten of the American Embassy in Oslo helped greatly by acting as interpreter and later sending me reports.

Thor Gudjonsson, director of the Freshwater Fisheries Service, Reykjavik and Seppo Hurme sent me reports on the rivers of Iceland and Finland respectively. I have been fortunate in enlisting the help of Dr. P. F. Elson and Dr. W. Harry Everhart who never failed to respond to requests for material dealing with the salmon in eastern Canada and Maine respectively.

My wife Elizabeth translated all the Spanish documents and Sven G. Karell the Norwegian, Swedish and Icelandic documents involved in the writing of this book.

My study was greatly facilitated by the courtesies extended by various librarians, especially the Librarian of the Ministry of Agriculture, Fisheries and Food in London, of the Centre Scientifique in Biarritz, Agricultural Librarian of Oregon State University, University of Washington College of Fisheries, and Edmond Gnoza of the Portland State College Library.

I would like to acknowledge with special gratitude the encouragement of Russell E. Train, President, and Samuel H. Ordway, Jr., former President, of the Conservation Foundation. The careful scrutiny and checking of the manuscript by Mr. Morley Kennerley, angler and conservationist, has enhanced both its readability and accuracy.

The book has been read in manuscript by the following persons, but all opinions and interpretations are strictly my own, and all errors of fact which may be found are due to the fallibility of the author:

Introduction–K. A. Pyefinch, Director of the Freshwater Fisheries Laboratory, Pitlochry.

Chapter 1–K. A. Pyefinch.

Chapter 2–Max R. Borrell, office of the Under-Secretary of Tourism, Madrid.

Chapter 3–Roger Bachelier, Bureau of Waters and Forests, Ministry of Agriculture, Paris.

Chapter 4–Dr. Arne Lindroth, Professor of Zoology, Umea University.

Chapter 5–Magnus Berg, Norwegian Fish and Wildlife Service, Trondheim.

Chapter 6–F. T. K. Pentelow, K. A. Pyefinch and Ian Wood, editor of *Trout and Salmon*.

Chapter 7–F. T. K. Pentelow, K. A. Pyefinch, and Ian Wood.

Chapter 8–W. J. M. Menzies, consultant to the North of Scotland Hydro-Electric Board; Hamish Mackinven, of the North of Scotland Hydro-Electric Board; F. T. K. Pentelow, K. A. Pyefinch and Ian Wood.

Chapter 9–Dr. Arthur E. J. Went, Fisheries Division, Department of Lands; and J. R. Williams, Electricity Supply Board, Dublin.

Chapter 10–Dr. W. Harry Everhart, Chief of Fisheries, Department of Inland Fisheries and Game, Maine, and Milton James, former Assistant Director of the U.S. Fish and Wildlife Service.

Chapter 11–Dr. P. F. Elson and Dr. A. G. Huntsman, Fisheries Research Board of Canada.

Chapter 12–K. A. Pyefinch and Dr. K. R. Allen.

Chapter 13–Major-General R. N. Stewart.

The National Geographic Society was kind enough to permit the use of its map of the Top of the World as a base for reference. The quotation on page 45 is reproduced with the permission of Messrs. Collins, publishers, London.

Chapters 2, 3 and 4 appeared in condensed form in *Salmon and Trout Magazine*, part of Chapter 4 in *Trout and Salmon* and Chapter 10 in condensed form in *Natural History*. They are reprinted with their permission.

I owe a considerable debt to Miss Kathleen Ash and Miss Sonja Eckhoff for their work in preparing the manuscript for the printer, and to Mrs. Betty Cox and Mrs. Jessie O'Brien for typing the manuscript.

ANTHONY NETBOY

Portland, Oregon
September 1, 1967

NOTE

No attempt has been made to convert Continental currencies into either British pounds or American dollars.

Where dollar equivalents are given for British pounds the pre-November 18th, 1967 rate of value of £1 equals $2.80 has been used.

Conversion tables equating kilograms with pounds are given on pages 410–11.

Introduction

The Atlantic salmon!

The words conjure up visions of a powerful, silvery fish renowned for its vast oceanic migrations and herculean upriver struggles. We see Magdalenian cave men huddling over a blazing fire roasting impaled salmon . . . Neolithic lake dwellers in Scotland and perhaps Switzerland spearing the gamy fish below their pile-built huts . . . and the encamped soldiers of Julius Caesar in Gaul attempting to catch the leaping giants in the rivers. It was the Romans who named the fish 'Salmo', the leaper.

'Salmo' was destined to become one of the noblest and most honoured (as well as most harried) of fishes known to man. Born in some humble river, it tarried there from one to four or more years; then, having attained the size of a man's finger, vanished utterly, only to return to this very stream one or more years later as a husky adult. It gave sport fit for kings and its savoury pink flesh was like no other.

Perhaps the cave dwellers (and lake dwellers) already knew some of the secrets of the salmon, its birth and departure from the river and punctilious homecoming. If so, the knowledge died with them because they had no written language. But their delight in and appreciation of this fish is commemorated in the pictures they carved on reindeer bone, smooth as ivory. Such objects have been found in the caves of the Pyrénées region of southern France and in north-western Spain at Altamira, where the river still flows which supplied them with salmon.

The Salmonidae family of fishes to which *Salmo salar* (L.) belongs may be traced to a common ancestor in the Pliocene epoch when modern plants and animals developed; the outlines of North America were almost the same as in recent times and in Europe the sea covered small parts of the north-west of the continent and a large area around the present Mediterranean. The Pleistocene (or Great Ice Age) which saw the rise of man is believed to have been specially propitious for the evolution of salmonid species into anadromous fishes–those which spend part of their lives in fresh and part in salt water and breed only in fresh water.

Being cold-water species, the Salmonidae thrived during the Ice Age when an ice cap covered the greater part of the northern hemisphere, blockaded the North American coast as far as Cape Hatteras, blanketed the British Isles, and laid down massive glaciers over Scandinavia and northern Russia, Siberia and Canada. When the glaciers began to retreat and vast quantities of fresh water poured into the northern seas, creating rivers and lakes, the Salmonidae adapted themselves to these new conditions. According to the French ichthyologist Edouard le Danois, 'great rivers which opened into the Arctic Ocean flowed freely, at least in summertime, and there was really little difference in salinity between river and marine waters. So the salmon formed the habit of going from the sea to the rivers to spawn; thereafter to return to the coastal zone to feed.'[1]

At this time 'the Baltic, the North Sea and the Irish Sea were still immense glacial valleys, while salt waters very diluted with fresh waters from the polar regions even washed the shores of southern Europe'. Melting of the glaciers in the Alps, Apennines, Balkan and Atlas mountains lowered the salt content of the surface layers of the Mediterranean. All these changes had an effect on the habits of the salmon (and other anadromous fishes). They left the high latitudes and gradually moved southward, frequenting all the great European rivers, not only those which flowed into the Atlantic Ocean but those like the Ebro, the Rhône and the Po which entered the Mediterranean Sea. In time, however, the glacial waters the salmon had always known departed from parts of Europe in the face of melting snows and encroachment of warm equatorial waters. This happened in the Mediterranean, which ultimately became too warm for the species–none is found there now. Only 'unwary fishes which had ventured into this sea at the end of the great glacial period have left some descendants in the lakes of Italy, Albania and even of Algeria', and these are landlocked. Other landlocked varieties of *Salmo salar* are found in various lakes in Russia, Sweden, Norway, and eastern North America.

In North America *Salmo salar* once probably inhabited rivers as far north as the tundra zone.

After thousands of years of adaptation to changing climatic conditions, *Salmo salar* established itself roughly in an area extending from latitudes 41 to 60 degrees north in North America and 40 to about 70 degrees north in Europe (map, page 24), when the landscape assumed modern features, entering rivers which were not too fully icebound and which flowed into, and gave access to, food-rich seas.

Related to the Atlantic salmon are the Pacific salmon (*Oncorhyncus* species), and sea-going steelhead trout (*Salmo gairdneri*) which seems to be biologically a Pacific version of *Salmo salar*.

When man first entered Europe the salmon were plentiful in hundreds of coastal rivers, often wandering far inland for hundreds of miles. They were found in Iceland, Ireland, Scotland, England and Wales, Portugal, Spain, France, the Low Countries, Germany, Switzerland, Denmark, Poland and all the countries bordering the Baltic Sea, Norway as far north as the rivers flowing into the Arctic, and Russia as far east as the Pechora River. They occurred in Greenland and ran up all the suitable waterways on the North American side of the Atlantic from Ungava Bay to the Housatonic which empties into Long Island Sound, and possibly the Hudson. Landlocked salmon swarmed in the streams draining into Lake Ontario and Lake Champlain. They were abundant in nearly every coastal river in Maine as well as in the Connecticut up to its headwaters near the Canadian border. Several hundred rivers in eastern Canada originally harboured regular runs of salmon. Indeed, before the white man came *Salmo salar* was probably as plentiful in eastern North America as Pacific salmon were in the United States and British Columbia.

Salmon is first mentioned in history by Pliny the Elder in his *Historia Naturalis*, written in the first century A.D. When the Romans colonized Gaul they found that the inhabitants were avid fish-eating people, and the most esteemed species were salmon in the west and mullet in the Midi. Demand arose for Gaulish fish in the markets of Rome.[2] With the collapse of the Roman Empire this trade vanished.

In the Middle Ages salmon fisheries were highly prized because

Top of the World Map showing part of globe originally inhabited by *Salmo salar*, including the oceans and major rivers.

Based on National Geographic Society Map *Top of the World*, with supplementary information.

they were important sources of protein food in areas where meat was scarce and expensive. Moreover, the Church's injunction forbidding the eating of meat on Fridays and during Lent made it necessary to assure a constant fish supply. In times of local famines, as in parts of France, the abundant salmon and eel and other freshwater fishes saved the population from starvation.

Magna Charta, the first charter of British freedom, contains a clause stipulating that rivers must be kept unobstructed by agents of the Crown so that migratory fish, including salmon, would have free passage to their spawning grounds. In fact, from earliest times the French, English and Scottish governments took pains to protect their inland fisheries and keep the rivers open. All the early British fishery legislation was concerned with salmon because it was the most valuable and also the largest food fish found in the rivers. Owing to the protection afforded by governments and the solicitude of proprietors, for rivers in western Europe were privately owned, salmon stocks remained at high levels almost everywhere, subject to the normal fluctuations of animal populations, until about the eighteenth century. In some areas there was not only plenty of fish for local use but salmon became an important export commodity.

With the growth of population, spread of agriculture, and especially the coming of the Industrial Revolution, man increasingly tampered with the salmon's habitat, and the leaping fishes could no longer thrive in many of their immemorial haunts. In the later nineteenth and early twentieth centuries we rarely hear of salmon gluts in Europe; instead the fish became increasingly scarce and expensive. They deserted one river after another.

The plight of *Salmo salar* is dramatized by the roll-call of famous rivers it has abandoned. The last naturally produced salmon was caught on the Thames in 1833 and legend says it was sold to the King for a guinea a pound. To mention but a few, salmon no longer come up the Seine or the Moselle; the Rhine (once probably the most productive river in Europe); the Gudenaa, Denmark's largest waterway; the Douro, Portugal's major river and prime salmon stream; the Miño, Lérez, Nalón and Nansa in Spain; the Elbe and Weser in Germany; the Oder in Poland; and the Kemi and Kokemäki in Finland. Some Swedish Baltic rivers once famous for their natural runs have been totally or partly supplanted with artificially-reared fish. The Vistula's runs have dropped precipitously.

The species has utterly vanished from Portugal, Switzerland,

Denmark, the Low Countries, and is in danger of extinction in France and Spain.

In North America salmon have deserted such major rivers as the Connecticut, Penobscot, Merrimack and Kennebec, not to mention many streams of less renown in the Maritime Provinces of Canada. No nation, in fact, frittered away its Atlantic salmon wealth more wantonly than the United States.

Table 1, which shows salmon landings from 1951 to 1964, presents a picture of the relative abundance of this species in the countries where it still exists in appreciable numbers. Denmark's total reflects the catches of Danish fishermen in the Baltic Sea and elsewhere, while the Greenland landings consist of fish which emanate almost entirely from European and North American rivers.

The River Rhine is a classic example of the ruin of a noble salmon fishery. One branch of the river starts in the Alps of eastern Switzerland, in a bleak mountain of almost 10,000 feet elevation. It flows through wild scenery to join the other branch, gushing out of a glaciated gateway, to form the Alpine Rhine, a substantial river with a rocky and boulder-strewn bed. In Switzerland, amid cerulean skies, the Rhine is a pure Alpine stream, and one may drink from it safely. A few hundred miles downstream it has a different colour and taste, and to drink it unpurified is to court disease and possibly death.

In Germany the river acquires the wastes of hundreds of industrial plants, sewage outflows from towns and villages, and sludge released by the incessant parade of barges. In the Alsace region French potash works pour over 10,000 tons of salts into the Rhine daily. When it crosses the Netherlands the river carries an estimated daily load of 40,000 tons of salts as well as 300 tons of petroleum waste dumped by 8,000 self-propelled freight barges. In some places the bed of the stream is already covered with a thick layer of petroleum sludge that is slowly settling into the ground and may eventually threaten water wells.

As one sails down the Rhine, especially from Mainz to Coblenz, past dreamy medieval villages, Gothic castles standing on islets or perched on beetling cliffs, past steep hillsides covered with vineyards or well-tended green fields, watching the highway on the shore crowded with trucks and motor-cars, while trains shoot past, disappear into tunnels and reappear, it is difficult to believe that salmon once teemed in these busy (and dirty) waters, within the memory of

Table 1
Atlantic salmon landings, 1951–1964
(1,000 kilos)

	1951	*1952*	*1953*	*1954*	*1955*	*19*
Denmark	1,136	1,348	769	986	626	9
England	26	NA	27	30	49	[illegible]
Finland	352*	383*	350*	300*	300*	3
W. Germany	142*	151*	82	117	157	2
Norway	896*	1,028*	1,111*	1,207*	1,269*	1,2
Scotland	1,376*	1,460*	1,244*	1,384*	1,477*	1,0
Sweden	1,133	821	438	511	320	6
Ireland	1,290	840	840	820	570	6
N. Ireland	NA	NA	333	307	293	2
Poland	NA	NA	NA	NA	41*	1
U.S.S.R.	NA	NA	NA	NA	1,582	1,24
Iceland	NA	NA	NA	NA	NA	N
Greenland	NA	NA	NA	NA	NA	N
Canada	NA	NA	2,060	1,670	1,210	1,2

* Includes sea-trout which may constitute 10–20 per cent of the total.
NA – Not available.

very old men. The huge fish came up from their sojourn in the distant sea, perhaps from as far as Greenland, and ploughed their way across Holland, Germany and France, to spawn in the headwaters above Basle. Many of those that survived the spawning ordeal negotiated the long journey back to sea and eventually, six to eighteen months later, returned to the river.

Up and down the Rhine men had fished for salmon for centuries, and their catches were in such great demand that Rhine salmon was a famous delicacy in Paris and Berlin and other places where gourmets met. At the bend of the river where the cliff stands sheer on which the Lorelei sat and by her beauty and song lured sailors to their destruction, there is a deep pool from which fishermen from St.

57	*1958*	*1959*	*1960*	*1961*	*1962*	*1963*	*1964*
11	912	955	1,084	1,691	1,544	1,156	1,745
31	35	45	94	47	63	47	61
00*	300*	293*	300*	300	265	368	465
52	201	250	226	361	223*	185*	298*
98*	1,239*	1,233*	1,422*	1,411*	1,671*	1,786*	1,600
00*	1,383*	1,304	1,179	1,063	1,800	1,365	1,913
67	322	393	480	602	365	387	647
20	750	740	620	610	1,299	1,284	1,333
A	411*	346*	303	247	486	498	593
85*	201*	239*	320*	52	293*	335*	357*
70	1,250	879	1,198	996	569	200	880
A	NA	NA	200	200	100	200	200
A	NA	14	60	120	300	463	1,384
00	1,600	1,700	1,600	1,500	1,700	1,800	1,887

e: *Bulletin Statistique des Pêches Maritimes*, International Council for the Explora-
f the Sea, and *Food and Agriculture Yearbook of Fishery Statistics* (Canada only), *Ire-*
Department of Agriculture and Fisheries.

Goar and Goarhausen used to take as many as 6,000 salmon yearly. In the North Sea estuary of the river Dutch set nets and seines made glorious hauls. . . . All that is now but a memory.

Even before the rapid growth of industry along the banks of the Rhine and some of its tributaries had befouled the once crystalline waters, hydro-electric projects made migration of fish to the headwaters in Switzerland quite difficult. By 1930 there was a series of dams on the main stem, 10 to 40 feet high, tapping the flow of the river for the generation of electricity. Several power projects on the upper tributaries further impeded fish migration: Bezner dam (18 feet high), Aarau (20 feet), Olten (27 feet), and Wather (66 feet), all on the Aar River, and Baden dam on the Limmat. As a result of these barriers built with poor or no fishways, the Upper Rhine became inaccessible while the polluted Middle and Lower Rhine, the busiest inland waterway in Europe, could no longer sustain salmon runs.

In the 1880s the Dutch section of the Rhine alone yielded millions of pounds of salmon yearly. 'The great draft nets at Kralingen dwarf anything seen in England and Wales', said A. D. Barrington, Chief Inspector of Salmon Fisheries for England and Wales, in his report for the year 1886. In 1885 the nets in this area caught 69,500 salmon, averaging 17·1 pounds, for a total of almost 1,200,000 pounds; those at Amerstol took 6,500 and at Gorinchen 6,000 fish, a grand total of 82,000.

In 1886 a convention was signed by the German Empire, the Kingdom of the Netherlands and the Swiss Confederation for protection of the salmon and other migratory fishes in the Rhine. It barred stationary nets that extended over halfway across the stream at low water, set close seasons in Dutch territory from August 16 to October 15 and above Dutch territory from August 27 to October 26; and forbade fishing for 24 hours beginning at 6 p.m. Saturday in the main river and tributaries below Basle. Further, netting and rod fishing were prohibited in the zones where the salmon were known to spawn, between the Rheinfall and Mannheim, from October 15 to December 31. The contracting parties also promised to make the greatest possible use of fish culture to augment the salmon stocks.[3] But this convention was of no avail. Catches held up fairly well through the nineteenth century, slumped around World War I, and petered out by the 1940s. Thus died one of the world's greatest salmon rivers.

When I was in France in 1963 I heard some talk of the possibility of planting salmon ova in 'Vibert boxes' on the French side of the river in Alsace, where promising nursery grounds exist. But it is difficult to believe that, even if the ova are successfully incubated, salmon can ever again thrive in what has been called the longest and worst sewer in Europe.

There is a little museum on the German side of the river at the Rheinfall opposite Schaffhausen, much frequented by tourists, where one may see photographs of salmon fishing in the good old days. At Stein-am-Rhein, a Renaissance Swiss village preserved in amber, there are 'Salmon Steubli' with their brass salmon signs swinging in the doorways, just as they did centuries ago. But not often is fresh salmon served there nowadays since it has to be imported from Norway or Scotland, or perhaps the Pacific coast of North America.

NOTES

1 Edouard le Danois, *Fishes of the World*, p. 32.

2 A. Thomazi, *Histoire de la Pêche*, pp. 224–5.

3 *Reports of the Inspector of Salmon Fisheries for England and Wales for 1886*, p. 32.

1

Life History and Migrations

What do we know about the salmon and how did we acquire this knowledge?

The English names of its various forms, 'parr' (juvenile), 'smolt' (transitional stage) and 'kelt' (spawned-out fish), which are Anglo-Saxon, suggest that the Germanic inhabitants of the British Isles made close observations of the fish. No important biological knowledge of the species, however, has come down to us from the medieval period. Meanwhile fairy tales were spun about the mysterious fish that spends the beginning and end of its life in the river and the most exciting part between in measureless seas largely unknown to man.

The theory of the salmon's return to the home river was published as far back as 1558 by Konrad Gesner in his *Historiae Animalium*. The Norwegian Peder Claussøn Friis (1545–1614) described the life of the salmon in the rivers and the sea almost as it is known today. Izaak Walton in *The Compleat Angler* (1653) says little that is authentic about the salmon but he refers to Gesner and mentions making experiments with English kelts.[1]

Scientific investigations of the salmon's life cycle date from the early nineteenth century, but the first epochal discovery–that every fish normally carries a record of its life (age, sex, stay in fresh and salt water, spawning mark) on its scales, as a tree does its rings–was reported by H. W. Johnstone in 1904. Other investigators had previously described scale reading on the eel, carp and cod, a technique which resolved many biological problems and dissipated numerous fallacies. Systematic tagging experiments on salmon began in Scotland around 1825 and were continued intermittently for the next forty years by river owners like the Duke of Atholl on the Tay, others on the Tweed. The earliest experiments on a rigidly scientific basis are credited to P. H. Malloch of Perth who started his salmon tagging in 1906. Subsequent studies in many countries firmly established the fact that salmon almost invariably return to their home rivers.

The high value attached to the salmon runs in all but a few countries where they are found has resulted in an ever-expanding programme of scientific investigations. No other freshwater species is receiving as much attention and consideration.

To compensate for the drain on stocks made by the inroads of civilization and to replant depleted rivers, the art of artificial breeding has been cultivated in many lands. It was an obscure German officer, Lieutenant Jacobi, who conceived the idea that salmonids might be artificially propagated and who first obtained positive results from attempts to fecundate fish eggs. In 1763 Jacobi published an article in a Hanoverian scientific journal in which he announced the successful production of salmon and trout fry in a hatchery at Naterlem. He had sent a memorandum of his work in 1758 to the French naturalist Buffon, who had it translated in 1783.[2] It was not till the 1840s, however, that practical experiments with this technique were undertaken in France and about the same time in Great Britain.

In the later nineteenth century it was widely believed that salmon populations could be maintained almost solely by the output of hatcheries. As the saying went, 'Where Nature fails, man steps in.' This assumption failed to materialize, mainly because there was little knowledge of the biology, diseases, diet, feeding and rearing habits of young salmon, either in Europe or North America. Successes were offset by numerous failures. As an example, the first salmon hatchery in England was built at Troutdale in Cumberland in 1868 and abandoned in 1883 because of a faulty water supply. Slowly, by trial and error, the knowledge needed for successful hatchery production was accumulated and it has now become an important arm of salmon production both in Europe (where the Swedes have advanced the art the furthest) and in North America.

In sum, when we add up what we know about the salmon in general and *Salmo salar* in particular we find, as Dr. J. W. Jones says, that 'the body of knowledge is considerable; but [we] must emphasize not only our ignorance of some aspects of his life, but also the provisional and speculative nature of our conclusions about other aspects.'[3] However, as Wilfred M. Carter of the Quebec Wildlife Service says, 'In many countries a race is on to unravel the mysteries still surrounding the salmon while there is yet time to prevent its disappearance from our waters.'[4]

River life

Every salmon that finds its way to the sea starts life as a pink blob, not much larger than buckshot, buried in the deep gravel of a cold stream. The eggs remain in this protected nest for 80 to 90 days in Britain, much longer in Arctic climates like northern Norway's–up to 180 days. Upon hatching the wriggling fish, called alevins, are about half an inch long and attached to a large yolk sac protruding from their bellies. They remain in the gravel until the yolk sac is almost absorbed, then they emerge into the water above.

You can see the shoals of fry (as they are now called) darting to and fro on the surface of the gravel in any salmon stream in spring. There is an abundance of aquatic life, caddis larvae living in protective cases, nymphs clinging to rocks. The parr take very little surface food but subsist mainly on winged insects in the nymph stage and occasionally terrestrial organisms like froghoppers, beetles and spiders. Salmon fry have also been found in parr stomachs.

The fish grow very slowly. As they develop they acquire brownish backs with black spots extending down the sides, with a few red spots in the vicinity of the lateral line; their bellies are light grey, creamy or silvery, depending on their habitat. Nine to thirteen dark bars, called parr marks, are clearly visible on each side. Now the fish are scarcely larger than a man's finger and, except for deeply-forked tails, closely resemble the trout with whom they mingle (and compete for food) in the rivers. Their enemies are numerous and deadly. Trout and eels gorge themselves on baby salmon; pike, perch, chub, roach and other fish prey on them. For instance, two Swedish investigators studied the fate, during their first twenty-four hours, of 30,000 salmon fry planted in the River Mörrum. Before planting, some of the predators, particularly perch, had been trapped and their total population estimated. As was expected, perch took the salmon in shoals. Again the predators were trapped and their stomachs examined. It was calculated that if all the perch had been eating like the captured ones, about 11 per cent of all the salmon fry planted would have been consumed in twenty-four hours–and the perch were spawning at the time, probably not feeding with their usual capacity.[5] Roach, ruff and pike also devoured salmon fry in the Mörrum.

Various water birds relish salmon. In the Canadian Gulf Islands of the Strait of Georgia I have seen squadrons of cormorants dive from their tree roosts and make delicious meals off the hordes of small grilse. Herons occasionally may be observed at the mouths of rivers standing motionless on their long legs waiting to snatch tiny salmon; gulls feed on these migrating young fish.

Depredations of the American merganser (*Mergus merganser*), called goosander in England, are notorious. The large white, black-headed males with peach-coloured breasts and orange bills and feet, accompanied by their less colourful mates and trim broods of ducklings, are fascinating to watch as they follow the winding course of a half-frozen creek or river, or gather on a lake or reservoir. However, they live to a large extent off juvenile salmon when available. The Canadian biologist H. C. White in 1957 reported that of some 1,200 mergansers shot in a duck-control experiment on the Miramichi River, 86 per cent had been feasting on salmon at a rate amounting to 1,900,000 parr annually! On the Indal River in Sweden Dr. Arne Lindroth found that at least half the food of mergansers consisted of salmon and trout parr, and in the year 1954 they may have consumed a substantial portion of the entire brood stock of this river.[6]

Another potent enemy of the salmon is the belted kingfisher (*Megaceryle alcyon*), usually found hovering above rivers or brooks. He flies with peculiar uneven wing beats, rattling as he goes. Somewhat larger than an American robin or European blackbird, he is particularly addicted to large parr, especially when water flow is low during the summer. He is well known and justifiably detested by hatchery men and river-keepers.

Controlled experiments in planting hatchery-reared Atlantic salmon on a ten-mile stretch of the Pollett River in New Brunswick revealed the tremendous damage inflicted by the merganser and kingfisher. By methodically destroying these birds–shooting the ducks and trapping and drowning the kingfishers–the average output of sea-going smolts was boosted no less than fivefold and perhaps more. With the possible exception of eels, no other species in the river benefited as much as the salmon.[7]

The length of the parr's life in the river varies with latitude. In the southern part of the salmon's range the premigratory stage is generally short. One or two years are sufficient for the young salmon to attain the smolt stage in the British Isles and two or three years in Canada, but two or three and even four years are common in northern countries (Table 2). The longer duration of parr life is attributed to slower growth due to poorer feeding conditions, coupled with the fact that the fish have to attain a certain physio-

Table 2

Age of salmon smolts at migration – various countries

Country	*River*	*Age (in years) by per cent of total*					
		1	2	3	4	5	6
Denmark	*Skerna*	11	84[a]				
	Gudenaa	26	60[b]	2			
Sweden	*Mörrum*	8	80	12			
	Ume		30	66	4		
	Lule		17	70	12	1	
	Viskan, Atran and Lagan		82·5	17·5			
Norway	*Mandal*		23	73	4		
	Orkla		30	64	6		
	Namsen		22	70	8		
	Tana		8	73	19		
Iceland	*Ellidaá*	1	16	80	3		
Greenland	*Kapisigdlit*				43	53	4
Canada	*Margaree*	1	57	39	3		
England	*Wye*	3	92	5			
Scotland	*Tweed*	6	91	3			
Ireland	*Shannon*	12	83	5			

[a] 1–2 years old–1 per cent. [b] 1–2 years old–12 per cent.

logical condition, in which size seems to be a factor, before they are ready to face the hazards of the sea.[8]

Now, parr marks and spots disappear as the salmon reaches the smolt stage, as if erased by a magic wand; tails lengthen and become more deeply forked. The fish acquire a silvery colour, caused by deposition in the skin of a substance called guanine. Already in March a thin guanine coat may be discerned on their bodies; in April they are fully dressed in sea livery. Internally, too, considerable changes are occurring, especially in the respiratory system and blood-stream, to enable them to live in sea water.

'The first spate in May takes the smolts away', says an old English rhyme. One morning we see them swimming in the clear water and a few days later, after a heavy rain, they are gone![9] Legions have been marshalled, as if by a leader's direction, and the descent to the sea has begun. They are usually only three or four inches long and weigh but two or three ounces.

Moving rapidly, the fish feed ravenously, as if eager to accumulate all the energy they can store up for the long, perilous journey ahead. They may be seen rising throughout the river, and in their frenzy to feed will snatch at almost any bait.

Natural obstacles are taken in stride, such as low weirs, millraces and foaming waterfalls. If the shoals of fish meet obstructions like hydro-electric dams they may hesitate and take thought, as it were. They use the fish passes provided for them, or go through the turbines or plunge over the spillway in their rush to the sea. An undetermined number may be lost, but the legions swim on. At some relatively high dams, as on the River Shannon in Ireland, a mighty battery of electric lights shepherds them around the edifice.

There may be other obstacles, not as easy to surmount as even a high dam: a moving wall of undissolved sewage, or foul, floating masses of refuse from a pulp mill, dairy plant, chemical plant, and the like. Smolts will swim past barges and boats and sometimes under log rafts in northern European rivers. They traverse towns and cities.

At last they encounter the fresh breezes of the sea which is their home, and are pulled forward by the welcoming tide. But even now there is no safety; the dangers, in fact, are greater than ever. As the smolts enter the estuary flocks of gulls and cormorants wheel overhead.

Mortality is heavy during the descent to the sea, perhaps in some proportion to the length of the river. The migration is not a continuous journey, but is usually accomplished in slow stages, past waterfalls, cascades, over spillways of dams or through the turbines of dynamos, free for the most part from predators in freshwater but subjected to polluted zones, and in the estuaries to birds of prey waiting to pounce on them.

Ocean life

When they reach the ocean anadromous fish are on the threshold of adolescence. Their physiological mechanisms, evolved from the remote Pliocene when they found their original marine environment overwhelmed in part by the flow of melting glaciers, enable them to adjust efficiently to salt water. We know little about this crucial transitional phase although various studies suggest that the salmon develops rather abruptly the ability to live in sea water. However, 'abruptness is a matter of degree and it seems certain that, owing to tidal stirring, there will always be a boundary layer of intermediate concentration in which smolts could remain until they get used to it. In larger rivers, where volume of fresh water is great, it is conceivable that the smolts can easily spend as long as ten hours in brackish water or dilute sea water, and thus have plenty of time to become acclimatized to the change of medium.'[10] And in this way they avoid the risk of being immobilized and falling easy prey to birds and other predatory animals. Nevertheless, mortality is high in the initial year at sea.

Now the salmon vanish from sight until they return to the home river as sleek, silvery adults, nimble and swift, capable of leaping or climbing over cataracts and waterfalls, or high dams, the prince of game fishes, and usually the largest fish in inland waters.

We know relatively little about their wanderings in the ocean, which may cover vast areas, and often half the Atlantic Ocean. Sir Alister Hardy says that they probably spend 'the greater part of the time either in mid-water or up towards the surface, feeding upon the . . . shrimp-like crustaceans which occur in immense swarms and make vertical migrations up towards the surface at night and down into deeper water by day'. They also take sand lance, herrings and other small fish but the red colouring of their flesh 'is thought to be derived from carotenoid and allied pigments found in the crustaceans of their diet'.[11] Perhaps they retain their shoaling habit in the sea.

The salmon spend varying periods of time in the sea, feeding ravenously. Many of them return after one winter as grilse, usually in summer, weighing anywhere from 1½ to 9 pounds, and even more, but the majority, in most countries, return after two or three winters and are considerably larger and heavier, their weight depending on the length of time spent on the feeding grounds. In some Scottish rivers, for instance, over 90 per cent of the returning adults may be one- or two-winter sea-fish; grilse form a large portion of the runs in some years in Ireland. In northern Norway, by contrast, Magnus Berg found that of 660 adults captured in Tanafjord only 2 per cent were grilse, 48 per cent had spent two winters in the ocean, 32 per cent three winters, almost 18 per cent four winters, and less than 1 per cent five winters.

No generalizations are possible about the size of adult salmon, although some countries like Norway and Scotland seem to breed heavier fish than others. Salmon weighing up to 70 pounds and more have been taken in these lands and the world's record, so far as I can ascertain, is a 103-pounder landed in the River Devon in Scotland.

Where do the salmon go when they leave the river? Where do they spend their feeding years?

Biologists have traced their movements by tagging hundreds of thousands of smolts, kelts and other adults on both sides of the Atlantic. Metal or plastic tags are inserted in their bellies or attached by wire near the dorsal fin. These fish are then sent on their way and finders are offered a modest reward for returning the tags to the organization listed with information about the place and method of capture. Recaptures have been voluminous along the coasts of Europe and Canada, and in the waters around Greenland, including the high seas.

W. J. M. Menzies, one of the leading students of salmon migration, says that two kinds of movements may be plotted as a result of tagging experiments in various countries. The great majority of the fish when recaptured are near the end of their journeys, about fifty miles or less from the parent river to which they invariably return. The rest may go a much longer way, sometimes many hundreds of miles. For instance, a few fish tagged at Titran in northern Norway wandered around the North Cape and wound up in the White Sea, a journey of 1,600 miles, where they were netted by fishermen; others tagged at Brevik, about one hundred miles south of the North Cape, were captured in Arctic waters in Finland and the White Sea. One of these hardy navigators landed in the Pechora River, 1,200 miles from Brevik. Norwegian salmon have been caught in Scottish waters.

The general movement of fish tagged on the north-west coast of Scotland seems to be through the Sea of the Hebrides and the Minch to the west coast of England. Some of them were recaptured in the River Tweed while others travelled in the opposite direction and were found in Yorkshire waters. Some fish leaving the rivers of the west coast of Ireland make circumisland migrations, and one is known to have swum all the way to south-west Sweden, a journey of about 700 miles completed at an average speed of 25 miles per day.[12]

A few smolts released in the Gave d'Oloron in southern France were recovered in the ocean a considerable distance off the coast of Brittany, perhaps heading towards Greenland where we now know salmon from both Europe and North America join in feeding migrations. Although only a few inches long and weighing but a few ounces when released, these French fish had travelled 15 to 18 miles per day.

A large amount of tagging has been conducted in the Baltic rivers. Smolts released in northern Sweden and northern Finland are known to travel in a southerly direction to reach waters rich in crustaceans and small savoury fish; some of them in six months tally 800 miles and grow to a size of 12 to 18 inches and weigh 1 to 1½ pounds.

The Canadian biologist A. A. Blair tagged 450 grilse and large salmon on the east coast of Newfoundland. A few went as far as northern Labrador. The record was made by a grilse that sped along at an average speed of 32·5 miles per day over a distance of 792 miles. J. R. Brett, who has made elaborate studies of what he calls the 'swimming energetics of fish', says the salmon has the stamina of a race-horse.

This statement is borne out by the fact that millions of salmon swim all the way to west Greenland waters from rivers in Canada and Maine, Scotland, Ireland, England and the east and west coasts of Sweden. Some of the 217 tagged salmon[13] so far recovered in the Greenland fishery had journeyed almost 2,000 miles from their natal rivers, and one, a smolt, went in 18 months from the Wear in Durham to Upernavik on the north-west coast of Greenland, a distance of about 2,500 miles.

Greenland waters and the high seas between Labrador and Greenland are now known to be feeding grounds for hordes of European and Canadian Atlantic salmon.

On the whole, homeward-bound fish do not seem to move in clearly defined patterns. Sometimes they follow a circular route, or drift with the tidal current, but always with a conscious sense of direction. Thus many a specimen caught in a net staked to a tide-lashed coast and released, returned to that vicinity and became enmeshed in the same gear.

There is evidence that salmon utilize one-direction staging areas, perhaps established as far back as the Pliocene epoch. Here shoals assemble, like armies on the march, and disperse towards various rivers. Port-aux-Basques in the Gulf of St. Lawrence is one of these identifiable rendezvous and Brevik in northern Norway is another. 'Brevik', says Menzies, 'is at least a junction for the salmon of apparently all the rivers of the north coast of Europe as far eastward as the River Pechora.'[14]

It is noteworthy that so far no salmon tagged in Norway or Iceland have been found in the Greenland fishery, indicating that these races have different feeding grounds from the French, Spanish, Irish, British and Swedish fish, who inhabit the Atlantic Ocean.

Fish intercepted on their homeward trek have usually had their last supper, so to speak. They will not eat again until they have spawned and returned to the sea. In the river they live off the fat accumulated in the ocean.

In the ocean, as in fresh water, the salmon is not always in motion. 'The great depths of the sea form a special and unique environment', as Marston Bates says, and 'it is always dark and always cold, regardless of geography'. The layers of the ocean teem with uncountable numbers of animals, specially the kind which salmon like to eat.

In the ocean the gluttonous fish grows in length and girth until its body becomes saturated with food. It may be the dawning mating instinct, or the siren call of fresh waters far away pouring into the restless seas, that lures it homeward. Whatever the cause, it sets out, alone or with cohorts, upon the most dangerous adventure of its extraordinary life . . . the return to the river it had left as a juvenile.

River life again

How does the fish, after an absence of so many years, find its particular river or creek where it was born, or had been deposited (if hatchery-reared) as a smolt? Does it have a supersensitive direction finder which enables it to 'feel' its way home? Does it navigate night and day by a system of celestial mechanics unfathomable to man but just as accurate as his vaunted radar? Scientists have long pondered these mysteries but cannot agree on the answers. Some biologists believe that the fish depends upon the currents, the varying salinities and chemical ingredients of the water, the physiographical features, or a combination of all of these. 'Is it the taste of the water', as Marston Bates says, 'that guides the salmon to its home river, that tells it which branch to choose until finally it ends in the mountain stream where it spawned years before?'[15]

Perhaps the olfactory sense is the prime determinant, as Frank Buckland said. 'When the salmon is coming in from the sea, he smells about till he scents the water in his own river. This guides him in the right direction, and he has only to follow up the scent . . . to get into fresh water, that is if he is in a travelling humour. Thus a salmon coming up from the sea into the Bristol Channel would get the smell of water meeting him. "I am a Wye salmon", he would say to himself. "This is not the Wye water; it's the wrong tap, it's the Usk. I must go a few miles further on", and he gets up steam again!'[16]

The early fish in the river are in prime condition, and are most eagerly sought by fishermen. Their bodies, sometimes a yard or more long, are solid with fat and muscle, well-proportioned, blue-black and silvery, and their flesh is pink and firm. Set nets, bag nets, traps or other fixed or floating gear await them as they swim cautiously towards the river. Seals and porpoises trail them. This is the end of the journey for a large proportion of every run.

In the river the arrival of schools of salmon may be so stealthy as at first to go unnoticed. One may vigilantly reconnoitre the mouth of a stream and hardly be aware that they have come home.[17]

In many British rivers, shortly after the spring runs of full-grown salmon come in, schools of the smaller grilse appear, slender, graceful fish that make long, spectacular leaps out of the water. These are followed by further runs of full-grown salmon. The runs usually peak in July and taper off during the hot August days, but resume in

September and October, when the late-comers leave the sea with relatively little time to spare if they are to mate that year. Atlantic salmon spawn usually from November through January.

Having run the gauntlet of the estuarine nets, the fish may have to elude nets in the tidal reaches of the river, and sometimes farther upstream. Anglers cast barbed hooks with artificial flies that stir their attention. They must negotiate weirs, where many are taken; crawl and leap over waterfalls; pull themselves up fish passes at dams or be lifted by hydraulic devices to the safety of reservoirs.

To follow salmon upriver is a fascinating spectacle. Their ascent is a staccato series of stops and starts, periods of movement broken by interludes of rest. They surmount one formidable obstacle only to be confronted by another, including their chief predator, man. They have to swim against the current, and if they slacken their efforts the water will carry them down, back whence they started. They must push forward or find a quiet pool where they can lie behind rocks, or seek safety at the edge of deepening water. They move mostly at night or early morning when the light is dim and the water murky.

I watched a salmon approach a waterfall not provided with a fish pass on the River Sella in Spain. It was trying to climb over the cascade so that it might continue the journey towards the head-waters where spawning would occur. Diving into the deeper eddies, turning its head against the falling water, it brought all its muscles into play as it edged up the smooth rock down which an abundance of water was falling. Twisting itself into the shape of a bow, then straightening itself out, it managed to climb partly up the face of the rock, then stretched itself on the level surface and with a short run leaped, like a flash of lightning, over the last portion of the cascade. I saw it disappear upstream in the murky water, seeking a hollow place or shelter where it would rest and then set out again.[18]

Commonly no obstacle daunts the fish. They may linger for days or even weeks around a waterfall, and when an opportune time arrives with an increase in water flow, opening up a broader path, they begin the climb from rock to rock, doggedly hanging on until they reach the top. In like manner they push themselves up fish ladders at dams, swimming steadily until they pass the counting board and reach the calm waters of the reservoir. On the short coastal rivers of Spain, Brittany or Normandy, the ascent may be relatively easy and swift. But on great European rivers like the Loire or Shannon a journey of hundreds of miles may be required. This may take many months, or longer. Salmon are bold, determined and patient travellers, keeping their way without faltering, always making for the head of the stream, the higher reaches.

In their inexorable travels what signposts do they 'read'? In Trøndelag, Norway, I saw a brook flowing into the Stjørdal River that was scarcely wider than the span of a tall man's legs and only 18 inches deep, yet every autumn a small number of salmon dash in to spawn. How do they find these obscure places?

According to Louis Roule and other biologists, it is the dissolved oxygen content that attracts them. When they come to the meeting place of two streams they may find two different kinds of water; different in the amount of dissolved oxygen. Invariably they go where the waters are most richly aerated. This theory, however, is challenged by the Canadian biologists, A. D. Hasler and W. J. Wisby, who believe that odour is the crucial factor in guiding salmon to their home stream.

During its upstream migration the fish's sexual organs develop steadily; the male becomes heavy with milt and the female with roe.[19] As summer melts into autumn the salmon approach their grand climacteric. The male acquires the characteristic hook jaw of the spawner. Both male and female have lost their silvery-blue sheen. The female is now light brown to bronze in colour, sometimes greenish as though corroded by the sea, while males have livid skins, pink-silver or even reddish. Fish may arrive at the spawning grounds in a bruised and battered condition, bodies lacerated and skin discoloured by fungus. They have lost the lice acquired in the ocean, are much thinner than when they began their upstream migration, and their stomachs are empty and shrunken. Some specimens have net marks on their bodies, wounds from bites of porpoises or seals, or scars in their jaws from the barbs of hooks. In October or November one may see a parade of fish moving upstream, pressing forward against the current, their dorsal fins sticking out of the water, literally pushing themselves over the shallows.

By November all but a few of the voyagers have reached their destinations. Most of the lower pools in the river, the beats precious to anglers, are empty. The tides rise and fall in the estuaries but hardly any salmon are visible. Fishermen's nets have been put away and anglers have laid aside their rods. River-keepers, fish wardens and fishermen may now be found in English or Scottish country inns, or in French or Spanish bistros, reminiscing about the past season over a pipe of tobacco and glass of beer or cognac, lamenting the big ones that got away and congratulating themselves on the bigger ones they landed. Meanwhile, up in the headwaters, deep in the forests, the salmon are going through the complex rituals of courtship and mating.

This strange performance, which puzzled many writers from Izaak Walton to our own day, has been accurately described and cinematically recorded by Dr. J. W. Jones of Liverpool University. The general pattern may be summarized as follows:

The males and females spend a considerable time resting in the pools at either end of the spawning bed though the dominant male will quite frequently interrupt his rest, prod a female with his snout, push against her, or bully any other male. Dominance may be an indication of imminent readiness for spawning. . . . The next stage is the movement of a female out of the pool and over the gravel. After a series of such exploratory wanderings, the female starts cutting a bed; and as bed-cutting continues, the dominant male quivers with increasing frequency and intensity alongside her. Periodically this female, called for convenience the *tenant*, rests from her activities and either drops back into the pool, or remains stationary in the depression which has resulted from her cutting. The males may fight intermittently, and other females may appear to challenge the tenant female for possession of the bed, although they rarely if ever displace her. . . . As the cutting continues, the tenant tests the results of her activities with her ventral fins, particularly the anal; and when she has made a saucer-like depression about six inches deep, her efforts appear to be directed principally to perfecting the shape of the bed. The end-result is a hole at the bottom of which the current is much reduced: at the bottom of the hole there are two or three large stones between which she can thrust her anal fin as she presses her body into the shape of the bed. When, after hours or even days of fidgety cutting and feeding, the bed is suitable she assumes the 'crouch' position, opens her mouth, and is joined by the male. He also opens his mouth and quivers violently; and the eggs and sperm are extruded simultaneously. Immediately . . . the male moves away, generally into the pool below, while the female moves a foot or so upstream from the bed, and by vigorous cutting sends down gravel to fill the depression and cover the eggs. In most spawnings nearly all the eggs are ejected into the crack between the stones at the bottom of the bed, where they are difficult to see and reasonably well sheltered from the shower of gravel which the female afterwards sends down. The 'covering-up' sequence is usually continued at the beginning of the next spawning sequence.[20]

One female may go through eight sequences, each a bit farther upstream, before she has dropped all her eggs. In some instances Lilliputian male parr, sexually mature, participate in the spawning act alongside towering adult males and females. Each male usually mates with more than one female.

Epilogue

After spawning, all Pacific salmon die, their cycle complete, the curtain drawn on their hectic lives. *Salmo salar* may meet a different and happier fate. Exhausted, both male and female drop downstream, usually tail first. The swift current may stir them to sudden, short-lived bursts of activity. They may even rise to an angler's fly. Mostly, however, they lie for a time in quiet places, thin, discoloured, empty of feeling, patiently awaiting the rain which will take them down to the sea.

Far more females than males, proportionately, survive the spawning ordeal. Most kelts fall prey to disease: their carcasses can be seen floating in rivers in winter or early spring.

A certain number of mended kelts from every year's run reach the ocean and eventually find their way back to the feeding grounds (wherever they may be), and return to the river as 'clean fish' to spawn again. J. A. Hutton, who examined the scales of about 11,500 Wye salmon between 1908 and 1920, found that 7·7 per cent had spawned twice, and of these only one in ten was a male. The survival rate varies with each river, partly due perhaps to stream conditions. In short and slow rivers spawning may not be as exhausting as in long and rapid rivers. The time of entering the stream may also be an important factor. In northern Norway, says Magnus Berg, many of the male salmon spawn twice. On the River Eo in Asturias, according to the Marques de Marzales, only 1·5 per cent of returning fish had spawned previously, while in Ireland Dr. A. E. J. Went found that the proportion of previous spawners ranged from less than 1 per cent in the River Liffey to 9·5 per cent in the Erne one year and less than 1 per cent in the River Boyne to 15·4 per cent in the Erne the next year. In the Add, a small, west-coast Scottish river, Menzies discovered that 34 per cent of the incoming run one year had already spawned at least once. This was probably a record.

Very few kelts recover from their second spawning and live to try again. In the Wye, 8·4 per cent of all incoming fish sampled by Hutton had returned to the river twice, 0·7 per cent three times, and 0·02 per cent four times. Went reported that on the Irish rivers he studied, 3 per cent came for a third spawning and less than 0·1 per cent for a fourth. The known record is held by a salmon from the River Add which spawned five times and died at eight years of age! However, the longevity record is held by a kelt caught in Loch Maree, Scotland, which was thirteen years old when it spawned the fourth time.[21]

The fishes which have run through the cycle and lived to produce another generation are but a very tiny fraction of the multitudes that set out from the river as smolts. It is believed that under the most favourable conditions less than 1 per cent eventually return to the river, and for every two adults that mate two offspring find their way back safely to the spawning grounds, other things (including man's predation) being equal. Mortality is high in the first year of ocean life (where disease is inconsequential)–up to 90 per cent in the Baltic Sea, according to the Swedish biologist Borje Carlin.

Of the hordes of fishes that return to the river, a large proportion are taken by netters and anglers, and so have fulfilled their destiny of providing man with food and sport. Some individuals fail to find their natal waters, cannot negotiate fish ladders, are blocked by impassable dams, or suffocate from deoxygenated waters, and thus die without spawning. The survival and maintenance of the species, in short, depends on man—on his providing them with clean and passable waters and nursery grounds conducive to perpetuation of the race.

NOTES

1 Izaak Walton and C. Cotton, *The Compleat Angler*, p. 132.
2 L. de Boisset and R. Vibert, *La Pêche Fluviale en France*.
3 J. W. Jones, *The Salmon*, p. 1.
4 Wilfred M. Carter, 'The Reproduction of Salmon in Scandinavia and the British Isles', *Atlantic Salmon Journal*, June 1964.
5 Jones, *op. cit.*, p. 22.
6 Arne Lindroth, 'Mergansers as Salmon and Trout Predators in the River

Indalsälven', p. 132. Similar results were found by Derek Mills in analysing the stomachs of 157 mergansers shot on Scottish lochs and reservoirs. The goosander and red-breasted merganser are predators in Scottish waters.

7 P. F. Elson, 'Predator-Prey Relationships between Fish-eating Birds and Atlantic Salmon', p. 67.

8 G. Power, 'The Evolution of the Freshwater Races of the Atlantic Salmon (*Salmo salar* L.) in Eastern North America', pp. 87–88.

9 The rise in temperature with the coming of spring and the low light intensity may have as much influence on smolt migration as rain or the rise in the water level, according to H. C. White.

10 Jones, *op. cit.*, p. 40. See especially A. G. Huntsman and W. S. Hoar, 'Resistance of Atlantic Salmon to Sea Water', *Journal of the Fisheries Research Board of Canada*, (4) 1939.

11 Alister Hardy, *The Open Sea*, Vol. II, p. 87.

12 See W. J. M. Menzies, *The Stock of Salmon*, pp. 43–66.

13 One hundred and forty-six of the fish had been marked in Canada, 2 in the United States, 6 in Ireland, 28 in Scotland, 33 in England and Wales, and 2 in Sweden.

14 W. J. M. Menzies, *op. cit.*, p. 66.

15 Marston Bates, *The Forest and the Sea*, p. 147.

16 Quoted by J. W. Jones, *op. cit.*, p. 75. Recent investigations make us incline towards this theory.

17 See Roderick Haig-Brown, *Atlantic Monthly*, January 1964.

18 For a scientific account of the leaping ability of salmon, see T. A. Stuart, 'The Leaping Behaviour of Salmon and Trout at Falls and Obstructions'.

19 It is believed that the number of eggs is related to size of fish. According to S. A. Pope, O. H. Mills and W. M. Shearer, 'The Fecundity of Atlantic Salmon', a 27-inch specimen lays 5,000 to 6,000 eggs.

20 J. W. Jones, *op. cit.*, pp. 100–1.

21 *Ibid.*, pp. 131–4.

1a. An old Roman bridge over a good salmon pool on the River Deva-Cares, Spain. Roman soldiers probably fished at this spot nineteen hundred years ago.

1b. An excellent salmon beat in the upper reaches of the River Deva-Cares, one of the few remaining salmon rivers in Spain.

2

Melancholy Fate of the Spanish Salmon

Spain, which faces the Mediterranean and the Atlantic Ocean, is a land of enormous climatic and scenic contrasts but basically it may be divided into two parts. The northern and western portion is marked by a north-west European climate with ample rainfall, well distributed throughout the year, supporting deciduous forests and humid types of agriculture. The rest of the country generally luxuriates in sunshine (a relatively scarce commodity in northern Europe), is sparsely forested, and is noted for its sheep and goats, olive and orange groves and vineyards. This is the dusty land of Don Quixote. It is not salmon country, although during the great Ice Age this fish inhabited some of the rivers, like the Ebro, flowing into the Mediterranean.

North-west Spain, green and lush, with a rugged coast framed by the Picos de Europa mountains towering up to 9,000 feet above sea level, is the home of the salmon. Here the rivers are swift and cold, laced with many waterfalls and rocky ledges, and strewn with gravelly beds ideal for spawning. The waters flow murmuringly through the mountains and down the green valleys, often passing forests of chestnut, oak and poplar, and pour into the sea in the *rias* of Galicia and the estuaries of the Cantabrian coast.

2a. Sixty-metre-high Palombera hydro-electric dam on the River Nansa, completed in 1950. In spite of the fish pass, the Nansa salmon have been practically exterminated; thus Spain lost one of her best salmon rivers.

2b. Long salmon pass under construction at the Palombera dam on the River Nansa, Spain, built to comply with the law, but completely useless.

This part of Spain sheltered some of the original members of the human race. It is still a tranquil and rather remote kind of area except for hectic cities like La Coruña, El Ferrol, Santander, Oviedo and Bilbao; possessed of a pastoral quality, with villages not much changed since the Romans ruled the land and built cobblestone roads and arched stone bridges, some of which still stand, as on the Cares and Sella Rivers.

From the wooded areas which skirt the Atlantic coast one passes to the foothills where the ground is intensively cultivated. Small apple orchards are predominant, cattle graze, little dairy farms abound, and rye, wheat and corn grow easily. The chief mode of transportation is the donkey which the peasants ride sideways, as in Greece. The softness of the landscape, the clouds which continually play hide-and-seek with the faces of the mountains, and the well-watered valleys give north-west Spain—the home of the salmon—a unique and attractive trade mark.

Salmon rivers

At least fifty Spanish rivers from the French to the Portuguese borders once harboured salmon. In the province of Galicia they are mostly 20 to 40 miles long, with a few like the Ulla and Tambre running to 70 miles. In Asturias they range from 15 miles (the Barcia) to 85 miles for the Nalón, while in Santander and Guipuzcoa provinces they are usually shorter. However, productivity is not necessarily related to size and some of the lesser rivers like the Sella, Umia and Pas were as well-stocked with silvery fish under pristine ecological conditions as the much larger watercourses. The greatest of salmon rivers, and once one of the richest in Europe, was the Douro which in its 500-mile course drains a large part of Spain and Portugal as it drops from its source in Pico de Urbion in the Iberic Mountains, across Old Castile and Leon, to the sea at Oporto. Next in size is the Miño, a 200-mile Galician river which rises in the Sierra de Meira and flows through the provinces of Lugo, Orense and Pontevedra to reach the sea at the Portuguese frontier. Both of these rivers no longer contain any salmon.

When the earliest human inhabitants perhaps 15,000 years ago entered the Cantabrian coast they found an inexhaustible food supply in the rivers. Fish were caught by the cave-dwellers with crude spears and by paleolithic man with flinty weapons. The prehistoric Iberians and Celts, the Phoenicians and Greeks who followed them, barely exploited the ichthyological riches but the Romans used the rivers more fully. They probably shipped Spanish salmon to the great central food market at Rome where this exotic fish was regarded as a delicacy fit for Lucullan feasts.

Salmon thrived in the pastoral and agricultural ages, not only in Spain but everywhere in Europe, because the rivers were uncontaminated and unblockaded, and their passage to the spawning grounds was assured. The balance between animal and human populations was maintained until man's numbers increased and his destructive hands were felt not only on the land but in the waterways.

Figure 1 shows Spain's remaining salmon rivers.

The salmon runs

Salmon enter the Spanish rivers between February and June. Those entering early tend to be larger than the later arrivals. The adults weigh between 7 and 25 pounds, with the heaviest ascending the rivers in the winter months. Spawning occurs between November and January and the eggs hatch in two to three and a half months, depending on the temperature of the water.

Most of the smolts (called *esquin*) migrate to the sea after 12 to 18 months of freshwater life and remain there from one and a half to four years. The Marques de Marzales, who made important contributions to our knowledge of the Spanish salmon, found that 60 per cent of the spawning fish on the River Eo had spent two years in the ocean and all but a few of the remainder three years. This age composition is believed to be typical of Galician streams. Only 2 per cent of the upstream migrants examined by Marzales had spawned previously but this low figure, he said, was 'not surprising since many net and rod fishermen capture kelts (called *zancados*) on their descent to the sea'.[1]

There is little information about the oceanic movements of the Spanish salmon, since almost no scientific research has been done on the species in recent decades; certainly no tagging experiments that I am aware of.

From riches to poverty

'Our rivers in past centuries produced fantastic quantities of salmon', says the authoritative Enrique Camino. Fishing rights were the patrimony of ancient abbeys and noble houses and the good fishing places were intensively exploited from at least the eleventh century onward. One of the chief fishing methods was to build a stockade consisting of two lines of stakes planted crosswise along the entire width of the river with nets at the centre. At these places, called *postas* or *apostales*, catches were often munificent. There are records of disputes over the right to fish at some of the *postas* in the fifteenth and sixteenth centuries. Remains of such ancient weirs were still to be seen in the River Pas in our own century.

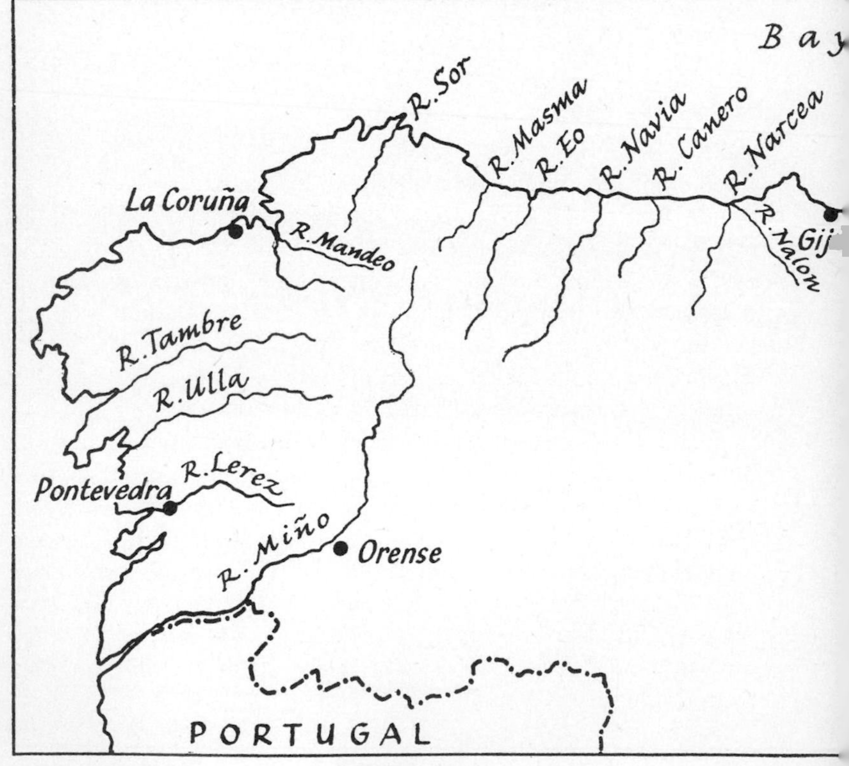

Figure 1
Spain's remaining salmon rivers.

Protection of the inland fisheries was a royal tradition from at least the time of King Alfonso el Sabio, who in 1258 promulgated an edict prohibiting trout fishing from All Saints' Day (November 1) to March 1. An ordinance of Juan II of 1435 was specifically directed against poachers. Anyone caught throwing quicklime, henbane, daphne, mullein or any other poisonous substance into the streams to kill or deaden fish was subject to a fine of 2,000 maravades, an enormous sum in those days. Philip II in the next century reaffirmed and amplified the law of 1435 with regulations pertaining to closed seasons, fishing apparatus and fishing practices prejudicial to the fishery. It was forbidden to fish with 'cloths of straw, or linen, or sheets, or with hand baskets'; 'to dry up sources of rivers and leave them dry'; nor could anyone fish when 'little salmon are

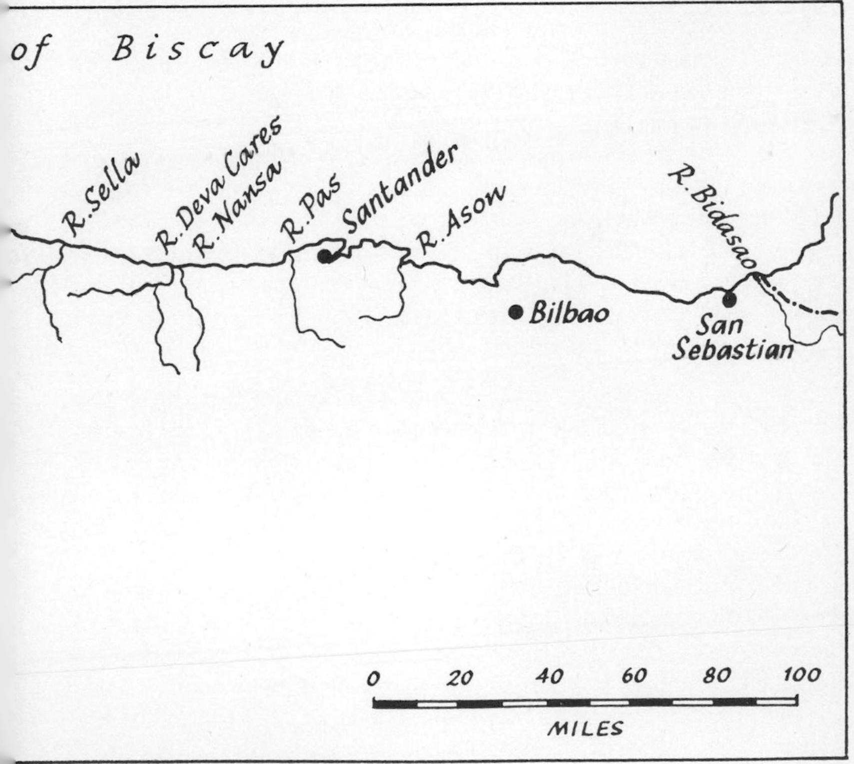

running or when fish are spawning'. Each province could issue local regulations regarding the kind of nets that could be used 'according to the quality of fish in each river so that fish [would] not be wasted'. These statutes did not apply to the royal dominions, but covered the holdings of the grandees and ecclesiastical establishments.[2]

Various modifications were made in the regulations in succeeding centuries. Carlos IV in 1795 among other things redefined the right to fish in inland waters, thereby bolstering seigneurial privileges and also taking steps to specifically protect anadromous fish. His edict is worth quoting:

First. 'The right of fishing in rivers is . . . as free and general as that of navigation, and by the same token, exclusive authority to fish in any determined place can be derived only with the royal privilege or from possession which assumes it.'

Second. 'Whatever the origin of this exclusive right, it never assumes authority to obstruct free navigation of the rivers nor the right to fish away from the place determined by the same privilege.'

Third. It is clear that the right to fish does not 'give one the authority to place across the rivers any stockades that, by shutting off passage to boats and the ascent of salmon and other fishes, usurps the free right of navigation and fishing [which belongs] to the riparian [owners] upstream'.

Fourth. It is ordered 'to dismantle all stockades which cross a river completely or any of its tributaries, as contrary to the nature of the fishing privileges and incompatible with free navigation and general fishing rights for the entire length of the river'.[3]

Not only were there ample harvests of salmon but the stocks thrived because of the protection afforded by legislation, the respect for property and law, and especially appreciation of the inland fisheries in an era when fish provided a large portion of the protein needs of the Spanish people. According to Sañez Requart in his *Historical Dictionary of the National Fishing Arts*, published from 1791 to 1795, 2,000 salmon were caught daily in the province of Asturias alone. 'Considering the quantity and quality of the rest of the rivers in the north of Spain,' says Camino, 'it is not venturing too much to suppose that . . . no less than [a total of] 8,000 to 10,000 fish per day were caught [in all of Spain] at the end of the eighteenth century.'[4] On the basis of Requart's calculation, the total annual catch during a three-month season, such as now prevails, might have been as much as 700,000 to 900,000 fish, weighing perhaps 7,000,000 pounds.

We know that income from salmon fisheries was often quite considerable. The municipality of Pravia, for example, obtained more than 100,000 reales annually in 1780 and 1790 from the fishing rights it owned. (By the middle of the nineteenth century the return had fallen to only 8,000 reales.) And, as in other countries, we hear legends–never verified–of servants and field workers on the manors of Asturias and Santander begging their masters not to be served salmon more than twice or thrice weekly.[5] Such a situation would suggest that salmon was an inexpensive food.

Amid the political and economic upheavals of the nineteenth and early twentieth centuries, the riches of many Spanish rivers disappeared. Mills were built which diverted the flows by impoundments, ignoring Carlos IV's injunctions that channels must be kept open to allow fish to pass at all times. Large and small hydroelectric dams cropped up on northern and western rivers where the bulk of Spain's water power is found: usually they had no fish ladders or inefficient ones. Many excellent salmon streams were thus sacrificed to dams, some of which provided but trifling amounts of electricity. In some instances these impassable obstructions were permitted to remain even after the power plant, factory or mill had been abandoned. There was a basic belief that the nation needed kilowatts more than salmon. A few people, like the late Marques de Marzales, protested against this policy, but in vain.

Compounding this evil was lax enforcement of regulations which encouraged illegal and excessive fishing. Many rivers were looted. Peasants living eternally on the edge of poverty found the salmon an irresistible attraction. One nightly raid on a river with trident or net was quite profitable. If the salmon refused to be roused from their resting places, an old sock filled with chloride and skilfully tied to the end of a stick was dipped into the water, and the fleeing fish were quickly killed.

Motorized transportation facilitated illegal fishing. In the early hours of the morning a truck would arrive at the riverside, a rowboat and hoop net were shoved into the water, and the team of poachers quickly scooped up many fish. Haunts of the salmon were ascertained in advance by a member of the gang posing as a rod fisherman with a licence in his pocket. The River Pas, for instance, is ideally situated for poachers. Its banks are shaded and it flows through deep ravines so that sentinels can be posted on the heights. There are caves where notes can be hidden for accomplices. Thus it was not uncommon for poachers to take sixty salmon out of a single pool in one night and sell them the next day in Bilbao.[6]

The *paisano*'s love of the river did not always stop him from snatching an illegal fish or two. In Spain, it is said, a man will abandon his work, his cattle, and even his woman for an opportunity to catch a salmon. Should he return at the end of the day empty-handed, he may get a cold reception from his family.

I stood on a little Roman bridge over the River Cares one cloudy spring afternoon. Mist had erased the ridges of the mountain. The salmon pool with its clear waters, reached by a long foot-trail, was dimpled with mayflies and other insects. High above me an eagle soared. Birds chirped in the trees. Several anglers in hip boots were fishing from the banks, and one was wading in the middle of the stream which gurgled happily as it flowed past us. In this very place, perhaps, Roman legionnaires fished for salmon on a warm spring afternoon twenty centuries ago, dreaming of their distant homes. Fish were abundant then. Now they were scarce. Not a single salmon was caught that afternoon on this beat. All but one of the anglers went home discouraged. He retired with his gillie to the *refugio* provided by the Government and planned to resume fishing after a siesta. 'If I don't catch one today, there's always tomorrow', he said philosophically.

There was a contrasting scene on the River Sella the following day. A local fisherman was slowly playing his line with a big, wriggling salmon at the end of it. As word spread that he had a strike, half the nearby village rushed to the river. Deftly the angler brought in the fish, gaffed him, and laid him on the grass. The spectators applauded. A few shook his hands and shouted 'Ole!' It was a lucky day for the *paisano*. At about $2.50 per pound, the salmon would fetch almost a month's wages at the going rate for unskilled labour in Spain.

Overfishing, dam-building, excessive abstraction of water for irrigation and other uses, and poaching are regarded as the major causes of the decay of the salmon runs in Spain, but divided governmental jurisdiction was also a factor. Maritime fishing was controlled by the Ministry of Marine and river fishing by the Ministry of Development (Fomento). The Ministry of Marine permitted netting throughout the week, opened the salmon season on February 15 (which some experts like Marzales regarded as a month too early) and permitted nets to be placed 100 yards apart where twice that distance would have better served the interests of conservation. However, 'the major weakness of our fisheries legislation', said Marzales, writing in the 1920s, 'consists in the leniency of its enforcement. There are not so many technical defects [in the laws] as there is weakness in their application, and this increases their inefficiency even more.'

Fish wardens were not only scarce: they were lazy and ineffectual. Sanctions were not applied with the necessary rigour because jurisdiction over offenders was in the hands of the municipal judges. As a result, many abuses went unpunished. 'When the judge does not appreciate the importance of his decisions, the legal precepts are not fulfilled, [and] transgressions are not castigated, it matters little whether legislation is good or bad, complete or defective, advanced or archaic', said Marzales. What Spain needed was a radical reform of the statutes pertaining to freshwater fishing, and in fact a commission was actually struggling with this task in the 1920s but its work came to naught.

An interesting sidelight on the plight of Spain's salmon stocks was the status of the two international rivers, the Miño and Bidasoa. The 1893 Treaty of Commerce and Navigation with Portugal provided for joint control of the Miño, but the fishery regulations that were issued proved to be calamitous. In 1912 the Spanish Government renounced the treaty and thereafter no regulations were in effect. Salmon eventually disappeared from this river. On the Bidasoa, fishing was controlled by a convention between Spain and France dating from 1886. Regulations were considered technically acceptable but they did not prevent the rapid deterioration of the runs, because of excessive fishing and dam-building. Today only a few hundred salmon are taken annually in the Bidasoa.

By the 1930s the impoverishment of many salmon rivers was readily apparent. Typical were the major Galician streams. On the Eo some fifty persons fished commercially in the vicinity of the village of Abres, five miles from the estuary of Ribadeo; their nets worked day and night, including weekends. Even smolts were taken. Upstream migrants that managed to escape the barrage of nets were greeted by three dams at the end of tidewater. The first obstruction was manageable; the second, about seven feet high at Lauredal pool, had no fish pass but was negotiable in flood; the third, a hydroelectric dam about ten feet high, was equipped with a defective ladder. Despite these difficulties, some 2,000 salmon were still caught annually in the Eo in the late 1920s. It was capable, however, according to Marzales, of providing a harvest of 50,000 fish a year.

The Sella, an Asturian river, was plagued by a plethora of nets in the non-tidal zone, fishing for parr and smolts was permitted, and several small dams with ineffective ladders made upstream fish passage difficult. About 3,000 salmon were taken in 1927–one-tenth of its real capacity.

The Narcea, a fisherman's delight, with 70 well-known salmon pools, was rendered partly uninhabitable for salmon by washings from a coal mine. Here too an incredible amount of illegal fishing was permitted; the nets operated not only throughout the week but in the closed season, assisted by stockades resembling the *postas* of earlier centuries. As a consequence, the Narcea yielded barely a thousand salmon yearly when its potential was 50,000!

On other waterways the picture was equally gloomy. The Nalón, renowned for centuries among fishermen, was almost emptied of salmon by 1930 owing to pollution. The Deva-Cares still yielded some 2,000 fish annually, but this was a small fraction of its former production.

While Asturian rivers had suffered enormous losses, the outlook was not much brighter on rivers of Galicia, Santander and Guipuzcoa provinces. In 1931 an estimated 10,000 salmon were caught in Galicia, 5,800 in Asturias, 4,000 in Santander, and merely 200 in the Basque rivers, a grand total of 20,000 fish. Compared with the eighteenth century this was a pitiful harvest. As Civil War erupted in 1936, and all protection was withdrawn from the rivers, respect for fishing laws disappeared and restocking ceased, the decline of the salmon runs was accelerated.

A sportsman's paradise?

By 1940, when the Civil War had ended, only a dozen tolerably good salmon streams remained in Spain. Clearly, drastic action was needed if the resource was not to become extinct. Accordingly, General Francisco Franco, himself an ardent angler, inspired the promulgation of the law of February 20, 1942, which was designed to prevent further deterioration of the inland fisheries. Its most important provision was the banning of nets in all salmon rivers, including their estuaries. By this move Spain handed over the resource entirely to the sport fishermen. Subsequently the Government took control of many of the better salmon beats and set up a system of management. The Rivers Eo, Narcea and Sella were designated as national fishing preserves managed by the State Tourist Bureau.

A National Service of River Fishing and Hunting was created in the Ministry of Agriculture in 1945 to supervise freshwater fishing. A modest programme was launched to rehabilitate a few of the more promising rivers, mainly by restocking with young salmon (bred in trout hatcheries), laddering some dams and waterfalls, and dynamiting some useless dams and other obstructions. No systematic research, however, a necessary concomitant of any restoration programme, was undertaken. Poaching and illegal fishing were ruthlessly stamped out. If a person is apprehended in the act of illegal fishing he may go to prison for as much as ten years. With the enlarged corps of wardens and the ubiquitous Guardia Civil (National Constabulary) in evidence, it is better to take any measure to escape than to be caught red-handed.[7]

Many country people, accustomed to obtaining salmon furtively, actually welcomed the new dispensation which allows them to fish from sunrise to sunset by purchasing a professional's licence for a modest fee. In fact, most of the rod and reel fishermen became professionals, and in 1966, according to Max Borrell, at least 80 per cent of the 7,233 fish caught were killed by professionals.

The rivers were divided into restricted zones called *cotos* and free areas. In the latter anybody who possesses a licence may fish during the season, while on the *cotos* one must have a special permit specifying the date or dates when he can fish. Every salmon killed must be registered with a warden and receive a tag, blue if captured in the *cotos*, red in the free zone. Only red-tagged salmon may be sold, and the penalty for selling a blue-tagged fish is enormous.

For the convenience of anglers the Government has built stone chalets (*refugios*) furnished with chairs, dishes, tables, fireplaces, washrooms and lounges. Cement sidewalks along the banks, suspension bridges, and improved access roads and trails provide amenities of a high order.

What has happened to the salmon runs under the new deal?

On the whole, it seems that outlawry of the nets, restocking and restoring the rivers and rigidly controlling fishing have improved the runs moderately, but did not bring them back to the level of the

Table 3
Salmon catches in Spain, 1949–1966
(*numbers of fish*)

Rivers	*1949*	*1950*	*1951*	*1952*	*1953*	*1954*	*1955*	*195*
**Sella*	715	822	900	915	1,052	2,871	1,068	1,2
Deva-Cares	701	813	1,025	1,198	1,285	1,776	1,437	1,9
Ason	200	320	558	621	798	1,321	702	1,0
**Narcea*	666	750	782	800	810	788	622	1,1
Navia	200	288	300	321	360	576	725	1,1
**Eo*	187	220	221	242	258	544	465	4
Ulla	51	60	78	100	128	443	339	3
Pas	10	15	22	29	32	69	39	1
Bidasoa	29	30	35	38	40	224	45	1
Nansa	48	60	78	90	95	146	80	
Others	101	35	35	44	54	54	372	2
Total	2,908	3,413	4,034	4,398	4,912	8,812	5,894	7,8

* National fishing preserves.

1920s. Catches rose from the very low records of the 1930s, reached a peak of about 9,000 in 1954 and 1959, slipped again sharply, and in the last few years made a modest come-back (Table 3).

The roll-call of defunct Spanish salmon rivers reminds us of the fate of New England streams in America. Few or none of the fish come up the Miño, Eume, Sor, Oro, Landro, Jallas, Mandeo, Masma, Allones, Mero, El Puerto, Tambre, Ulla and Verdugo Rivers in the province of Galicia; the Barcia, Canedo and Nalón in Asturias; the Nansa, Saja and Miera in Santander. Galicia, once so rich in salmon, may be written off entirely except for the River Eo, where the runs are quite meagre. Only one salmon river is left in Guipuzcoa, the Basque province: namely, the Bidasoa, which in 1966 yielded but 324 fish. Asturian streams have held up much better. The famous rivers of Santander, like those of Galicia, harbour few salmon except for the Ason.

957	*1958*	*1959*	*1960*	*1961*	*1962*	*1963*	*1964*	*1965*	*1966*
978	992	2,781	1,381	984	1,151	1,705	1,036	1,505	1,162
002	982	1,696	1,220	732	781	866	1,782	1,592	1,063
801	732	1,541	917	552	559	474	768	1,105	1,343
630	353	1,298	785	389	592	555	529	826	1,197
811	755	701	374	280	175	276	234	774	764
191	191	312	390	56	185	361	293	366	348
281	152	96	99	115	140	268	265	295	97
127	82	136	109	79	135	111	84	165	305
75	65	94	180	96	87	61	205	152	324
51	20	129	51	44	68	30	23	48	36
270	194	256	153	96	197	275	333	396	594
217	4,518	9,040	5,659	3,423	4,070	4,982	5,552	7,224	7,233

Source: Ministerio de Informacion y Turismo (Subsecretaria de Turismo).

In fact, there are now only about five rivers of any consequence in all of Spain: the Sella, Deva-Cares, Navia, Narcea and Ason. They accounted for 76 per cent of the total salmon catch in 1966. And even their future is by no means secure. For example, a large hydro-electric dam is to be built on the River Sella, and doubtless other streams will be pre-empted by power dams, paper mills, and the like as Spain's economy expands.

Moreover, the runs are in grave danger of overfishing, according to Max Borrell, Sports Technical Adviser to the Under-Secretary of Tourism. 'Rod and reel fishermen', he says, 'fish from dawn to dusk, every day of the season, with all kinds of baits and lures, such as flies, spoons, devons, prawns, worms and what have you. These market fishermen send most of their catch to Madrid's fish market where it is auctioned at prices ranging from 400 to 500 pesetas ($6.50 to $7.30) per kilogram at the beginning of the season (March) and a minimum of $4.00 per kilogram after Holy Week and until mid-July, end of the official season.'

Twenty years ago the sale of national fishing licences hardly reached 10,000. In 1965 over 190,000 were issued and more than 150,000 were sold in 1966, said Borrell. 'On a good fishing day, in the River Sella, one is likely to see from 300 to 500 professionals fishing with "everything". Once upon a time nets almost exterminated the salmon; now, unless drastic steps are taken, the runs will be very much depleted by a multitude of hooks. Professionals are only allowed to fish in the best pools for 30 minutes if others are waiting to do so, but I have seen over a dozen waiting their turn. Even children queue up, not to fish, but to sell their turn to a professional.'

Borrell believes that 'it would be wise to forbid all methods of fishing but the fly, shorten the season, and limit the number of fishing days for market fishermen. If this is not done (and I doubt that it will) *Salmo salar* in Spain will go the way of the carrier pigeon in America.

'There seems also to be no way to prevent the electrocution of the fish. Kilowatts take precedence over salmon. We have failed to evolve any plan that would safeguard the fishery as our rivers are being developed. We have lost the battle of fish versus dams and coal.'[8]

NOTES

1 Marzales' study is reprinted in *El Salmon y Su Pesca en España*, p. 42.

2 Marzales, *op. cit.*

3 *Ibid.*

4 Camino, *El Salmon y Su Pesca en España.*

5 Luis Pardo, 'A Modo de Sintesis: La Riqueza Salmonera en España', in *El Salmon y Su Pesca*, p. 366. Max Borrell adds: 'After many years of research spent by Camino and me on this subject, we came to the conclusion that what was offered [the servants and field workers] were kelts, either dead and found by the banks, or those which were easily netted.' (Personal communication, October 24, 1964.) In a later communication, February 18, 1966, Borrell adds that he found a few ' "rental contracts" in which it was stated that if the land tenants could not meet their obligations in wheat rentals, they could put in the difference in fresh salmon, at the current market price, or in poultry'!

6 Enrique Camino, *La Riqueza Piscicola de los Rios del Norte de España*, p. 18.

7 See M. R. Reeve, 'Where Salmon Fishing Reigns Supreme', *Country Life*, February 28, 1963.

8 Personal communication, March 16, 1966.

3

Dissipation of the French Salmon Resource

La belle France!

The traveller sensitive to natural beauty quickly falls in love with the landscape of France, its endless variety, its mosaic of mountains, glaciers, forests, valleys, marshes and dunes, its rocky coasts and sandy shores, and above all with its rivers and canals that reach into every corner of the land. The rivers of France have been eulogized by poets, lovingly depicted by the Impressionist painters, and even described in tone poems. Their very names evoke images of dimpling waters flowing across fields of wheat or corn, or neatly-terraced vineyards, or wandering lazily around grassy meadows, or darting through dark pine forests, or pouring down narrow defiles along flower-carpeted banks.

The salmon rivers

Most of the French rivers emptying into the Atlantic Ocean, from the English Channel to the Bay of Biscay, once harboured stocks of anadromous fish – shad, sturgeon, eel, sea-trout, and especially salmon. Salmon used to ascend to the upper reaches of the Seine which rises on the Plateau de Langres and then return as kelts to the English Channel. Centuries ago Parisians used to catch salmon from the banks of the Ile de la Cité, incredible as it may now seem.

The Loire cuts a 625-mile arc across the centre of France from the Cevennes Mountains to the Bay of Biscay, which it enters at St. Nazaire, the outport of Nantes. This glorious waterway, with its many tributaries, the Cher, Vienne, Indre, Allier and their tributaries, flows through the Val d'Orléans, Val de Blois, Val de

Touraine and Val d'Anjou. It presents a pleasant landscape 'with meadows on the flood plain, market gardens on the lower terraces near the towns, large fields of wheat on the broad upper terraces, and vineyards and orchards everywhere'.[1] The Middle Loire flows through ancient towns rich in historical lore, like Orléans, Blois, Tours and Saumur, and past regal châteaux, each standing on some prominent bluff or spur, like Amboise, Chenonceaux (built on a bridge over the Cher), Blois and the ruin of Chinon. Phenomenal runs of salmon used to ascend the Loire and spawn in the uppermost waters of the Allier and Upper Loire in the Massif Central (see Figure 2).

The Gironde, formed by the confluence of the Dordogne and Garonne Rivers, originates in the Spanish Pyrénées and follows a serpentine course of some 350 miles to its entry in the Bay of Biscay below Bordeaux. It flows through the famous Médoc wine district and once it too attracted huge runs of salmon that spawned in the headwaters.

The idyllic Adour, strictly a Pyrénéean river, rises in the Roncesvaux pass where Charlemagne suffered a disastrous defeat by the Basques in the ninth century (an incident which inspired the medieval epic, *Chanson de Roland*). With its many branches the Adour embroiders the landscape of Béarn and Gascony and pours its waters into the Bay of Biscay below Bayonne. Some of its tributaries arch northward and others south-eastward to become mountain torrents that provide ideal nursery grounds for salmon.

For example, the Nivelle, a major affluent of the Adour, flows through oak-beech forests in the foothills of the Pyrénées, gathering up the waters of many brooks and rills. Lively brown trout can be seen darting between the rocks. Occasionally, a majestic salmon jumps out of the water to show its vitality, and perhaps to look at the surroundings. Eels are numerous and devour the baby salmon.

The Nivelle meanders through a rather narrow valley dotted with Basque villages. There are mouldering houses, little shops and unobtrusive inns. There may be a Romanesque cathedral whose spires form a landmark in the valley. One may see old men fishing from the bridges, with boys at their sides. This is fishermen's country, and

---

3a and 3b. Bayonne, France. *Inscrits Maritimes* fishing for salmon with a seine.

trout are still plentiful although the salmon have become quite scarce.

When I visited the valley of the Nivelle rain was falling gently; the green slopes of the mountains were obscured; water dripped down the red tiles of the roofs of farmhouses with their whitewashed walls and brown shuttered windows. Pigs and chickens scurried to the shelter of the barns. Village streets were empty. The women were busy at their household chores while in the bistros men talked of going fishing the next day if the rain ceased, because the river would rise and salmon might come out of their hiding places and start moving upstream.

Many other French watercourses once teemed with salmon and other anadromous fish: the short, swift rivers of Brittany and Normandy; the Meuse, Moselle and Rhine and their numerous affluents. No other country in Europe, probably, was better endowed with inland fisheries—and none frittered them away so completely.

Profile of French salmon

The general biological characteristics of the French salmon are similar to those of the Spanish, English or other British races of the species. The larger fish, weighing seven kilograms and over, enter the estuaries of the Adour and Loire from November to March and move upstream promptly but are not usually in a hurry to reach their destination. They arrive at the spawning grounds in the following November or December, and may spend up to a year in the river. Smaller fish of three to five kilograms, called *Madeleines* (because St. Madeleine's Day is celebrated on July 22), enter the rivers from March through July and also spawn in November or December. Very few *Madeleines* are found in the Adour or Loire, but they are now the only salmon ascending the Breton and Norman rivers.

4a. Sorde-l'Abbaye (Gave d'Oloron), France. Micro-central (rating 6kW) blocking fish passage. Note that in September 1966, in very dry conditions, the entire flow of the Gave went through the turbines.

4b. Sorde-l'Abbaye (Gave d'Oloron), France, looking upstream on the canal (abbey on left) leading to the micro-central. Note the crest and downstream face of the dam (right). This is about 400 yards long and has no fish ladder. Not a drop of water was going over it in September 1966.

The eggs incubate in 80 to 90 days and the parr usually stay in the river until the spring following their hatching; sometimes a year longer. Dr. Richard Vibert found that about 60 per cent of the smolts in the Adour were yearlings, and the rest were two-year-olds.[2] May is the month of departure for the smolts.

Any productive watercourse is populated at a given time by salmon of various ages and states of development. Juveniles are going downstream in shoals while adults are fighting their way upstream. There are several hundred smolts for every adult. The young are resplendent in their silvery dress while the adults (who do not eat) are daily losing weight and some of their brilliant coloration. There are *Madeleines* that spend one year in the ocean, and 'spring salmon' two years or more in the sea, and larger fish with three or four years of ocean feeding behind them. There are also a certain number of kelts returning for a second (or third) spawning. In the Adour, Vibert found that 4 per cent of the adult salmon were kelts.

Finally, the river harbours spawned-out fish lying in pools or below the rocks, inert and desolate. Some of them have enough vitality left to attempt the journey back to the sea, while the remainder are doomed to die and their carcasses will float downstream to be eaten by predators.

The fishery before the Revolution of 1789

In France the right to fish was originally a royal right. Navigable and floatable streams belonged to the king, and like all Crown property, were inalienable and imprescriptible. During the ninth and tenth centuries, when the feudal system replaced the primitive monarchy, the king more and more frequently assigned fishing rights to clerics and laymen. At first these were granted for the life of the recipient and were revocable, but as the monarchy was weakened by the rise of a strong nobility, they tended to become hereditary. In brief, as the vassals acquired the rights attached to a fief, fishing privileges went with them. Owners often leased their fisheries. For example, the Priory of Ministrol-sur-Loire in 1375 granted a lease on the fishery of Gonfolens on a share basis: the Bishop of Puy obtained one-fourth of the yield, the Prior of Nozières a fourth, and the two lessors one-fourth apiece. The monks of the ancient house of St. Ilpize, established in 510, controlled the fishing on their domains on the Allier River; in the ninth and tenth centuries these lands became part of the duchy of the Counts of Auvergne; later they fell into the hands of the Seneschal of Beaucaire; and finally were held by the powerful family of Rochefoucault. All these owners derived revenues from one of the best salmon streams in the kingdom. Some municipalities, wishing to commemorate the natural bounty of the rivers, incorporated the salmon in their coats of arms.

Landowners seem to have been usually solicitous of migratory fish and took pains to keep the waterways unobstructed and assure passage at difficult places. Sluices were provided at mill dams to allow salmon and sea-trout to move upstream. A Béarnais statute of 1662, for instance, required that 'all dikes and dams must have a sluice or passageway of a height deemed necessary by experts to permit fish to ascend or descend at all times. Proprietors were ordered to put in such fish passes within three months, and they must maintain them; in case of negligence, the Estates would proceed to do it and charge the cost to the said proprietors.' In Brittany, weirs at the mouths of rivers were generally designed to trap large salmon but permitted the smaller ones to escape.

Salmon along with eel, lamprey and shad supplied the peasants with food, especially when the grain harvest failed and famine threatened. The fisherman was an important member of his community, and sometimes, as in the Basque town of Oloron Ste Marie where two excellent salmon streams meet, the Gave d'Ossau and Gave d'Aspe, the people enshrined him and his fish in sculpture on the portal of the Romanesque cathedral. The salmon of Normandy and Brittany, of the Rhine, Moselle, Gironde, Loire and Adour, were as famous among Frenchmen as the Thames, Wye, Humber or Tyne salmon among Englishmen, or Tweed, Dee or Tay salmon among Scotsmen.

Because of its abundance, salmon in the Middle Ages was a dietary staple wherever it was found. It was boiled in wine, smoked, or made into paste or powder. In the valleys of the Lower Auvergne and Lower Loire the knights celebrating a jousting victory, or some other fête, often called for a dish of salmon among the dozen courses they were accustomed to devour at a sitting. The fish was brought by pages on a pewter platter to the sound of trumpets, its head and eyes and intestines intact. Servants handed round sauces and spices. No forks or knives were used–food was eaten with the fingers.

Salmon acquired a high reputation among gourmets. Thus

Abraham de la Framboisière, royal physician of the sixteenth century, extolled 'the tender flesh of the salmon, oily, sweet, very appetizing and excellent to the taste, preferable as a delicacy to all other fish'. Church dignitaries, nobility and members of the royal household appreciated it. For example, the menu of a banquet given by the canons of Brioude in 1719 included among sixteen courses the head of a salmon cooked *à la Hollandaise* and served in white wine with pomegranates.[3] The gourmand Louis XIV was not fond of fish but his successor, Louis XV, had a preference for freshwater species like perch from Lake Geneva and salmon from French streams. Among the capital dishes created by French chefs, and widely imitated, were *saumon à la royale*, *saumon à la Chambord* and *saumon Impériale*, said to be worthy of standing beside those regional masterpieces of French culinary art, *sole Normande*, *bouillabaisse Marseillaise*, *pic Anjou* and *burbot Franc-Comtoise*.

As in other countries, the kings of the Middle Ages tried to protect the fisheries. The oldest statutes relating to freshwater fishing date from the reign of Charlemagne and are probably the prototype of all such legislation in Europe. His successors issued decrees authorizing vassals to fish on certain rivers and streams (regarded as royal or seigneurial preserves), listing species that were permitted or forbidden to be caught, etc. (Until the eleventh century only fishing for salmon and eels was specifically regulated; other species appeared in the edicts of later kings.) In the thirteenth century the right to fish on the Seine was apportioned to the Abbey of Saint-Germain-des-Prés between Sèvres and Pont au Change and to the Abbey of Saint-Magloire from there to the Île Notre Dame. The area from this point to Villeneuve-Saint-Georges and on the Marne was designated as 'royal water' on which fishing privileges were disposed of annually, partly on the basis of furnishing fish for the royal table.[4]

Ordinances in the Middle Ages dealt with nets and other engines, with meshes, close seasons, minimum size of marketable fish, etc. A sense of conservation pervades these statutes for some devices were regarded as inimical to preservation of the resources and could be used only at certain times and prohibited at others. The edicts of Charles IV and Philip VI in the fourteenth century are notable for their long lists of permissible and non-permissible gear and modes of fishing. They specify the kind of violations which will be punished first by destruction of gear and if repeated by monetary fines. Efforts were made to protect the fish during the spawning season; close-mesh nets were outlawed so as to preserve the young fish; steeping of linen or hemp in the streams, as was the custom in Normandy, Picardy and Bourbonnais, was forbidden during the spawning season. It was permitted to fish for salmon at least six months of the year, using nets with meshes of 40 millimetres and the minimum size that could be taken was 40 centimetres. It was illegal to poison the waters to stupefy fish; blockade the entire width of a river with weirs; fish at night; use drag nets; stir up the waters; employ explosives or firearms. French documents contain detailed descriptions of the kinds of nets that could be used in freshwater fishing. 'In fact,' says Thomazi, 'the names and methods of fabrication have changed but the fishing devices have hardly altered for two hundred years or more.'[5]

By the time of Henry IV in 1597 excessive violation of the laws must have become alarming for an edict declared that 'with an infinite number of engines [which have been] prohibited by the ordinances, fishermen are depopulating the rivers, streams and brooks. They are [therefore] forbidden to fish with any gear, even legal ones, which have not been previously marked by our officers.'

By the middle of Louis XIV's reign the fishery laws had become chaotic and often contradictory. The Seigneurs added their regulations to those of their Sovereigns. From one province to another and one district to the next the rules changed, and there were rivers on which the two banks were not under the same authority. Louis' minister Colbert therefore abrogated all previous statutes and in 1667 enunciated a new and uniform fishery code for the nation which was not substantially modified until 1829. However, in his laudable endeavour to regulate and conserve the freshwater fisheries Colbert also granted the right to fish in the estuaries and tidewater on navigable streams only to sailors of the Royal Navy (called *Inscrits Maritimes*), a move designed to stimulate enlistments. This right became in effect prescriptive, led to overfishing in later centuries, and assisted in the ruin of the anadromous resources.

Until the Revolution of 1789, at least, the freshwater fishes were generally in ample supply, subject to normal fluctuations of abundance. That salmon were plentiful is attested by chroniclers of the various regions and also by the well-established custom of masters to serve it *ad nauseam* to their servants and workers. In areas where salmon spawned landowners were known to collect emaciated kelts, preserve them, and feed them to their menials. As a result, servants sometimes rebelled and insisted they would not eat salmon more than twice a week. This situation was common in Brittany, Limousin, Auvergne, the Adour basin, and in the Allier valley.[6]

Despite the abuses known to have occurred, such as poaching and destruction of smolts, excessive fishing at different times and in different places, the salmon runs continued at high levels because the rivers remained unpolluted, and spawning grounds were protected, or were not blockaded by impassable barriers. The Seigneurs made sure that a certain proportion of the runs would reach the headwaters and mate to produce succeeding generations. Weirs and barrages were provided with free gaps to float timber and pass fish, or were low enough to permit salmon to leap over them, at least at high water. Fishing seasons were reasonably observed, and waterways were usually well tended.

Although statistics are scarce, some conception of the wealth of the French rivers may be gleaned from the fact that in the eighteenth century, according to Louis Roule, Brittany alone produced as much as 9,000,000 pounds of salmon annually in good years, bringing an aggregate income of some 200,000 livres to the proprietors of the rivers.

But the halcyon days of the French fishery passed as revolution, industrialization and growth of population posed inimical and often ruinous threats to the stocks of salmon.

Salmon in retreat

Dissipation of the inland fisheries began with the French Revolution. Decrees of the Legislature and Convention of 1792 and 1793 abolished the exclusive rights of the Crown, Church and nobility to hunt and fish on the lands of the kingdom. The Republic proclaimed free fishing for all citizens on all rivers. Hitherto barred from sport by high walls and harsh trespassing laws, the populace began to pillage the resources. 'What belongs to everybody belongs to nobody', was a common saying; hence, citizens helped themselves to all the fish and game they could obtain. Under the Consulate the fishing rights on navigable waters were restored to the state, and rod fishing was permitted without formality on state lands. Riparian owners recovered their fishing rights on non-navigable waters subject to general and local laws governing the fishery. The ordinance of April 25, 1829, reconfirmed this general state of affairs and specified in detail permissible and non-permissible types of gear, close seasons, and penalties for violations. It remained the fundamental fishery code of France until 1941 but was poorly enforced.

When I asked Roger Bachelier, Principal Engineer in the Bureau of Waters and Forests (*Eaux et Forêts*), charged with supervision of inland fisheries, what were the chief causes of the loss of France's salmon runs, he replied: 'Before the Revolution, monsieur, there was respect for private property in France. During the Revolutionary era people went wild, hunting and fishing without restraint. That spirit never really died.'

The consequences of unrestrained exploitation of the fishery and neglect of the rivers began to be noticed after the Bourbon restoration. Around 1830, for instance, a former Army surgeon observed that the Allier River around Brioude 'is no longer as populated with fish as it used to be. The species taken are barbel, eel, lamprey . . . dace, grayling, rarely trout and more rarely carp. Salmon is scarce and dear. It sells for three and even four francs the pound and old men have seen it sell for 40 and 50 centimes and even 25 centimes the pound.'[7]

Industry early learned to take advantage of the waterways of France. The entrepreneur set up his tannery, textile mill, flour mill, lumber mill or paper mill on a little river or brook and diverted the water by means of a flume or weir. In order to obtain the maximum head, he did not as a rule open the sluice gates to permit fish to pass. Usually he also had the right to draw all the water he wanted, and if this caused the flow to drop at times to levels dangerous for fish life, he shrugged his shoulders unconcernedly.

It was not till well after the middle of the nineteenth century that serious declines in salmon runs began to arouse the authorities. A law was promulgated in 1865 requiring all owners to build fish ladders at impoundments, with indemnification by the state. However, it did not stipulate that adequate streamflow was to be maintained at all times to permit fish to hurdle these structures, nor did it apply to pre-existing dams. In consequence, the law did not help to arrest the diminution of migrating fish.

Émile Moreau in his *Histoire Naturelle des Poissons de la France*,

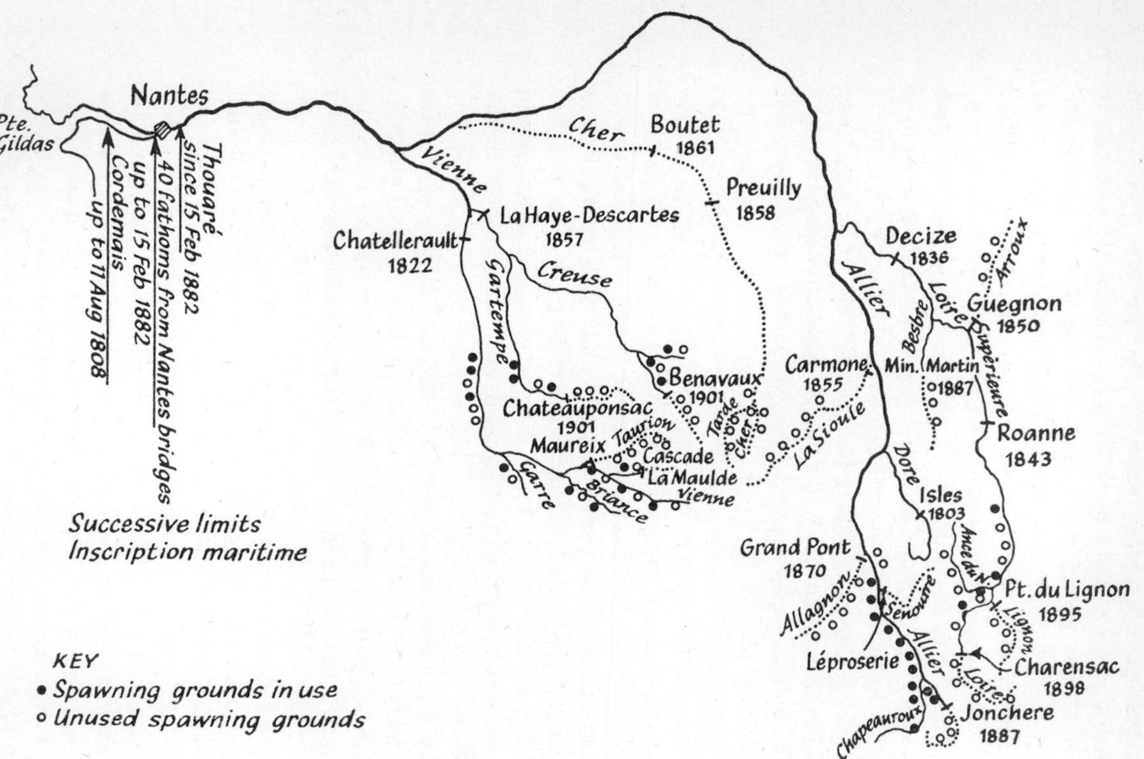

Figure 2

Migratory routes of salmon in Loire Basin, end of nineteenth century, with major obstacles.

published in 1881, said that salmon were already rare in the Moselle 'which it ascends to Épinal and even beyond; quite rare in the Meuse and its affluents Semoy and Chiers'. It used to be quite abundant at Monthermé, where about forty men were occupied in fishing for salmon fifty years before. The Meuse was closed to the fish by impassable dams, but they were still quite common in the Somme; rare in the Seine above Quillebeuf. Arriving at Montereau, salmon abandoned the Seine and went up the Yonne. They also ascended the Cure, a tributary of the Yonne. They were much less numerous than formerly in the Rille, and very rare in the Orne.

Moreau noted that the rivers debouching into the English Channel, such as the Sienne, Sée and Selune, were still rich in salmon. The fish were also found in considerable numbers in the *grèves* of Mont St. Michel and in the Rivers Odet and Ellé, but had become scarce in the Aulne and Blavet since those streams were canalized and locks erected. The Loire River system, however, seemed to be still rich in salmon, and there were distinct runs in spring, summer (*Madeleines*), autumn (*becards*), and winter. They abounded in the Vienne but had almost disappeared from the Allier, where they were being re-established by the planting of fry (Figure 2).

Continuing his survey of French rivers, Moreau found that salmon runs were slender in the Charente, and had declined in the Dordogne and Garonne Rivers. They did not go very far up the Adour. In fact, they left the main river at Bayonne to ascend the Nive and enter the Gaves, and were fished in great numbers at Peyrehorade. 'Unfortunately,' said Moreau, 'there are an excessive number of fisheries on the Nive.' The Nivelle still had good stocks of salmon and so did the Bidasoa.

Failure to enforce the law of 1865 is one of the main reasons for the disappearance of salmon from various rivers which were dotted with mill dams and later hydro-electric dams not equipped with fish ladders. This evil notably affected the Loire basin. In 1900–1 Chateauponsac dam, 5 metres high, was built on the Gartempe River and Benavaux dam, 10 metres, on the Creuse, both tributaries of the Vienne River, which is a major affluent of the Loire (Figure 3). In 1907 the La Roche-Bat-l'Aigle dam, 5½ metres high, was added to the Creuse. Since these structures were not provided with fish passes they condemned both rivers to sterility. The erection in 1918–20 of Bec-des-Deux-Eaux (Maisons-Rouges) dam, 5 metres high, also without fish passage facilities, just above the confluence of the Vienne and Creuse, sounded the death knell of the salmon in the Vienne basin.

The Upper Loire was blockaded in 1957 by the towering Grangent power dam, 50 metres high, which submerged 20 kilometres of headwaters that used to be ideal nursery grounds for salmon. The licensee for this project was not required to install a fish pass, although it was strongly urged upon the Government by Waters and Forests, which was endeavouring to open up the Upper Loire to salmon by laddering low dams downstream and planting salmon ova in 'Vibert boxes'.

These are but a few examples of the consistent destruction of French rivers by power projects built without any regard to migratory fish. 'Actually,' says Bachelier, 'it would be neither difficult nor too expensive to provide a salmon lock which permits fish to reach the reservoir above the dam, regardless of its height. But rarely are possibilities of spawning found above the dam, having been inundated by the impoundment or by other reservoirs upstream; and there has not yet been found means of permitting salmon spawned upstream to descend to the sea through a large reservoir which has practically no current.'[8]

'Formerly, whenever man modified the course of a river, whenever he built a dam or lock,' says Couture-Spicer,

> he took special pains to preserve conditions favourable for the free movement of aquatic fauna. It is not necessary to go far [in our rivers] to find the remains of fish ladders. We say the remains because many are now in ruins.
>
> Fish, salmon and trout particularly, could freely move against the current to reach their spawning grounds. It was good to see them jump from pool to pool, propelled by the powerful energy of their tail in order to reach the reservoir and lose themselves finally in some subtributary where they would find peace and tranquillity.
>
> Modern hydro-electric dams, which reach 100 metres or more, preclude fish ladders. The cost would be excessive and moreover no fish, unless he were a champion, could hope to surmount such a ladder without completely exhausting himself. These projects which we admire for their technology, these dams which furnish electricity without which we could scarcely live each day, well merit their name. [But] they bar access to superb spawning grounds, which are now totally abandoned.[9]

The licence for a hydro-electric plant 'required the licensee to maintain at the tailrace, a flow adequate to safeguard the general interests [in the river] and, if necessary, a flow equal to that which prevails at the intake', but in practice this stipulation was often ignored because it was too costly. 'Fortunately,' says Bachelier, 'navigation locks on the Aulne and dams on the Allier River and Gave d'Oloron remained passable to salmon; if not, fish of eight kilograms and larger would have totally disappeared from France and there would remain only salmon of three or four kilograms in a few Breton and Norman streams.'[10]

A major factor in the melancholy fate of the salmon stocks was intensive and remorseless netting. As the fish returned to the estuaries of their parent streams the nets of the *Inscrits* awaited them *en masse*. 'Until recent years the *Inscrits Maritimes* could get away with anything', said Commandant Latour in his book, *The Salmon in Breton Rivers*, published in 1928. 'They had no consideration for regulations governing coastal fishing, knowing full well that nobody would have dared or dreamed of enforcing them.'[11] Their nets at times virtually blockaded the rivers. 'I have seen with my own eyes the length of the towing path of Quimper lined with seines and each would take a dozen large salmon in one sweep . . . and more.' The fish which passed the first breastwork of nets were confronted 200 or 300 metres upstream with a second, and so on for a considerable distance. Only a minimum number of fish managed to escape. 'And one wonders how that happened', added Latour tartly.

The nets worked night and day, all week, without interference by the authorities. Although the weekend was supposed to be a close period, the netsmen flouted this regulation. As a consequence, they sometimes took as much as 85 or 90 per cent of the total catch in the river.

In his *History of the Loire Salmon* Bachelier provides ample evidence of the role played by abusive netting in the estuary and tidewater. The fishermen blocked the migratory routes in the Loire with their nets, ignored the prohibition against night fishing, and worked during the close season unperturbed and undisturbed. Thus a survey by the Bureau of Bridges and Roads (*Ponts et Chausées*) revealed that on the Lower Loire the *Inscrits* captured 5,936 salmon during the open season from January 10 to August 30, 1890, and 3,046 fish in the close season from October 16, 1890, to January 10, 1891. No government agency could control them, and beginning

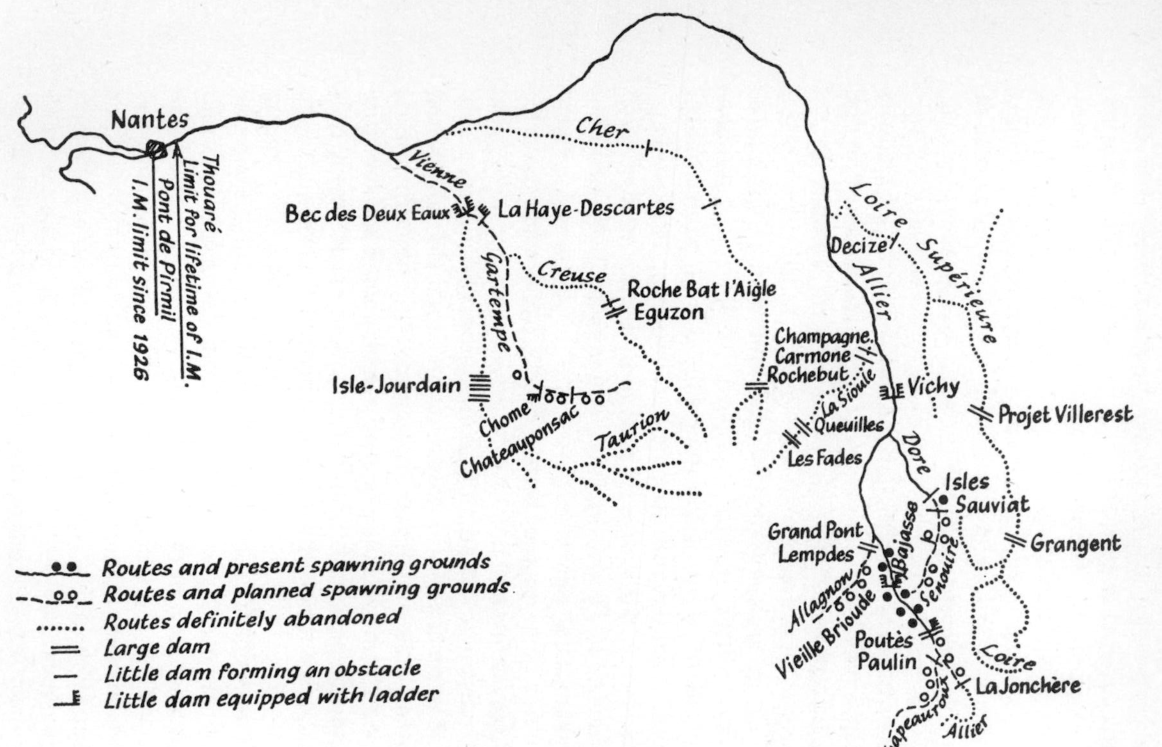

Figure 3
Current migratory routes of salmon in Loire Basin, showing abandoned spawning grounds.

with 1902, adds Bachelier, 'they had a powerful protector in the person of Camille Pelletan, Minister of Marine'.[12]

Licensed by the Ministry of Marine, the *Inscrits* were permitted to use almost any kind of gear. A ministerial order of September 30, 1934, authorized them to fish with drag nets as well as hoop nets of any length or mesh size. They continued to wreak havoc with the Loire salmon stocks, already gravely imperilled by impassable dams on the tributaries, until the end of World War II. By then some of the major affluents were sterile, the runs had been grossly depleted, and netting was no longer lucrative enough to attract many *Inscrits*. Opportunities in industry in Nantes and St. Nazaire called many of them. The drastic reduction in catches in the Loire Basin is shown in Table 4 and severe amputation of migratory routes in Figure 3.

In assessing the causes of the destruction of salmon populations, poaching must not be ignored. 'Modern poaching is a veritable industry of water pirates and thieves who, by every means from nets to explosives . . . are devoted to intensive devastation of our rivers', wrote L. de Boisset and Richard Vibert in their authoritative book, *La Pêche Fluviale en France*, published in 1944. Nowhere in Europe perhaps was poaching so well organized and justice so lax.

The evil became widespread during World War I when the price of salmon rose sharply and policing of the rivers was understandably relaxed. After the war it continued unabated, attracting many shady characters. Usually these people operated in gangs, like bootleggers in the United States during the Prohibition era. Two men worked the banks of a stream while others acted as look-outs. Their favourite gear was the trident, a light and demountable iron tool, easily hidden in one's jacket. Thus armed, the poacher explored the river with an innocent air, usually puffing casually on his pipe, scrutinizing every pool and hollow, climbing a tree sometimes to get a better view. Practically every water where desirable fish might be found was known to these gentry. They lurked near the approaches to dams and weirs, around bridges and watergates, and wherever salmon rested on their upstream journeys. So well did they 'case' the streams that rarely did a big fish moving out of its hiding place escape their attention.

Quickly inserting the trident into the handle, the poacher dispatched the salmon in a matter of seconds. If a warden or angler appeared in the distance, the trident was quickly hidden in the grass.

Table 4
Estimated salmon catches in Loire Basin
1891–1962 (selected years)
(*numbers of fish*)

Year	*Maritime Zone*[a]	*Basin total*
1891	15,000	NA
1892	21,000	NA
1893	30,000	NA
1895	20,000	NA
1896	8,000	NA
1897	3,000	NA
1898	5,700	NA
1901	6,200	NA
1910	1,800	NA
1915	1,100	NA
1920	3,100	NA
1925	5,000	9,500
1930	2,770	6,000
1935–36	3,480	4,500
1941	NA	10,000
1945	6,000	NA
1950	1,570	2,000
1955	682	1,100
1960	562	1,150
1961	1,243	2,250
1962	592	1,350

[a] Represents estimated catches by the *Inscrits Maritimes.*

Source: R. Bachelier, *L'Histoire du Saumon en Loire.*

Sometimes fish were taken behind the very backs of wardens and under the noses of persons who had leased the water. On the spawning grounds, where salmon are off-guard and easily descried, poachers were able to decimate them, usually leaving the females behind, 'not for sentimental reasons or because they had the foresight to provide themselves with future victims,' says Latour, 'but because, stripped of their eggs, they fetched much less than the males'. Even smolts were taken in shoals, usually at impoundments, and sold for fertilizer or pig feed.

These marauders operated at night as well as in daylight. Carrying an acetylene lantern, they carefully scouted the bed of the river usually at the headwaters. Any salmon that were discovered were quickly killed and taken away, or hidden and picked up in the morning.

Night prowlers were more difficult to catch than daylight poachers. Warned by dogs of the approach of strangers, they quickly extinguished their lanterns. If the warden or gendarme appeared, they blinded him with the lantern light and effected their escape among the tangled undergrowth and trees along the banks. If apprehended in the deeper part of the stream, they would duck into the water up to their necks and hide till their pursuers disappeared. Then, throwing the fish into baskets, they would jump on their bicycles or motor-cycles and dash home.

In some instances fish pirates used rakes to stir the big salmon out of their resting places and then forced them into an enclosure where they could be easily netted. Occasionally dynamite was used to root out the fish, even chloroform was used to drug them.

The fishery code of 1829 was almost useless in suppressing illegal fishing. It was difficult, for instance, to prove that a person was selling or transporting illegal salmon during the open season if the fish was of legal size. The only evidence might be trident or spear marks on the skin, but this was too flimsy to stand up in court. Even if a person were caught and convicted, he would receive a nominal fine which need not be paid at once. He could run up numerous convictions and fines while continuing to fish illegally night and day. Henri Boyer, Vice-President of the Association of Fishermen of the Upper Allier, said in 1930 that he knew people with up to thirty convictions who not only continued to fish but bragged about their records. 'Poaching has attained since the war the status of a national institution', he exclaimed. 'The devastations particularly affect the waters of angling clubs whose members are powerless and discouraged by the apathy of the Administration.'[13] Equally disheartened were wardens and forestry officers (guardians of the rivers) whom poachers regarded as harmless nuisances.

Periodically, the courts granted amnesty to offenders, thereby relieving them of the necessity of paying their accrued fines and at the same time whitewashing their reputations. Now assured of impunity, they stepped up their operations. When judges were requested by angling groups to press for payment of fines or take steps to incarcerate notorious poachers, they were told: 'These people are insolvent and there's nothing to be got from them.' Yet some of these alleged paupers took a thousand francs' worth of salmon weekly out of the rivers, owned their own homes and also had an automobile, or at least a motor-cycle for rapid transportation. 'It is infinitely regrettable', said Boyer, 'to see professional poachers . . . continue freely to ravage the watercourses of an entire region and sell their fish openly in close seasons. . . . In every region a half-dozen of these characters have a monopoly on the exploitation of the streams, which they grossly abuse.'[14] Occasionally a poacher would actually be imprisoned for three months, at most six months. After that he would blithely return to the river. The black market for salmon consisted of inns and restaurants, but sometimes the fish were peddled to rural housewives. In recent years poaching has been greatly curtailed by means of an enlarged police force employed by the national government under the supervision of Waters and Forests and by local fishermen's groups.

Divided administration

An important factor in the deterioration of freshwater fisheries has been the confused and divided authority of government agencies. At the top level of responsibility, if we can call it such, are three bureaux. The Ministry of Marine has jurisdiction of the rivers up to the end of tidewater; Bridges and Roads controls canals; and Waters and Forests under the Ministry of Agriculture is charged with setting rules and regulations pertaining to fishing on inland streams above tidewater, policing the rivers and conducting fishery research. Another agency in the picture is the Hydraulic Service which issues licences for hydro-electric schemes. Aside from establishing the general fishing regulations and endeavouring to enforce them, the role of Waters and Forests is purely nominal. It cannot tell an owner or club how to manage the water; it can only offer advice and hope it will be followed. Where so many bureaux are involved conflicts are naturally generated and vested interests will triumph at the expense of natural resources. This has been the experience not only of France but of Spain and other countries.

> We would not pretend [said de Boisset and Vibert] that all the services charged with fishery responsibilities have always had in full degree all the desirable technical competence. The reasons are many. They stem in large part from . . . lack of comprehension in the seats of power of the national interest in the inland fishery. Regulations were made that were poorly adapted to biological conditions, permits for hydraulic projects were too readily granted, industrial diversions [of water] were tolerated in ignorance of the proper methods of attenuating them. . . . All true. But we should not ignore the patient efforts of certain forest officers who fought the evils they saw, efforts which were futile because of the lack of co-ordination of the services, lack of comprehension of the public welfare, and we must say, egoism, anarchy, and ignorance.[15]

Occasionally agreements were negotiated by the government bureaux that were in the interest of fishery conservation. Such was the pact promulgated by an interministerial committee in 1929. It set aside seven rivers–the Aulne, Ellé, Allier, Adour in part, Gave d'Oloron, Gave de Mauléon in part, and the Nive–on which preservation of the salmon runs shall take precedence over industrial use and hydro-electric licences will no longer be granted. On seven additional rivers–the Canche, Sienne, Sée, Sélure, Élorn, Scorf and Gave de Pau–salmon shall have a place equal to that of industry and licences for power dams will be granted only on the basis of an understanding between the Hydraulic Service and Waters and Forests, and with certain restrictions relative to the height of dams, design of fish passes, etc.

This unprecedented agreement served to postpone or prevent further encroachments on a few migratory fish routes. In fact, rivers in the first group still account for a large portion of the annual salmon catches, and those in the second, located, except for the Gave de Pau, along the Norman–Breton coast, supply most of the remainder.

Another interministerial committee which met in 1934 and 1935 to study measures for mitigating excessive netting in the estuaries was less successful. The agreement reached on November 23, 1935, stipulated merely that nets used by non-professionals–that is, not

Inscrits–shall be closed down thirty-six hours each week if a committee of local people and interested administrators deemed it necessary. The Minister of Marine, arguing against including the *Inscrits* in this restriction (which the foresters strongly demanded), said: 'We do not deny that certain new measures are justifiable under the circumstances but would it not be better to make sure at first, by regulations rigorously applied, of the impossibility of polluting streams frequented by salmonids, severely control poaching, impose ladder designs at dams, and finally, if these measures are insufficient demand new restrictions on the rights of fishermen whether they operate in the maritime or freshwater zones?'

As de Boisset and Vibert commented, 'This thesis, of course, rests on a sophism. When we are faced with a grave danger we do not waste time establishing priority of safety measures. We employ all of them simultaneously. If to save the fishery we first attack pollution; then, if this is insufficient, poaching; then, if this is still inadequate, apply restrictions on hydro-electric dams; if, after exhausting all these means, we agree to impose restrictions on fishing in the estuaries the action would be meaningless because there would no longer be any fish.

'When foresters request free movement for the salmon over the dams the electrical engineers often reply, "To what good? First get rid of pollution in the estuaries, the famous biologic blockade which the salmon cannot pierce. When the fish can enter the river, we will talk about dams." . . . While these academic discussions were being held, the salmon runs continued to decline . . . the fish disappeared from more and more rivers.'

Although there are no reliable statistics because the French Government has never required reports of catches from those who hold fishing licences, de Boisset and Vibert estimated in 1944 that salmon catches had fallen to 6,000 to 7,000 in Brittany, 5,000 to 6,000 in the Loire basin, and 10,000 to 18,000 in the Adour basin, a total of 21,000 to 31,000 annually. In contrast, a hundred years earlier some 10,000 salmon were sold in the market of Quimper alone.

By World War II France was importing at least ten times as much freshwater fish as it was exporting, and most of the imports were salmon. In 1936, 4,500 metric tons entered the country, of which 53 per cent comprised canned Pacific salmon from the United States, a situation that was intolerable to patriotic Frenchmen. 'In a country like ours,' said de Boisset and Vibert, 'endowed by nature with such riches in its rivers there ought to be on all our tables the fresh salmon of France, superior to all the salmons from overseas.'

Attempts at conservation

Between the two world wars attempts were made to halt the steady depletion of the freshwater fisheries, partly at the instigation of dedicated public servants and partly under pressure of anglers' associations. These activities centred around (1) a modest programme of rehabilitating promising rivers, and (2) developing a *modus operandi* among government agencies to promote fish conservation.

In the 1920s Waters and Forests sent members of its staff to Norway to study fish passes. As a result of this mission the Bureau launched a programme of laddering obstructions on some of the Pyrénées rivers. Altogether ten dams were equipped with fish passes in the Adour basin in the years 1933 to 1938: on the Nive, the Gave d'Aspe and Gave d'Ossau (which together form the Gave d'Oloron), thus reopening 180 miles of spawning grounds which had not been frequented by salmon for centuries. In the 1940s the neighbouring Gave de Pau was similarly rehabilitated. Co-operation of angling clubs and the Syndicate of *Inscrits Maritimes* permitted the temporary extension of the close season in the Adour basin by two months; fishing for kelts was suppressed; a weekly 24-hour closure was instituted in the estuary; and poaching was curtailed by means of an enlarged staff of wardens.

The results were rather spectacular. Within a few years more salmon were found in the Gave d'Oloron than had been seen there since the beginning of the twentieth century. By 1950 the Adour was producing an annual harvest of some 20,000 fish taken by 300 *Inscrits* (who accounted for 60 to 85 per cent of the total) and 300 fly fishermen. However, according to a report by Fishery Inspector Richard Vibert of November 3, 1950, fears were already expressed that an excessive toll was being levied on the brood stock, not only by the remorseless netters but by fly fishermen who fished steadily throughout the season and sold their catches in the markets. Local anglers, anxious to exploit a bonanza, were antagonistic to outsiders who came to fish in the Gaves.

In the 1950s further work was done to augment France's salmon output both by local groups and government agencies, notably Waters and Forests. Waterfalls were laddered on the Aulne and Sienne Rivers; defective fish passes were repaired; ladders or locks were built at a few small hydro-electric dams; some unused dams were demolished. The nationwide survey of salmon rivers made by Waters and Forests in the autumn of 1962 nevertheless presented, on the whole, a picture of the decay and ruin of a noble fishery.

The Pyrénéean region, where salmon showed such a strong resurgence in the 1940s, still supplied a large portion of the national catch but the trend was manifestly downward. Some gains were offset by losses. Thus the rod catch had doubled on the River Nive in the preceding decade and the Gave d'Ossau also had improved runs. But the Gave d'Aspe had declined in productivity until a lock was installed at the Sœix dam so that fish could move upstream with ease. A natural gas development at Lacq completely destroyed the runs on the Gave de Pau.

On my visit to the Adour valley in 1963 I found local anglers downhearted. The boom in salmon fishing had collapsed, hotels which used to cater to anglers were in a depressed state. The annual salmon derby at Navarrenx was abandoned for lack of fish. The Centre Scientifique at Biarritz which, under Dr. Richard Vibert of Waters and Forests, had conducted important studies on the French salmon, no longer was interested in this species because of a lack of funds. Artificial breeding of salmon by the Government was ended.

In 1966, according to George Beall, one of the best-informed fishermen in the Basque region, the principal ray of hope for the salmon resource was the Committee for Protecting the Adour Salmon, formed in 1963, which represents all the angling clubs having salmon in their waters. It was working towards common management of the resource on a watershed basis and was closely allied with the National Association for Protection of Salmon Rivers (called ANDRS). The committee planned to have a salmon hatchery in operation, while ANDRS hoped, among other things, to stop the spread of the 'micro-centrals', a menace which first appeared on the Allier River. These are small, privately-owned hydro-electric dams not producing enough power to justify their being taken over by the government agency, Électricité de France. They are usually not equipped with fish passes or ladders, and, having been abandoned by their original owners, are bought at bargain prices by speculators who repair them and sell the power to the government at a profit. (Under French law Électricité de France, which generates and distributes electricity for the nation, must purchase all generation offered for sale and incorporate it into its network.) Owners of such installations operate them without the necessary authorization or consent of Waters and Forests, regardless of the impact on the fishery. Thus a micro-central on the Gave d'Oloron was purchased by a wealthy French perfumer who rebuilt it and elevated the crest of the dam without permission and practically cut off the best spawning grounds on the river. Under pressure of ANDRS, however, he had to remedy this situation but meanwhile the fish runs suffered. A similar problem on the Nive was being worked on by the Committee for Protecting the Adour Salmon in 1965.

The resource today

There is a general belief, though statistics are scant, that the French salmon stocks have reached a nadir. Catches in the Adour River between Urt and Peyrehorade for the years 1952 to 1961, as estimated by Waters and Forests, fluctuated between a maximum of 2,100 and a low of 300 fish annually, with an average of 1,500, compared to about 6,000 in 1928. These catches were made by the *Inscrits*, for there are practically no rod fishermen in this part of the river. Total catches in the entire Adour basin in recent years probably have been in the neighbourhood of 3,000 to 5,000 salmon yearly, of which the nets in the first 15 kilometres, from Bayonne up to Urt, take the lion's share. The number of netsmen (*Inscrits*) operating to the head of tidewater has dropped greatly. In 1964 there were probably only a hundred nets in use compared with about 600 in 1937. The year 1966 saw something of a comeback. The Nive had one of the best salmon runs in the twentieth century. An extra and vital month of close season, January 15 to February 15, probably made a considerable difference.

Meanwhile a further setback in the effort to curtail netting in the Adour had arisen in the form of *plaisanciers*, non-professional salt-water fishermen who use their nets to catch salmon exclusively, thus competing with the licensed *Inscrits*, who understandably are up in arms, for there is no control over them since they do not need a licence.[16]

The Loire system, or what is left of it, now offers the best possibility of augmenting the salmon stocks of France. Only the Allier among its tributaries remains relatively pure and unobstructed. It has made a considerable comeback in recent years, thanks to the planting of salmon eggs and fry taken from the Gave d'Oloron, a programme incidentally that had to stop because the Committee for the Protection of the Adour Salmon protested the diversion of its stock.[17]

Rod catches on the Allier rose from 540 in 1952 to an average of 1,400 in the years 1958–1962.[18] The runs had increased enough to bring back the wheel-type fish traps, laid aside for thirty years, which were so efficient that they had been partly responsible for depletion of the Allier salmon in the first place!

Despite better fishing on the Allier and in tidewater, the general outlook for the Loire salmon is dim. Bachelier says that only 200 hectares (about 500 acres) of spawning grounds, capable of supporting 1,000 to 3,000 spawners, remain in the basin of the Loire, compared to 2,000 hectares (about 5,000 acres) formerly which supported over 100,000 breeders.[19] In addition to other adversities, a complex of nuclear power stations is rising at Chinon, on the Middle Loire. When the four plants are completed the entire low-stage flow of the Loire, and the smolts as well, will go through the cooling towers, unless a way is found to by-pass them. Fish losses are certain to occur.

About a dozen small coastal rivers in Brittany still yield catches of small salmon, of which the Blavet, Ellé and Aulne are the best. Average annual rod catches on Breton rivers are estimated as shown on the next page.

Normandy has few salmon streams left of any consequence (Bachelier reported in 1962). Despite its short spawning area and abusive net fishing in the spectacular Bay of Mont St. Michel at low tide, the Sélune still supports a very small run; on the Sienne, migratory fish are blocked by hydro-electric dams; on the Sée, the *Inscrits* take nearly all of the small run; and on the Orne, where the government made some subventions to install needed ladders, a trickle of fish was coming back. Perhaps the Seine, most renowned river in Normandy, typifies the fate of anadromous fishes in France. When plans were made in the early 1950s to restore the canal lock

River	Salmon (up to 6 kilos)		
Blavet	700		
Ellé	400	–	1,000
Odet	100	–	200
Steir	100	–	200
Aulne	400	–	1,000
Élorn	100	–	300
Penze	50	–	100
Dossen	70	–	100
Douron	60	–	100
Guer	100	–	300*
Jaudy	20		
Trieux	60*		
Total	2,160		4,430

* Includes catches by netters.

at Posses, a fish pass was designed for it by Waters and Forests. However, the lock was rebuilt by Bridges and Roads without the pass, and the salmon coming up the Seine found their way barred by this, the very first lock on the canalized river.

What is the future of the resource?

All of France's stock of salmon now depends on fish spawning in the Pyrénéean Gaves and in the Allier River. In fact, according to Waters and Forests, there remain in the entire country but 2,400 hectares (some 6,000 acres) of available salmon spawning grounds, not all of which are being used.

Since government bureaux are either immobilized or have abandoned hope of improving the stocks, the main conservation efforts now rest with local fishing groups and their national organizations. A few of these are quite active, as we have seen. Aside from the campaign against the micro-centrals which has forced a number of their owners to modify the installations to accord with the needs of migratory fish, ANDRS can boast of the following achievements: (1) recognition by Électricité de France of the wardens' right to visit its reservoirs to check on and repress netting or trapping of fish; (2) the agreement by Électricité de France and the Ministry of Industry to keep in effect and reinforce the river classification agreement dating from 1929 which stipulates that no new dams will be built on specified rivers until it becomes necessary to utilize all the hydro-electric potential in the country, in which case the salmon rivers will be the last to be developed; and (3) an agreement by which Électricité de France undertakes to finance a study of ways to protect seaward migration of smolts, aimed particularly at the problem on the Loire. ANDRS is also mounting a campaign to curb the outdated privileges of the *Inscrits* by pushing for the limitation of netting in the estuaries. It hopes to achieve this result by a simple administrative measure modifying downstreamward the limits of tidewater as presently determined for the exercise of the *Inscrits*' rights.

Epilogue

The disappearance of the great bulk of France's salmon stocks constitutes an irreparable economic loss. The streams are still there and the waters flow, but the fish find them inhospitable. They knock at the door of a river, so to speak, and discover that the gates are closed. A canal lock or dam bars the way; the people who built it did not care enough to provide the fish with a means of entry. Or if they gain admittance to a waterway and manage to elude the nets in the estuary and tidewater, they may encounter a zone of polluted matter, a mass of lower forms of plant life, bacteria and filamentous fungi. Suspended in the water, these organisms absorb the oxygen dissolved in it and deprive the fish of *their* oxygen. Only those species which require very little oxygen, like the carp, can thrive in this environment. Salmon suffocate. Yet in France river pollution has been less damaging to salmonids than overfishing, poaching, and especially the large number of dams and other impoundments built without any concern for migrating fish.

As a nation France seems to have lost since the Revolution of 1789 the sense of fishery conservation that animated the monarchs and great landowners of the Middle Ages and pre-Revolutionary period. It has failed where other nations have succeeded, often after painful trial and error, in evolving a national policy which to a larger or lesser degree safeguards the fishery when a river is usurped for generation of electricity, irrigation of cropland, or other purposes. France, in fact, seems never to have enunciated a national water policy but permitted its rivers to become the victims of anarchic development, pollution, and despoliation, with the result that valuable fishes have diminished or disappeared in one river after another.

As we contemplate the fiasco described in this chapter, we may recall the comment of de Boisset and Vibert in their book, *La Pêche Fluviale en France*: 'Woe to the guardians of the public wealth who, through ignorance or the crime of carelessness, have permitted the property of which they were the keepers to slip through their hands, since they can be sure that God on the Day of Judgment will make them pass on the left side.'

NOTES

1 *Standard Encyclopedia of the World's Rivers and Lakes*, p. 146.
2 Richard Vibert, *Recherches sur le Saumon de l'Adour*, p. 116.
3 Henri Boyer, *Le Saumon dans le Haut-Allier*, p. 26.
4 A. Thomazi, *Histoire de la Pêche*, p. 276.
5 *Ibid.*, p. 424.
6 R. Felix in his book on the Allier salmon says that there were contracts between masters and apprentices before the Revolution which stipulated that salmon could not be served more than once a week! (*Le Saumon Sa, Sa Vie, Pêche dans l'Allier*, p. 69.)
7 Henri Boyer, *op. cit.*, pp. 82–83.
8 Roger Bachelier, personal communication, November 25, 1964.
9 *Naturalia*, June 1963, p. 54.
10 Personal communication, November 25, 1964.
11 Commandant Latour, *Le Saumon dans les Courses d'Eau Bretons*, p. 43.
12 Roger Bachelier, *L'Histoire du Saumon en Loire*, p. 19.
13 Henri Boyer, *op. cit.*
14 *Ibid.*, p. 145.
15 De Boisset and Vibert, *La Pêche Fluvial en France*, p. 172.
16 Personal communication from George Beall, June 13, 1966.
17 Personal communication from George Beall, October 17, 1964.
18 Roger Bachelier, 'Situation Actuelle du Saumon en France', October 26, 1962.
19 Roger Bachelier, *L'Histoire du Saumon en Loire*, p. 42.

4

Baltic Jig-saw Puzzle

'The Baltic area', said the Swedish biologist Gunnar Alm, 'must, on the whole, be considered a fairly uniform and enclosed area as regards the propagation and migration of salmon' (Figure 4). Whether their home address, so to speak, is a river at the head of the Gulf of Finland or farther north in the Gulf of Bothnia, or several hundred miles south in Sweden, the Baltic salmon are fairly homogeneous and mingle freely in the sea.

River life

In his study, *Salmon in the Baltic Precincts*, Alm showed that the fish usually migrate to the sea in Germany and Poland after one year in the river; in Denmark and southern Sweden after two years; and in mid- and northern Sweden after three years. Many fish spend four and even five premigratory years in Baltic rivers. The urge to leave home is thought to depend to a large extent on the size of the parr while their growth rate is affected by temperature and food supply which consists largely of pupae of insects (species of *Ephemeroptera*, *Trichoptera*, *Plecoptera* and *Diptera*).

It is thought that the northern Scandinavian rivers, flowing through vast woodlands, are not as rich in food as southern rivers which flow mostly through crop and grazing lands. Also, the lower water temperatures and shorter feeding period in the north, where the rivers are frozen or ice-coated several months of the year, slow down the fishes' growth and delay their descent to the sea. Smolts leave Scandinavian waters in the spring when the temperature is about 50 degrees F. They are then five or six inches or longer.

Figure 4
The Baltic area.

Life in the sea

In May or June the rivers send forth shoals of young salmon into the Baltic, perhaps as many as ten million each year. They share the wine-dark sea with some 300,000 million herring, million million sprats and one billion cod. Here they find feeding grounds as rich as those their cousins enjoy in the north Atlantic. During their first year they seem to feed on insects floating on the surface of the water; later they turn to a fish diet.

Sea life, however, is extremely hazardous. According to the Swedish biologist Dr. Borje Carlin, only 10 to 20 per cent of the smolts are still alive after the first year. The rest are victims of predators; few die of disease. Of the survivors, a varying number of males will return to their home rivers as grilse; 30 per cent may be captured by fishermen in the open sea; 15 per cent may succumb from natural causes; and 10 per cent may return to the rivers as full-grown adults. Very few members of any given year-class are left in the Baltic after three winters there.

Smolts from northern Swedish rivers usually go straightaway to the south-western Baltic (Figure 5), travelling probably mostly at night, along the coast. They linger there, cramming down nutriment constantly, feeling safer from predators as they grow larger. According to Alm, most of the fish that have not returned to the rivers as grilse remain in the southern Baltic during their second winter; then a certain proportion go north to home waters; the remainder, not due to spawn for one or two years more, stay in these agreeable places or visit the eastern Baltic. Eventually they return to their home rivers by much the same route as they came, a journey of several hundreds of miles.

Some fish tagged on the island of Bornholm and in Poland were recaptured the same year far to the north in the Kemi River in Finland and the Torne River on the Swedish–Finnish border. Such relatively quick, long-distance journeys are not uncommon.[1]

A great deal has been learned about salmon migrations from the study, begun in the eighteenth century, of hooks found embedded in fishes' mouths. Salmon caught in the Bay of Bothnia were found with hooks used in the southern Baltic fishery, while specimens taken in southern waters bore hooks employed only in the northern Baltic. From hooks biologists have traced voyages from Angermanland in Sweden to the coasts of Estonia and Latvia, and from the island

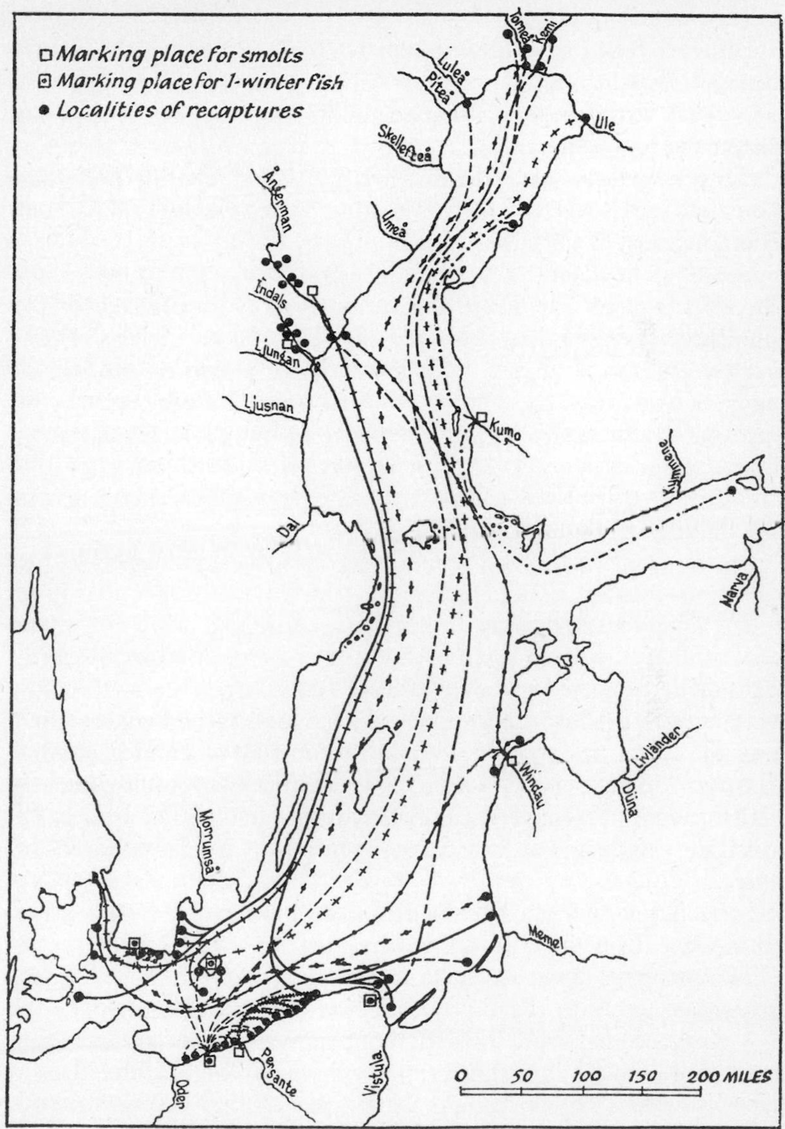

Figure 5

Migrations in Baltic of marked salmon (after Alm).

of Bornholm (in the vicinity of which fishing fleets make huge catches of salmon) to the Bay of Riga and Bay of Bothnia.

Alm believed that salmon from northern Sweden and northern Finland tend to migrate to the southern Baltic, and fish from the central coast of Sweden often cross the Baltic to the coasts of Latvia, Estonia or Lithuania.

Thus we can picture the Baltic Sea, which is 900 miles long and 50 to 400 miles wide, as a melting pot where fish from many lands come together, wander in small groups or in shoals, swim with the currents, in calm and relatively warm waters in summer and under the ice in winter. Their lengthy odysseys may seem patternless to us but they are inspired by an insatiable appetite and–who knows?–perhaps by a kind of wanderlust and curiosity. They crisscross the vast sea in search of sprats, herring, stickleback and sand-eels, the fish that comprise the staple of their diet, adding four to six pounds a year, growing more quickly in summer than in winter when they go closer to the surface.

Swedish river fishery

Salmon are known to have inhabited about fifty Swedish rivers of varying size in their pristine state, of which three-fourths empty into the Baltic Sea and the others into the Kattegat and Skagerrak.

Salmo salar is now found chiefly in the central and northern Baltic rivers. This is a region of soft and undulating landscapes, covered with forests of spruce, birch and pine, and sparsely settled. Here are the mighty Dal River, regarded as the boundary between central and northern Sweden, the Ljusnan, Ljungan, Indal, Angerman, Ume, Skellefte, Lule, Kalix and Torne Rivers (Figure 4).

Salmon enter fresh water from the sea during the summer and spawning occurs in the very large headwaters during October and November. Small tributaries seem to be unsuitable for spawning due to severe climatic conditions. Fish returning for the first time to Swedish rivers have been on the average two or three winters in the sea.

Four salmon tagged in Sweden have been recovered so far in the Greenland fishery. The two smolts that journeyed to the Sukkertoppen area from the west coast,[2] taking about eighteen months to cover 2,270 nautical miles, indicate that this may be the rendezvous of all or most of the west-coast salmon. More sensational was the discovery of two fish, released as smolts in the Lulea River in the Gulf of Bothnia, off the east coast of Greenland. These were not only the first foreign salmon recaptured in east Greenland waters but the first known to have left the Baltic for a journey that may have encompassed over 3,000 miles–the longest sea voyage on record for Atlantic salmon! The recaptures of the Lulea fish, says Dr. Paul Hansen, the Danish biologist in charge of Greenland fishery investigations, 'are of special interest owing to the fact that the Baltic stock of salmon always has been considered as a local stock and very few . . . tagged in the Baltic have been caught outside the area'.

The rapid-strewn waterways of northern Sweden flow past villages of red wooden houses, fields where cattle graze, and little towns with white stucco churches surmounted by slender black spires. In the north settlements are few and far apart and are located mainly along the highway and on the coast. Railway bridges of astonishing dimensions cross the rivers as they rush down to the sea; massive log rafts are floated to the sawmills and pulp mills which line the lower reaches, all the way from the Dal River to the Torne.

In the winter six feet of snow blankets the north and the soil is frozen. The white-barked, leafless birches are etched against the leaden sky while the pines and spruce form symmetrical patterns of green on the landscape. Darkness comes early but even in daylight villages seem asleep. Rivers are frozen. Huge icicles hang from the boulders at waterfalls, and the flow is but a trickle. Young salmon are hibernating in the deep water, waiting for spring and the warming sun to call the insect world on which they feed into life.

From Stockholm the highway runs north through endless, thinly-stocked forests almost to the Arctic Circle. At Haparanda it crosses into Finland, then turns south to Helsinki, passing many fine salmon rivers, but now only two still harbour considerable quantities of anadromous fish. This bleak land of forest and tundra may be inhospitable to man, who is an interloper, but it is well suited to the salmon that were here long before he set foot on Baltic shores.

In the large valleys of Norrland salmon fishing has been a prominent industry for centuries. Fish were caught in many ways. The oldest method was a stationary structure into which they were lured. The Lapps, earliest inhabitants of northern Scandinavia, built barrier-traps across the narrows of a river.[3] During the Middle Ages the seine was a familiar sight. The Vikings stored plenty of fish in the holds of their long black ships to sustain them at sea and during their raids on the coasts of Europe.

I stood at the mouth of the Ume River where it flows into the Baltic. It was a warm autumnal day. The river was flanked by a thin forest of silver birch. In the fading golden twilight no human habitations could be seen. Some farmers were setting their eel traps. The honking of migrating geese broke the stillness. Now and then a fish leaped out of the water in a swift arc-like movement. There was not much time for it to reach the spawning grounds because soon the days would be quite short and ice would cover the river. The scene had not changed much since the fierce Norse warriors mounted their invasion of Russia from this very locality.

Until fairly recently the fishing industry had flourished in Norrland, providing farmers with a food supply in an area where meat was scarce, and often with additional income. Crawls (fish pens), pole traps, float nets and seines were used. Fish were even taken in the spawning season. According to a report by Carl Bystrom of 1867, salmon from the Angerman River fetched fairly high prices: six to seven (American) dollars per lispund (18¾ pounds) in the spring and four to five dollars per lispund in the summer. Salmon caught far upriver were lean and poor and brought only two to three dollars per lispund.

Most of the lower-river catch was sold at Härnösand on the coast, whence it was transported farther south, but a goodly portion was disposed of locally, for fish was the main source of protein food. Uno Lappea, a fishery officer in Lulea, relates, for example, that about 900 pounds of salmon were consumed yearly in his parents' household early in the twentieth century. In his native village of Kengis it was not uncommon for a single family to consume fifty salmon a year. The fish were salted down in wooden barrels soon after being taken from the river; after a couple of days they were removed, the mucus and brine scraped off, and salted again in large, well-cleaned vessels kept in cellars specially built for the purpose. This supply

---

5a and 5b. Näs smolt-rearing station, summer and winter views. The station was built to produce 125,000 smolts per year for the Lule River in northern Sweden.

commonly lasted until the hay harvest was completed the next summer.

Salmon was prepared in rather simple ways: baked, or partly steamed on top of potatoes in a boiling pot. Kidneys and liver were ground up into a pudding and the roe was salted and eaten. Such dishes harked back to Viking days.

Originally, Swedish salmon fisheries, as in other European countries, belonged to the Crown and were granted to various subjects for services rendered. They are now either owned by the Government or by individuals whose titles are derived by descent from the original grantees or by purchase from their descendants or the Crown. There are peasant holdings with fishing rights handed down from generation to generation for 400 years.

The usual arrangement in the nineteenth century and before was joint ownership of seines or weirs by several farms with the catch divided up according to an ancient custom–the number of people in each household.

Harvests fluctuated widely. In some years they were munificent and in others lean. We hear of apprentices and servants complaining they were forced to eat salmon too frequently. For instance, Crown Forester Yngve Bostrom relates that in the summer of 1917, when he was on assignment in the village of Brannland on the Ume River, the sawmill owner treated him to salmon at practically every meal. When he expressed his delight about the menu, his host said, 'Salmon is something one can tire of,' went to his desk, and drew out an ancient document called a 'service contract' which contained stipulations not only about wages and vacations but a clause stating that servants were not obliged to eat salmon more than ten times a week![4]

Uncertainty of the runs was the most certain aspect of the fishing industry. One year's harvest foretold little about the next. The general trend of the catches, however, was downward. Farmers in the Angerman Valley attributed the decline to the 'mass of large and small steamers which in recent years have begun to ply the

---

6a. Hatchery at Näs with conventional wooden troughs and hatchery boxes fed by water which is pressure-filtered and aerated.

6b. Netting out and loading smolt at Näs into a 'fish pullman' or transport tank on a truck.

waters', to increased logging, and to overfishing the lower stretches, not suspecting that there was possibly a periodicity in biological numbers unrelated to man's activities. Although overfishing was most often cited as the cause of reduced catches, there was hardly any offshore netting for salmon in Sweden before the twentieth century.

The salmon curve

'The fishing fluctuates from year to year to a high degree,' said Carl Bystrom in 1867, speaking of the Angerman River, 'so that where five years ago a fisherman could catch 2,100 lispund (39,000 pounds) and the following year 1,400 lispund (26,000 pounds), the next two years yielded only 300 lispund (560 pounds) and 200 lispund (375 pounds).'

That fishing luck depends to some extent on weather is well known. In the spring weather and water levels in the river played important roles. Low water deterred the salmon from going upstream while high water attracted them. Seining crews knew that their chances of success depended on whether the fish came along their side of the river or their neighbour's. Beyond these changes in the characteristics of the river and habits of the fish there was a more important factor–the size of the salmon population. When the runs were heavy the possibilities of a good catch were high; when they were slender, the odds were less favourable.

The question widely asked is: on what factors do the good and bad years depend? In his classic study of salmon catches in the rivers of northern Sweden for the period 1850–1950, Lindroth found that fluctuations were remarkably synchronized in the Baltic region as a whole. 'Whether the rivers are regulated or unregulated, pure or polluted, with or without power dams, with or without accessory artificial propagation, the trend of the catches in most of them is very similar.'[5] There must consequently be similar forces at work in the different waters or in the sea where the international stocks mingle.

Discounting fishing intensities, Lindroth concluded that 'the recorded long-term fluctuations are due to fluctuations in the salmon stock'. Thus, the problem centres around population dynamics, about which little is known for so complex an animal who has moreover a limited biotic efficiency compared with the herring or cod. In brief, discussing the long-term trends, Lindroth ruled out environmental changes such as variations in water levels and water temperature in the rivers as major causative factors; nor did he find any correlation between the rise and fall of salmon populations and those of predatory river fishes.

Are the fluctuations produced by undeterminable factors in the sea? Some investigators like Gunnar Svärdson see a significant relationship between the occurrence of severe winters in the Baltic with a maximum ice cover and a peak salmon yield some years later. He also believes there is a connection between the prevalence of porpoises in the sea and the size of salmon stocks in the rivers. Lindroth is inclined to accept the first theory but rejects the second since, upon examining the stomachs of some fifty porpoises, he discovered that they were crammed with sprat, herring, cod and other very abundant fishes, but no salmon!

The biological explanation of the long-term swings in catches, dramatically illustrated in Lindroth's 'Salmon Curve' (Figure 6), is still obscure. 'The main factors must be sought in changes in the biological balance induced by climatic factors', he concluded. Cyclical fluctuations in populations of fish and birds that prey on salmon, and insects and fishes that constitute their food supply, may be influential. Little or no information, however, is available to throw light on these aspects of the mystery.

The total river catch in all Baltic lands in recent years has been in the neighbourhood of 250 metric tons annually. Although netting has been greatly curtailed by hydro-electric dams, Sweden still accounts for one-half to two-thirds of all the salmon taken in the Baltic rivers, the Soviet Union for the major portion of the remainder, Finland for perhaps 10 per cent, and Poland for an insignificant amount.

Rod fishing is quite limited because the salmon is rather unwilling to take the bait in fresh water. There are only three or four Swedish rivers where angling occurs and these are extremely hard fished or in poor condition. Fishing is closely regulated. Close seasons are fixed by individual river but is usually from the middle of September to the break-up of the ice, or to a fixed date in the spring (which may be as late as June 1 or June 15). Fixed and floating gear must shut down one or two days a week.

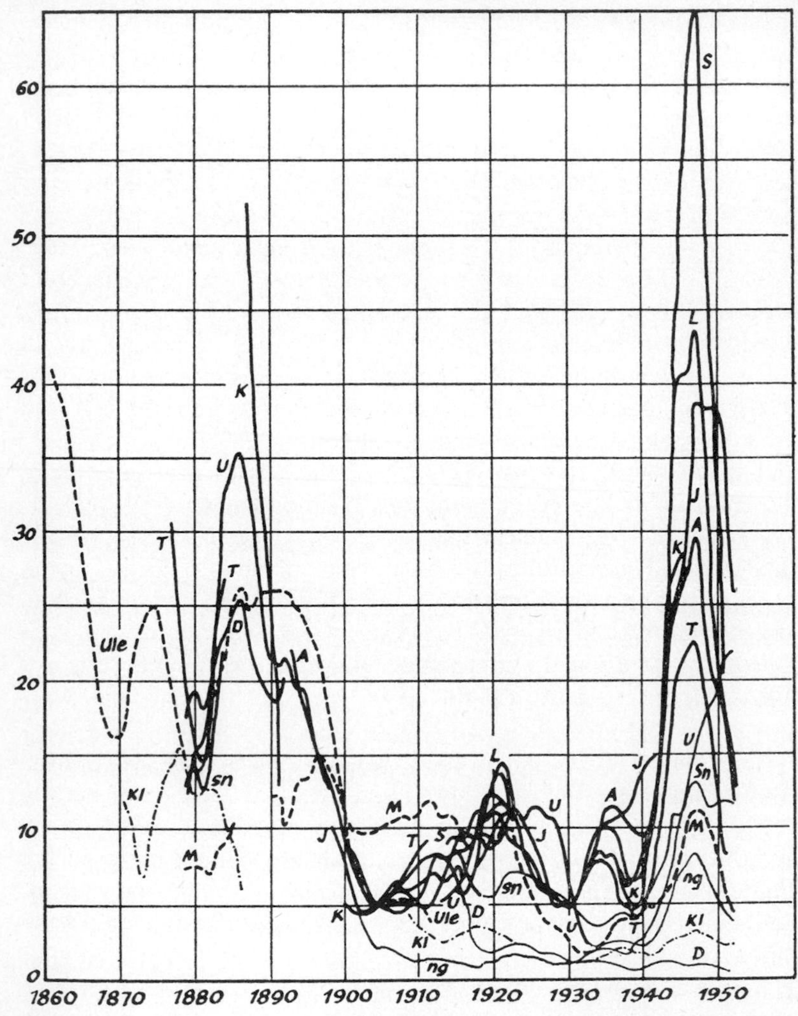

Figure 6

Commercial salmon catches in Swedish rivers (arbitrary weight units of moving five-year means). Thick lines: undamaged periods. Thin lines: after curtailment by power developments.

KEY to Figure 6

River	Abbreviation	'10' in height scale = ton	Years represented
Ule	Ule	24	1860–1912
Torne	T	31	1877–84, 1903–11, 1917–23, 1933–48
Kalix	K	13	1887–90, 1900–23, 1931–48
Lule	L	31	1885, 1915–23, 1931–
Skellefte	S	5·4	1914–
Ume	U	12	1879–1908, 1913–
Angerman	A	16	1893–
Indal	J	16	1898–
Ljungan	ng	15	1894–
Ljusnan	sn	21	1879–84, 1915–
Dal	D	21	1879–92, 1897–
Mörrum	M	20	1879–85, 1890–
Klar	Kl	20	1870–86, 1903–22, 1932–47

High-seas fishery

Baltic salmon are now for the most part commercially exploited in the open sea (Table 5) where they are captured by gill nets and floating longlines. Hundreds of fishing vessels issue from Danish harbours, from Swedish fishing villages, from Kiel in Germany, from Gdynia and Danzig in Poland, in search of salmon. They operate around the Danish island of Bornholm, in the southern Baltic, and farther north between the Swedish islands of Öland and Gotland. They also fish the eastern Baltic off Mememland down to Brusterort and in the Bay of Danzig. A typical 40-ton Danish cutter carries a crew of four. The Danes, who produce few salmon in their country, account for about half the total Baltic catch.

Fishing is a ceaseless routine of drifting, laying nets and hauling them in; of back-breaking work in cold winds and strong currents. The crew have to handle their tackle in rain and fog that make passing ships almost invisible. The waters around the island of Bornholm, where the main salmon fishing effort is concentrated, are frozen on the average one winter out of five, and there are times when the entire sea is covered with ice. The fish must be cleaned and packed in narrow, cramped quarters even as the vessel is tossed by the waves or pushed by the ice. As soon as one night's haul is landed, the gear must be readied for another. There is little time for rest.

Salmon are taken by means of longlines or drift nets. The Danes,

Table 5
Salmon catches in the Baltic area,* 1940–1964
(*metric tons*)

	Sweden							
Year	*Rivers*	*Coast & Sea*	*Den-mark*	*West Germany*	*Poland*	*USSR*	*Finland*	*Total*
1940	85	176	49	NA	NA	62	162	534
1941	151	267	77	NA	NA	NA	413	908
1942	165	345	126	NA	NA	NA	403	1,039
1943	246	592	153	NA	NA	NA	323	1,314
1944	215	700	142	NA	NA	NA	224	1,281
1945	548	1,233	156	NA	NA	NA	224	2,181
1946	613	1,474	475	NA	277	79	475	3,393
1947	421	1,218	630	NA	475	161	395	3,300
1948	410	1,248	851	NA	394	280	289	3,472
1949	365	1,105	843	NA	283	185	260	3,041
1950	351	1,339	1,317	192	365	155	399	4,118
1951	211	1,098	1,096	136	82	151	352	3,126
1952	221	790	1,350	144	43	149	383	3,080
1953	171	412	753	75	24	117	350	1,914
1954	100	472	962	121	43	96	400	2,184
1955	107	298	609	158	17	109	200	1,497
1956	142	670	961	285	156	71	300	2,585
1957	132	340	893	345	133	61	200	2,104
1958	107	288	892	194	135	NA	150	1,766
1959	114	358	933	243	79	NA	150	1,868
1960	114	425	1,096	217	100	NA	200	2,152
1963	NA	371	1,133	180	335	200	368	2,587
1964[a]	NA	631	1,721	NA	357	235	465	3,407

* Includes river, off-shore and open-sea fisheries. [a] Preliminary.
Sources: Gunnar Alm, 'The Salmon Catch and the Salmon Stock in the Baltic During Recent Years', the Swedish Salmon Research Institute and the International Council for the Exploration of the Sea.

who have the largest fleet, use mostly long, shallow, large-meshed nets. The boat and the nets drift through the night. Only a lantern indicates their presence.

Longlining, which involves more complicated gear, consists of a main line to which a nylon line 52–66 feet long, baited with hooks, is attached. A cutter may set 1,500 to 2,000 hooks during the night, each with a piece of hornfish, herring or sprat. The operation begins with the placing of a buoy in the water, followed by other buoys at intervals of every 80 hooks, the whole forming a procession up to 18 miles long, marked by 25 or more buoys. Every buoy carries a numbered flag and usually a battery-charged lamp. Since salmon bite better in poor weather, gear may be set in a strong wind. Navigation equipment permits the skipper to pinpoint his position when setting and picking up his lines.

Since the Baltic is heavily travelled by small and large craft, longlines are often severed and sometimes destroyed. Fish in the nets are bitten and mangled by seals which trail the fleets. A good night's catch may average two salmon for every hundred hooks set out.

Around noon the lines are pulled in and the fish, gleaming in their silver-lead hues, their scales shiny and their bodies exuding great strength, are taken aboard with a hand net, immediately eviscerated and packed in ice. If the catch is good the work may take many hours and after that the lines must be set again.

Salmon fishing with large, powerful boats is carried on almost the year round in the eastern Baltic but is most profitable from September through April. There is little activity in summer when the fish disappear into the lower depths (Table 6).

Danish fishermen take their cargoes to Bornholm while the Germans, who also fish the eastern Baltic, land theirs mostly at Kiel. Comparatively little of the valuable catch is sold domestically by the Danes; the bulk goes to foreign buyers. Although Sweden plays a minor role in the fishery, it supplies from natural and artificial production as much as 60 per cent of the stocks in the Baltic, with the remainder coming chiefly from rivers in Finland and Soviet Russia.[6]

The high-seas fishery has grown rapidly since 1950. Studies of catches indicate, according to Dr. Borje Carlin, director of the Swedish Salmon Research Institute, that 'very young fish make [up] too large a percentage of the total catch, which means a waste of not unlimited resources'. The size composition of the 1964–65 Danish

Table 6
Danish salmon catches in eastern Baltic Sea
July 1964–June 1965

Month	*Catch (metric tons)*	*Per cent*
July	0	0
August	53	3
September	171	10
October	219	14
November	169	10
December	248	16
January	215	14
February	132	8
March	154	10
April	122	8
May	79	5
June	27	2
Total	1,589	100

Source: O. Christensen, 'The Danish Salmon Fishery in the Eastern Baltic in the Season, 1964–65'.

catch, totalling 402,000 fish, for example, was as follows: 1–5 kilograms, 61 per cent; 5–7 kilograms, 20·5 per cent; 7–9 kilograms, 15·2 per cent; and 9 kilograms or more, 3·4 per cent. In other words, one out of two fish weighed less than 9 pounds and three out of five less than 11 pounds.[7] 'It is shown by using a model of the Baltic salmon based on tagging experiments', says Carlin, 'that a reduction of the fishing effort in the sea leads to an increase of the value of the total catch. The number of fish caught by the fishermen on the coast and in the rivers would increase considerably. The number of fish caught in the high seas will be reduced, but this would be fully or nearly fully compensated by an increased mean weight and a higher price per kilo.'[8]

In order to lessen the exploitation of immature salmon the leading nations involved in the Baltic fishery, Denmark, Sweden and the Federal Republic of Germany, signed an agreement which became effective on March 1, 1966, that stipulates: (1) nets of natural fibre shall be 165 mm. wide and nets of synthetic fibre 157 mm. wide; (2) the span of fish-hooks on drift lines and set lines used to catch salmon shall measure at least 19 mm.; and (3) salmon which do not measure 60 cm. (23·6 inches) from the snout to the tail 'must not be landed, sold, offered, held on board, kept or forwarded, but shall immediately after catching be set out in the water again'. The provisions of this treaty apply in the entire fishable Baltic Sea, including the Gulf of Bothnia and Gulf of Finland. Other countries which participate in the fishery may ratify the agreement or put its provisions into effect.[9]

Fish and power too

The Baltic nations face the problem of maintaining their salmon runs in the face of expanding hydro-electric development which blockades spawning rivers. One prerequisite for Sweden's extensive industrial progress in recent decades, which has raised its living standards to one of the highest levels in Europe, is the harnessing of its waters to provide industry with inexpensive forms of energy. Its coal deposits are niggardly, it has no petroleum or natural gas, and its forests are too valuable to be converted into charcoal or fuel-wood. Sweden is one of the few countries in the world where 90–95 per cent of the electricity is generated from water power.

Eighty per cent of the nation's hydro-electric potential is found in the Norrland region which is also the major source of its salmon supply. Until the 1940s the demand for electric power could be met without encroaching significantly upon productive salmon waters except for such rivers as the Dal and Ljungan. Since World War II the insatiable thirst for power has brought hydro-electric projects into other rivers–the Ljusnan, Indal, Angerman, Ume, Lule and Skellefte. On waterways whose upper reaches had already been dammed, even the lower stretches have been pre-empted.

In the early phase of hydro-electric development Sweden adopted the conventional practice of installing fishways at the dams to permit salmon to ascend the rivers. It was also customary to plant fry or one-year-old parr in waters which provided favourable nursery grounds, mostly areas still accessible to running stock. As more power dams were erected the pattern became clear: each new project would destroy an additional section of a river until finally all natural production would cease. The Swedish power planners were consequently faced with a serious dilemma: they could abandon the salmon runs or find some means of replacing them. At this point their decision was simplified by the Swedish Water Courts, acting under a special Water Law, which would not approve requests by the State Power Administration or private power companies to build hydroelectric dams unless assurance was given that the destroyed salmon production would be replaced. In other words, instead of succumbing to the slogan, 'We need kilowatts more than salmon', as France and Spain did, Sweden was determined to have fish and power too. After much consideration it was decided that the only practicable way of maintaining salmon populations in harnessed rivers would be to replace lost natural stocks by rearing salmon in hatcheries and planting the smolts in the streams.

Figure 7 shows the present state of Sweden's salmon rivers, the reaches still accessible and those blocked off.

If you visit the Bergeforsen power plant on the Indal River, one of a network of thirteen generating stations stretching from Lake Storsjön down to the Gulf of Bothnia, and stand on the railing overlooking the water, you will see no fish migrating upstream. Logs from a half-mile-long anchored timber boom hurtle down the 425-foot chute at the rate of 21,000 per hour, tumbling over each other in their haste to reach the mills where they will be reduced to pulp for paper. At the rearing station below the spillway, which like most is far down the river, the big salmon are trapped as they return to the river and stripped of roe and milt. A plaque informs you that 'The station is built to produce fry and young migratory fish who, before the erection of the power plant, could reproduce freely in the river. Through the river they reached the sea, maintaining rich populations of salmon, sea-trout and river-spawning whitefish. Now, instead, the fry and young are liberated from the rearing station.

Figure 7 (opposite)

Swedish salmon rivers. Thick line: present accessible reaches. Double lines: former accessible reaches. Bar across river: fish pass. Arrow: trucking of spawners.

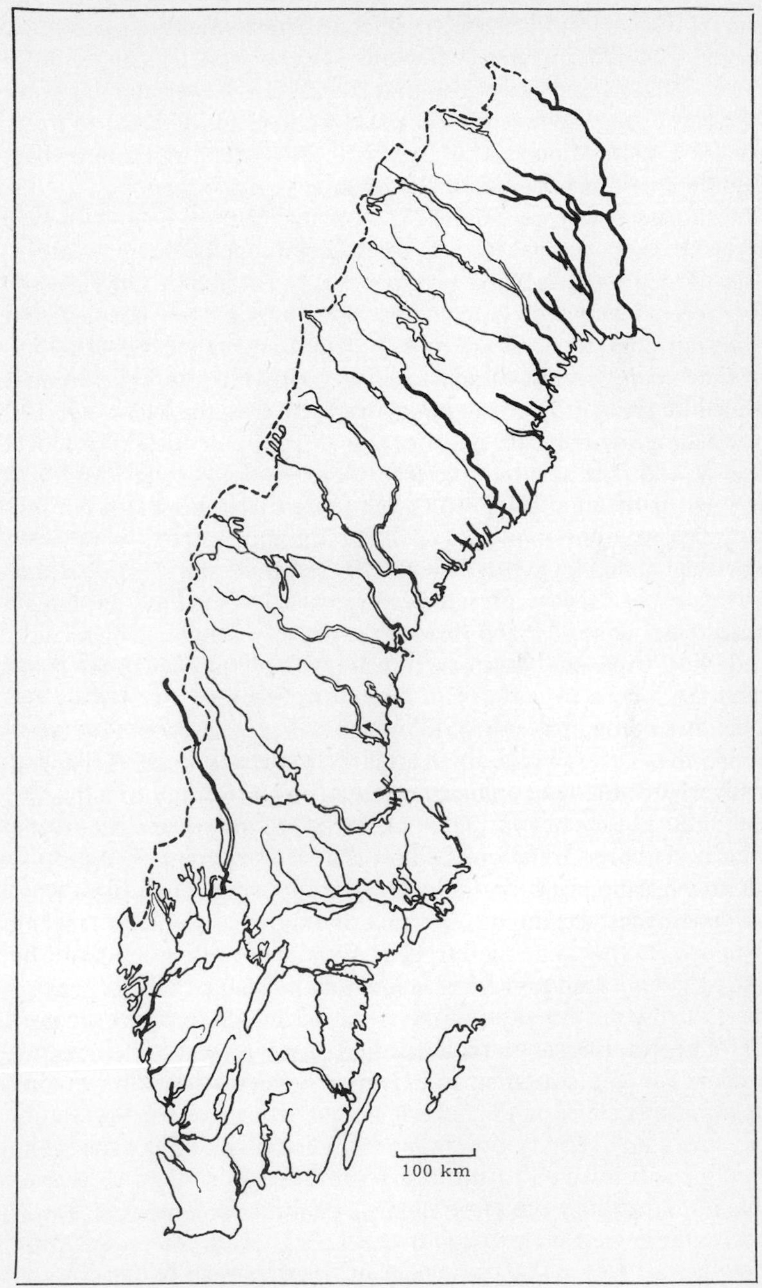
100 km

Annual planned production is 320,000 salmon smolts, 40,000 other smolts, 10 million whitefish fry and 150,000 whitefish fingerlings.'

The Water Courts stipulate that the private power companies or the State Power Administration must produce and liberate so many fish. The Water Courts also determine how much riparian owners should be paid for the loss of their fishings on the rivers.

'Fish passes were very useful at a time when only steep falls were exploited for power generation,' said Carlin, one of the main architects of the salmon-rearing programme, in 1959, 'but now also the river reaches with a low gradient are widely used for this purpose, and so the reproductive areas are more or less completely destroyed.'[10]

Since many rivers could no longer provide the environment needed for fry to grow to migratory stage, Swedish biologists decided to try an experiment on a scale new to European fishery science. They would raise salmon in hatcheries to the smolt stage and liberate them at the mouths of rivers below the dams. Financed entirely by the electric power industry, the programme started 'with more hope than actual knowledge about how it would work', said Carlin. On the whole, however, it has been remarkably successful although it had to surmount many difficulties, especially diseases which could (and did) wipe out almost an entire year-class of fish in some instances. There are now 17 hatcheries in Sweden operated by the State Power Administration and private power companies producing salmon that never see the river until their parr marks have changed to silver and their physiological mechanisms are ready to adjust to sea life. At the age of two years or less they are tossed into the rivers, given a 'God bless you!' and sent towards the hazardous Baltic.

Smolt-rearing plants on the main rivers are shown in Figure 8.

From modest beginnings in 1951 the output of smolts reached 1,659,000 in 1965 and the target is about 1·7 million annually by 1970 (Table 7). Fish passes and ladders are no longer built at Swedish power facilities and many of those installed in older projects are now idle. The planting of salmon fry and parr, carried on for many decades, has also ceased since it is now believed that it never had much positive effect on the fishery.

As the smolt-rearing programme developed the biologists wondered if the fish would have the same vitality and endurance as wild salmon, and exhibit the same homing instinct. To obtain information on these vital matters the Swedish Salmon Research Institute through 1963 tagged 800,000 smolts before they were released in the

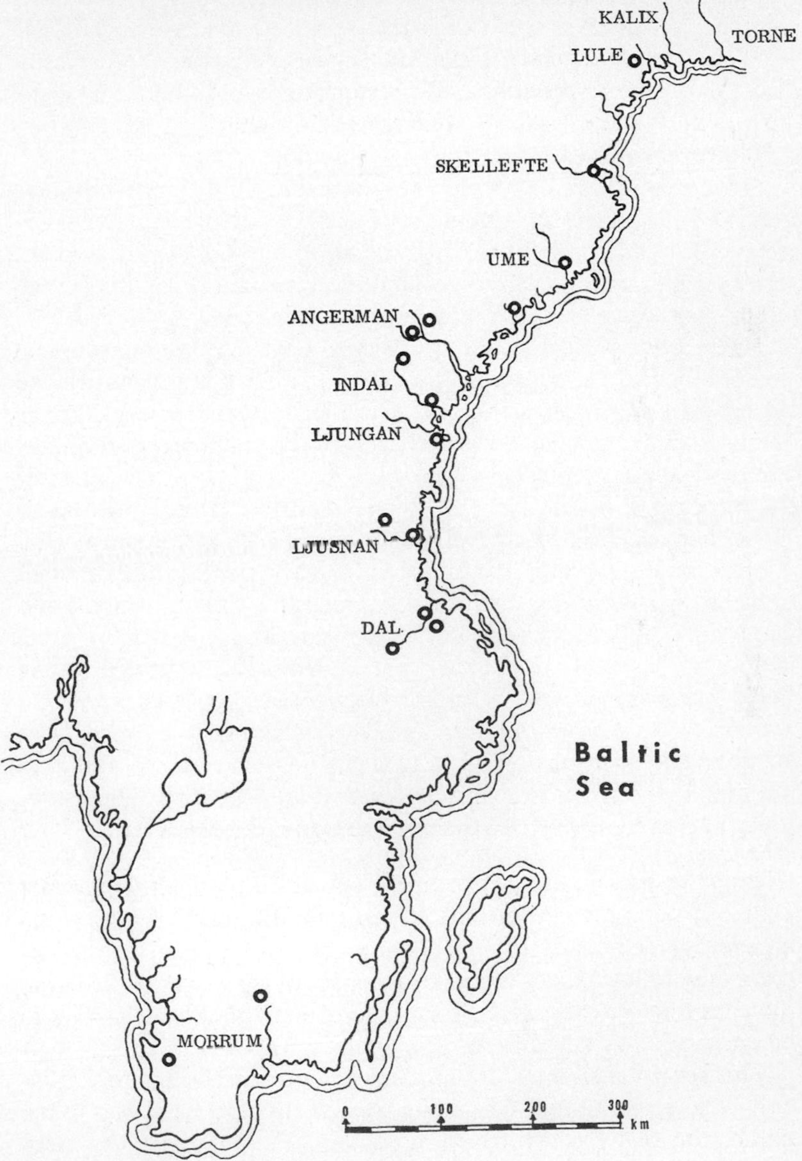

Figure 8
Main salmon rivers of Sweden and smolt-rearing plants.

Table 7
Preliminary survey of smolt production in Swedish Baltic rivers, 1900–1970 (*millions*)

River	*1900*	*1920*	*1940*	*1960*	*Projected 1970 Natural*	*1970 Artificial*
Torne	0·68	0·68	0·68	0·68	0·68	0
Kalix	0·25	0·25	0·25	0·25	0·25	0
Lule	0·54	0·54	0·54	0·50	0·01	0·53
Skellefte	0·11	0·11	0·11	0·10	0	0·11
Ume	0·35	0·35	0·20	0·25	0·25	0·10
Angerman	0·30	0·30	0·27	0·22	0	0·30
Indal	0·32	0·32	0·29	0	0	0·32
Ljungan	0·30	0·10	0·10	0·10	0·10	0·03
Ljusnan	0·4	0·3	0·3	0·1	0·10	0·30
Dal	0·3	0·1	0·05	0·1	0·05	0
Mörrum	0·3	0·24	0·11	0·11	0·11	0
Total	3·85	3·29	2·90	2·41	1·55	1·69

Source: Arne Lindroth.

rivers. The present average return is about 12 per cent (compared with 1–3 per cent in Norway), at least for Bothnian rivers, or 50 kilograms (110 pounds) of fish for every 100 smolts. From the returns it is evident that the stocks are in the order of those which existed in the rivers before they were blocked, and that the volume of fish to be harvested has not suffered.

This record is all the more remarkable since, according to Carlin, only 10 to 20 per cent of the smolts are still alive after one year in the Baltic, the rest are victims of predators. Few of them die from disease. Of those that survive the first year, a varying proportion, practically all males, will return as grilse and others will be captured by fishermen in the open sea. Perhaps not more than 1–2 per cent of

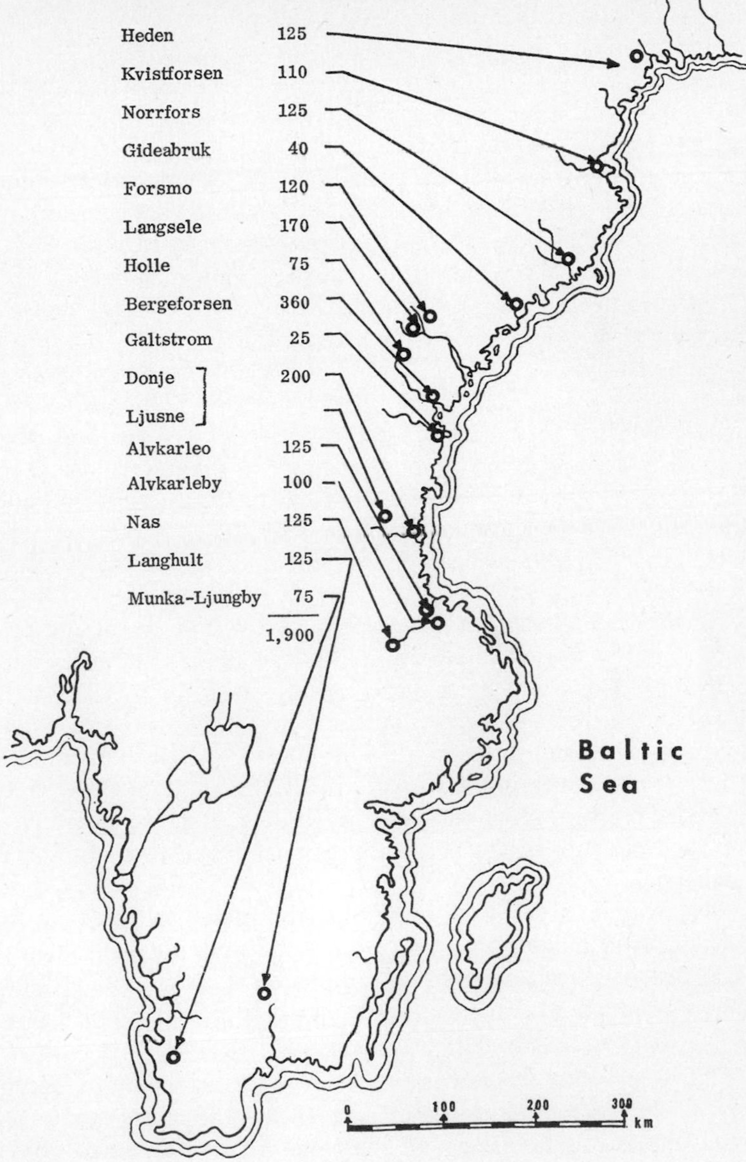

Figure 9

Swedish salmon hatcheries and smolt production (1,000's).

any year-brood of smolts will return to the rivers as full-grown adults. Less than 1 per cent of those which return to rivers are taken in waters other than the parent or 'foster parent' stream. Thus, an important discovery has been made by the Swedish scientists: the homing instinct is related to the place where the smolts are released and not to natal waters. In many instances eggs are taken from salmon captured in one river, the fry reared in a second, and the smolts liberated in a third. The adults from this group always return to the stream where they are liberated, even if they stayed there only a very short time before migrating to the sea. This phenomenon indicates that a hatchery can be located where it is most convenient and not necessarily on the river it may serve.

Salmon are now reared in central and south Sweden (Figure 9) and trucked in the autumn or spring in 'fish pullmans' several hundred miles to northern smolt-receiving stations and then planted in the spring in rivers at the foot of the lowermost dams. Here they return one to three years later and an adequate number are stripped of their eggs and milt to start new generations in the hatcheries. The kelts are usually permitted to recuperate and return to the sea.

Swedish salmon hatcheries are among the most efficient and productive in the world. They are models of automation: little trains drop tiny food pellets at regular intervals to the baby fish in the plastic or concrete 'antiseptic' ponds. Few persons are seen on the premises. The fish even obtain medical care from a 'fish doctor'. In a few years all rearing stations will exclusively use pelleted or crumbled food from the very start of feeding, after the alevin have absorbed the yolk sac, as is already done at Bergeforsen and other hatcheries.

The Salmon Research Institute at Älvkarleby, financed by the electric power industry, is dedicated to the study of physiological, ecological, genetical and technical problems associated with artificial salmon production. Among other things it is trying to breed races of fish that are resistant to disease in the hatchery, have superior

---

7a. Double bag-net fishing off the coast of Norway. Taken from a seaplane.

7b. A part of the drift-net fleet at Sörnaer, Finnmark, Norway. Drifters take a large number of salmon off the north Norwegian coast.

ability to evade predators in the sea, grow more quickly during the freshwater phase of their lives, and exhibit certain regular characteristics which will permit accurate predictions of the migratory cycle.

It costs about 50 cents (3s. 6d.) to rear a young salmon for two years; the scale of operations is lavish, the overall investment enormous. Hence Swedish biologists are moving towards the production of smolts in one year instead of two by means of growth-stimulating foods.

It is estimated that one out of every four salmon now caught in the Baltic Sea is the product of a Swedish hatchery. Danish fishermen reap the largest share of the benefits but, as Dr. Erik Montén, director of hatcheries for the Swedish State Power Administration, told me: 'The investment is only fair compensation for use of our rivers for hydro-electric generation. In fact, the costs of building fish passes at power dams and sacrificing the water needed for other purposes would be higher than the costs of rearing salmon artificially.' These expenses are borne by consumers in the form of slightly higher electric bills.

Table 7 and Figure 10 provide a picture of what has happened (and will happen) to Sweden's Baltic salmon rivers in terms of smolt production. By 1960 the most northern streams, Torne, Kalix, Lule and Skellefte, were still unimpaired. The Ume had lost about one-third and the Angerman one-fourth of its natural runs; the Indal was completely blockaded; the Ljungan had only one-third, the Ljusnan one-fourth, the Dal and the Mörrum one-third of their natural salmon stocks, but all were furnished with artificially bred fish to sustain the normal levels of production–as required by the Water Courts. It is predicted that by 1970 only the Torne and Kalix Rivers would still be free of power dams and remain natural salmon rivers; all the others of consequence would have to depend in varying degrees on smolt plantings. According to Lindroth, of the 3,250,000 smolts issuing into the Baltic Sea annually by 1970, about

---

8a. A salmon ladder in Vester River, Finnmark, Norway. The ladder, which is partly in a tunnel, was built in 1965, and the salmon entered it as soon as it was opened.

8b. A salmon ladder at a waterfall, Burfjord, Troms, Norway. One of about a hundred new, effective salmon ladders built in north Norway since World War II.

52 per cent will come from hatcheries and 48 per cent from the rivers' nursery grounds.

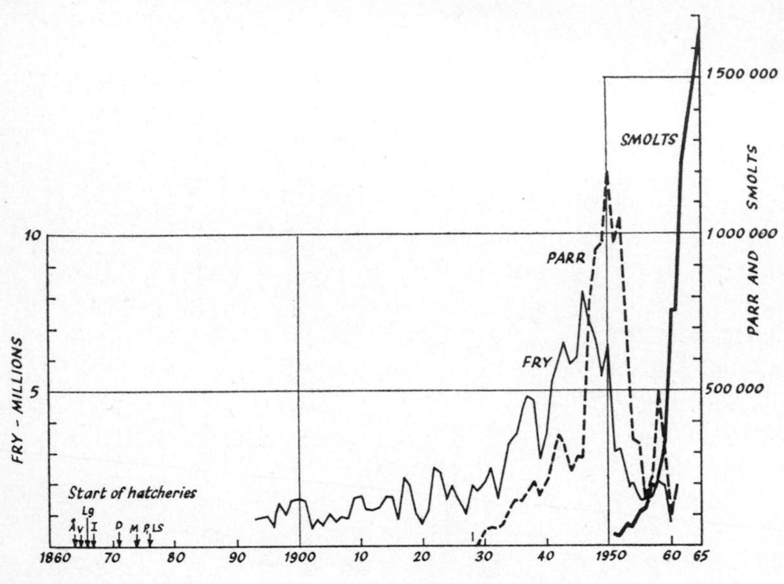

Figure 10

Swedish plantings of salmon in Baltic rivers.

Salmon in Finland

Well-wooded and well-watered, hardly any part of Finland is more than ten miles from a lake or river. The waters of the central plateau find their way to the coastal strip in a series of rapids and sometimes waterfalls which are a prime source of power in a country that has no coal. Many of the Finnish rivers have been developed for power purposes and their salmon runs have largely disappeared.

In 1948 the biologist T. H. Jarvi wrote: 'The two great salmon rivers of southern Finland have to a great extent–in fact, almost completely–lost their original conditions and simultaneously their importance as salmon rivers. Dams now block the ascent of salmon and consequently have done away with feeding areas for parr. Several fishing stations where my material was formerly collected have had to cease operations. This occurred in the western arm of the Kymi River at Ahvenkoski Rapids in 1931 and in its eastern arm, at Langinkoski Rapids and Kanninkoski Rapids in 1938. . . . This is also the case in the Kokemaki River. The construction of a power station at Pirila Rapids in Harjavalta in 1940 has stopped the ascent of salmon to the upper part of the Kokemaki River.'[11] Jarvi also noted in 1948 that the great Oulu River in northern Finland was obstructed by a power dam without fish passes and the excellent Kemi River was slated to be dammed close to the sea.

In 1962 Seppo Hurme published the first exhaustive study of Finnish salmon rivers ever undertaken, a task performed at the behest of the International Council for the Exploration of the Sea, the leading international scientific fishery organization in Europe, to which all the Baltic countries belong. Hurme's investigation covered 46 watercourses within Finland's present boundaries, including Swedish and Russian border rivers. He divided them into four groups: large (6), medium (20), small (16), and uncertain (4). On 13 rivers salmon and trout populations were extinct, including the large (and famous) Kymi, Oulu and Kokemaki Rivers. Salmon and trout populations had diminished greatly in many of the remaining streams and hydro-electric developments planned for the next few years will bring additional disasters to the salmon.[12]

On the 300-mile Kemi River which flows across Finnish Lapland with its birch forests and tundra, inhabited by herds of reindeer and their keepers, the Lapps, by lynx and elk, where in winter wolves hunt down their prey over the frozen wastes, a chain of hydro-electric plants is rising to supply the needs of industries in central and southern Finland. Seven installations are already in operation and six more will be built in the near future, providing a total of 860,000 kilowatts. To the south of Lapland flows the Oulu River which, although only one-fifth the length of the Kemi, has a power potential of 400,000 kilowatts that is being harnessed in ten plants which send their energy to distant industries. No provision was made to protect the salmon runs in these rivers, which are now deserted; yet the Kemi was originally one of the richest salmon waters in the Baltic region. There is, however, a scheme under discussion that would supply 100,000 smolts annually to the Oulu.

Power development is moving at such a rapid pace, says Seppo Hurme, that 'all of our rivers will be full of these dams in the next twenty to thirty years'.

Other factors that helped to deplete Finnish salmon rivers are water pollution, principally sewage and waste from industrial plants, but this problem is receiving some attention; systematizing of streams by such means as dredging and water-level regulation; the draining of swamps and wastelands which has caused large amounts of alum and humus to seep into fertile waterways, thus rendering them unsuitable to salmon and trout; lowering of water levels at the mouths of rivers which has hindered spawning fish from ascending them; and finally, floating of timber. Overfishing was a major factor in the decline of the runs on the Pyha and Siika Rivers in the Phjanmaa district. And even now, adds Hurme, with the stocks radically reduced, further depletion is threatened by the large catches of immature salmon in the Baltic fishery.

In short, Finland has only two good salmon rivers left, the Ii and Torne, and the latter it shares with Sweden! According to Table 8, its smolt production has dropped from 2,475,000 per year to only 625,000. Hurme estimates that several million smolts would need to be planted annually in the blockaded rivers to bring them back to something like their former productivity. But implementation of such an ambitious programme, which would have to be financed by the nationalized electric power industry, is quite remote; in fact, improbable. 'The state machinery works very slowly in handling such matters', he says tersely.[13] Finland thus takes its place besides France and Spain as preferring kilowatts to fish.

Atlantic salmon in Soviet Russia

The Soviet Union has numerous rivers possessing Atlantic salmon (Figure 11). They are divided into two groups: those which flow into the Baltic and those which empty into the White or Barents Sea. Baltic rivers include the 600-mile Niemen which rises in White Russia and flows through Lithuania; the Venta, a much shorter river, which also enters the Baltic through Lithuania; Gauja, longest river in Latvia, flowing into the Gulf of Riga; Salaca; the Neva which issues from Lake Ladoga and empties into the Gulf of Finland after passing through the once-beautiful and now dishevelled city of Leningrad; and the 600-mile West Dvina, that has its source in the Valday Hills, only a few miles from two other great rivers, the Volga and Dnieper. Flowing into the Barents Sea are such salmon streams

Table 8
Sources of Baltic smolt production
(1,000's)

Country and river	*Original smolt production*	*Recent smolt production*	*Present smolt plantings*
Sweden	4,145	1,585[a]	1,685[a]
Mörrum	350	100	0
Dal	400	50	100
Ljusnan	400	100	200
Ljungan	300	100	25
Indal	320	0	320
Angerman	300	0	300
Ume	400	250	100
Skellefte	110	0	110
Lule	540	10	530
Kalix	250	250	0
Torne	675	675	0
Others	100	50	0
Finland	2,475	625[b]	100[b]
Torne	325	325	0
Kemi	1,000	0	0
Ii	300	300	0
Oulu	300	0	100
Kokemaen	300	0	0
Kymi	250	0	0
U.S.S.R. (rough estimate)	3,000 (?)	2,000 (?)	0
Poland	1,000 (?)	100 (?)	0
Grand total	10,000	4,500	1,785

[a] Level about 1970.
[b] Level about 1960.
Source: Arne Lindroth.

as the Voronya, Teriberka, Kola, Tuloma and others of the Murman coast of the Kola Peninsula and Pechora; entering the White Sea are the Onega, the Mezen, and the North Dvina, all sizeable rivers, the Umba and Varzuga. The Pechora is probably the most fruitful of all these rivers and also the longest, cutting a 1,100-mile path to the Barents Sea. The Kara River which, like the Pechora, rises in the Ural Mountains, forms part of the border between European and Asiatic Russia and is now the easternmost limit of *Salmo salar*'s range.[14]

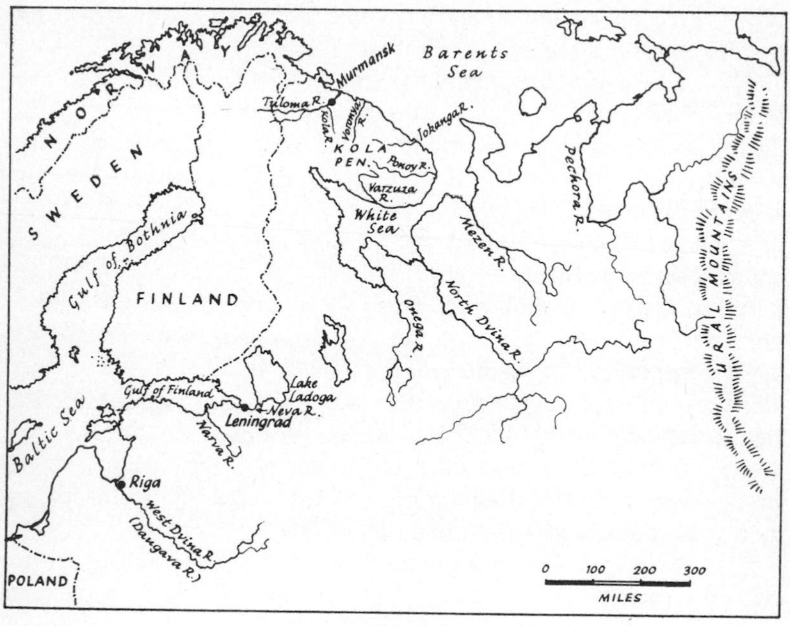

Figure 11

Atlantic salmon rivers in U.S.S.R.

Salmon journey far into the interior of some of these Russian rivers to find suitable spawning grounds. They are known to mate almost as far as the Ural Mountains in the Pechora system, some thousand miles from the mouth, and in the very headwaters of the Vistula (a Polish river). In contrast, the Neva salmon spawn in Lake Ladoga (which also contains non-migratory salmon), about 45 miles from the sea.

M. N. Vladimiriskaya gives us interesting details about the spawners in the Upper Pechora. Only large fish reach this outpost of the salmon's range. On the basis of her studies she says that 87 per cent are first-time spawners, 11 per cent second-timers, and 2 per cent third-timers–evidence again of the amazing stamina of the salmon which make the thousand-mile river journey and back in order to reproduce, not to mention those who manage to survive this lengthy migration twice. Migratory males compose 37 per cent of all the fish in the Upper Pechora, where it takes the eggs 250 days, or over eight months, to incubate. The smolts usually descend at the age of three-plus years, when they reach a length of five inches and weigh about nine ounces.[15]

The Soviets say that their total catch of Atlantic salmon in the Baltic, White and Barents Sea areas averaged 1,500 metric tons during the years 1954–56. No later statistics are available. This volume roughly equals that of any other country producing Atlantic salmon. Fishing is conducted mostly in the pre-estuary regions and in the lower reaches of the rivers. Floating and fixed nets and fixed and cast seines are used.

According to G. Nikolsky, the total yearly catch of salmon in these northern waters, exclusive of the Baltic, ranged from 800,000 to 1,800,000 pounds in the period 1946 to 1956. The Pechora River alone contributed 490,000 pounds in 1956 and the Archangelsk region 700,000 pounds. In that year over 37 million salmon fry and 1,100,000 fingerlings were liberated in the streams. Annual smolt production in Soviet Baltic rivers is estimated by Lindroth as 2,000,000, compared with 3,000,000 originally (Table 8).

The Soviets say they have instituted many measures designed to conserve their Atlantic salmon. Fishing is prohibited on spawning grounds and adjacent to dams, the number of fishing devices is limited, and a maximum catch is established. It is against the law to obstruct more than two-thirds of a river channel with nets, and the pathways of migrating fish must always be kept clear. Builders of dams are obligated to provide fish lifts or ladders, as at Kegum dam on the Daugava River, and on the Tuloma River on the Kola Peninsula. These installations have made it possible to maintain the salmon runs in both rivers.

There are said to be twelve hatcheries and rearing stations devoted to Atlantic salmon in the Soviet Union, and in 1962 they produced 10 million fry and an unknown number of smolts. The

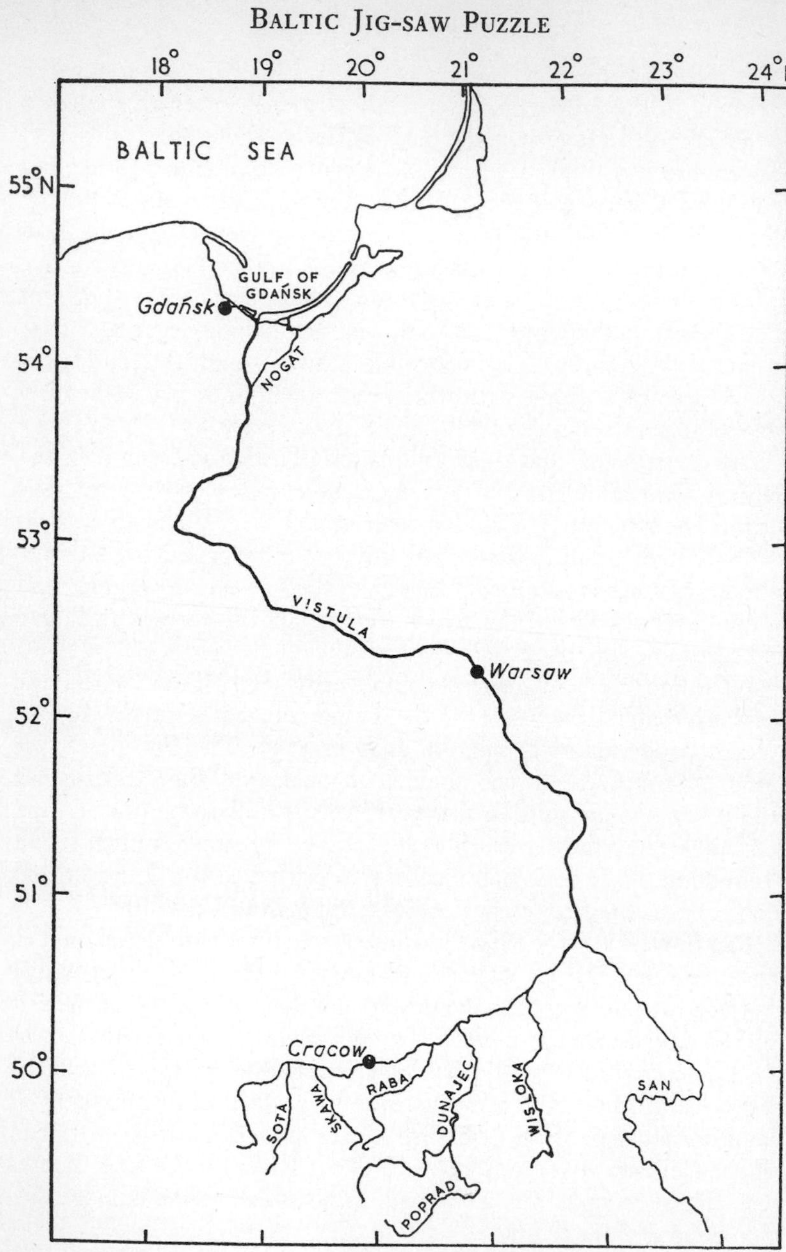

Figure 12

Tributaries of the Upper Vistula still harbouring salmon.

Russians are endeavouring to speed up the rearing of sea-going juveniles through the use of specially prepared feed mixtures containing, in addition to the usual components (dried blood and fish flour), algae, antibiotics and micro-elements. This combination makes it possible, they say, to rear smolts in ten months (compared with two years in Sweden).[16]

Salmon in Poland

Poland's salmon populations, once the pride of the nation, have declined drastically, like those of neighbouring lands. Two major Polish salmon rivers were the famous Oder and Vistula. The Oder rises in the Carpathian Mountains of northern Czechoslovakia and flows in a serpentine course of 560 miles to the Baltic at Stettin, while the 680-mile Vistula, also born in the Carpathians, passes Cracow and Warsaw on its way to the busy port of Danzig. Like the Rhine, these waterways are great transportation arteries and also carry the effluents of numerous factories and an abundance of other polluted matter, so that fishes cannot thrive in them. Salmon have disappeared from the Oder, and now enter, in small numbers, only the two upper tributaries of the Vistula, the Rivers Sota and Skawa above Cracow. No figures are available on the size of the Vistula (Figure 12) runs but sea-trout far outnumber them.

Polish salmon have a three- or four-year river life and are believed to frequent the northern part of the Baltic Sea for two or three years before returning to spawn.[17] The biologist F. Chrzan reported that many young salmon tagged in the Drawa River proceeded at first in a northern and eastern direction, heading towards the Bothnian Sea (Figure 13). Individuals in their second year of sea life were recaptured in the central part of the Baltic Sea but it was not known if they had migrated to the north Baltic previously. Polish fish apparently do not go to the western Baltic. A record journey of about 870 miles in a half-year was chalked up by a Drawa smolt, through the river and sea lanes, before being recaptured in the Bothnian Sea.

A small mature salmon, known to fishermen as *mielnica*, is unique to Polish rivers. These specimens are rarely larger than 20 inches and mostly are 13 to 17 inches and may be 4 to 6 years old, of which one year is spent in the sea. It is believed that the undersized *mielnica* is a product of poor feeding conditions in the sea.

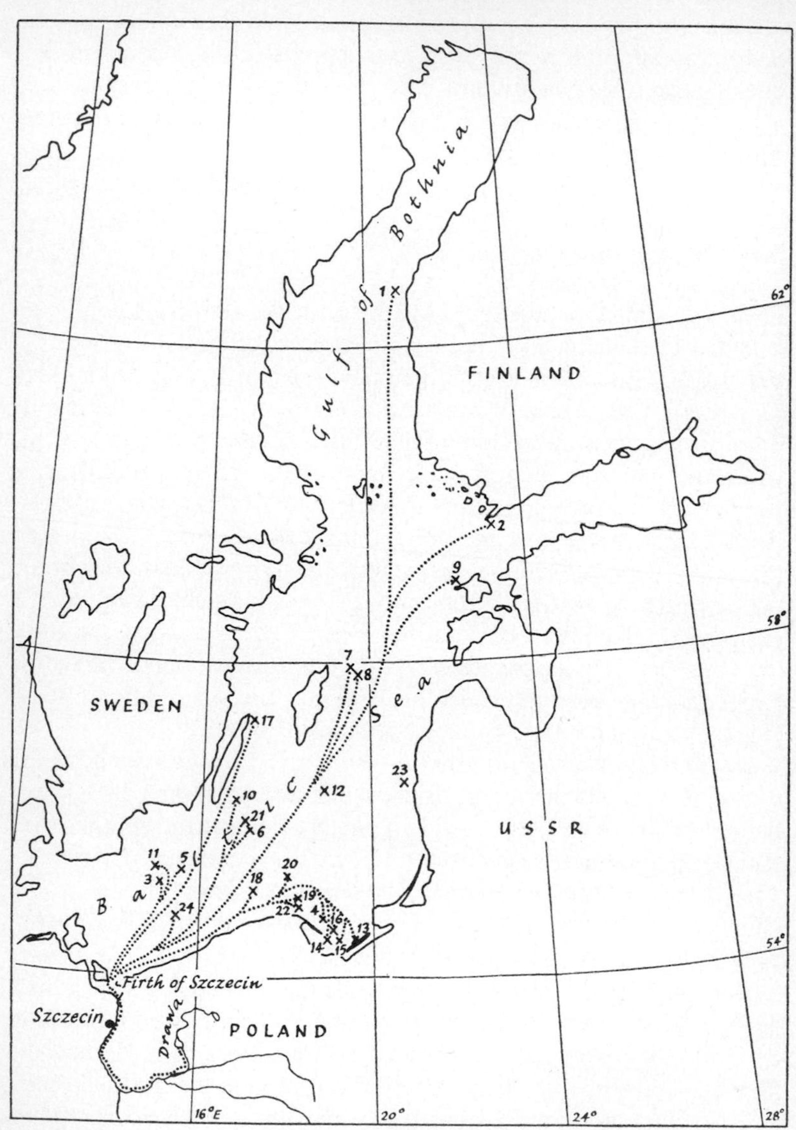

Figure 13
Migration of Drawa salmon.

Future of the Baltic fishery

Originally all the countries bordering the Baltic Sea contained teeming salmon rivers. Now Sweden, Russia, Finland, Poland and possibly East Germany make contributions to the melting pot, with Sweden and Russia providing roughly four-fifths of the total. Table 8, compiled by Dr. Arne Lindroth, shows that all the Baltic lands once contributed possibly 10,000,000 smolts yearly to the sea. Natural production is perhaps now only half of that level. Partly compensating for the tremendous losses of habitat and natural output in the various countries is the Swedish planting programme with a goal of almost 1,700,000 smolts per year to be released by 1970, the Finnish release of 100,000 smolts in the Oulo River and elsewhere, and the undetermined volume of Russian plantings.

Clearly the future of the Baltic salmon is closely related to the production of artificially-bred fish, mainly in Sweden. If it continues to be successful, and if other countries step up their hatchery output, the fate of the Baltic salmon will be fairly bright. There is little indication that either Poland or East Germany will undertake restocking programmes, or that they have any interest in saving the remnants of their once considerable resources. The enigmatic Russians are definitely interested in their Atlantic salmon stocks, are doing considerable research on this species, and are apparently contemplating the augmentation of their smolt-rearing programme.

NOTES

1 Gunnar Alm, *Salmon in the Baltic Precincts*, p. 43.

2 They were tagged in a tributary of the west coast River Atran in April 1961 and were recaptured twenty months later.

3 Roberto Bossi, *The Lapps*, p. 103.

4 Gunnar Svärdson, *Goda Laxar – Och Daliga*, p. 15.

5 Arne Lindroth, *Fluctuations of the Salmon Stock in the Rivers of Northern Sweden*, p. 137.

6 International Council for the Exploration of the Sea, *Procès-Verbaux*, Vol. 147, 1959.

7 O. Christensen, 'The Danish Salmon Fishery in the Eastern Baltic in the Season 1964–65', p. 2.

8 Borje Carlin in *Arsberattelse for Ar 1962*, Swedish Salmon Research Institute.

9 The Soviet Union could ratify the present agreement or sign a similar one with Poland, and Poland may ratify it and later conclude a similar treaty

with East Germany. Finland may either sign the agreement or place its provisions in effect unilaterally.

10 Borje Carlin, 'Salmon Conservation in the Baltic', 1959, p. 60.

11 T. H. Jarvi, 'On the Periodicity of Salmon Reproduction in the Northern Baltic Area', p. 5.

12 Seppo Hurme, *The Anadromous Fishes in the Baltic-Side Rivers of Finland*, pp. 191–2.

13 Seppo Hurme, 'Concerning Salmon and Trout Bearing Rivers in Finland which empty into the Baltic Basin', *Fiskeritidskrift for Finland*, No. 4, 1964.

14 Salmon are believed to have entered the Kara only in recent decades, owing to the warming of the climate.

15 M. N. Vladimiriskaya, 'Notes on Recent Salmon Investigations in the U.S.S.R.', I.C.E.S., *Journal de Conseil*, Vol. XXIII, No. 3, pp. 238–9. See also her article 'Young Salmon in the Upper Part of the River Pechora', I.C.E.S., *Procès-Verbaux*, Vol. 148, 1959.

16 Nikolai T. Kozhin, 'Atlantic Salmon in the U.S.S.R.', *Atlantic Salmon Journal*, June 1964.

17 Boris Dixon, 'The Age and Growth of Salmon caught in the Polish Baltic, in the Years 1931–1933', p. 69.

5

Norway's Salmon Upsurge

The coastline of Norway is about 1,250 miles long and extends over 12 degrees of latitude. The country is shaped like a kite, with the tail lying far above the Arctic Circle in the lap of Sweden, Finland and Soviet Russia. Mountains and fjords are the mould of the landscape and the ocean washes the shores with the warm current of the Gulf Stream, enticing hordes of migratory fishes out of the rivers and returning them in an endless cycle. So it has been for countless centuries.

All parts of Norway have salmon rivers flowing out to sea but the middle and northern counties are the main sources of the harvest. Cool and lively, the rivers often issue from the craggy mountains, bearing the milk of melting glaciers, and stumbling over waterfalls in their haste to reach the ocean. The coast from Oslofjord in the south to North Cape in the far north is indented by deep rock fissures. These fjords may run inland for enormous distances, like Hardangerfjord, which is 50 miles long and in places two and a half miles wide and two-thirds of a mile deep, acquiring the flow of numerous waterways to form 'rivers' of incredible splendour. Norway is characterized by spectacular fjords and deep valleys, large mountains, precipitous cliffs and deep dells into which waterfalls and rapids drop their burdens.

Each fjord may open to the right or left of the main stream and then break out again into smaller arms, forming a network of twisting channels. Geirangerfjord, for example, cuts a narrow, sinuous path into the interior, and in contrast to Hardangerfjord is nowhere more than a quarter-mile wide. The northern fjord country is sparsely populated, but a spruce hamlet with its gaily-painted houses may be found at the edge of a fjord's arm looking out to the sea.

Cataracts frequently veil the gloomy rocks with their eternal spray. Some of them reach huge proportions, like Skjeggedalsfoss in the River Skjeggedal in Hardanger which is almost 500 feet high, and reverberates like thunder through the valley.

When approaching Norway from the ocean the rugged mainland looms ahead, a panorama of deep blue or purple escarpments, especially in the west country. The mountains are steep, sometimes rising to 8,000 feet, and many are perpetually snow-covered. Innumerable islands fringe the coast, like strings of pearls, and ports nestle in the lee of the winds and storms. It is a land that breeds sailors and fishermen, and adventurous Vikings who still explore the seven seas.

In many districts the landscape is green, especially in the east, in Trøndelag, and parts of the north, and carpeted in spring and summer with a myriad of wild flowers. For at least two months the night sky is aglow in the Arctic Circle, and in Finnmark there is almost clear daylight at midnight during the middle of the summer. In the middle of winter the sun in this area hardly lifts itself above the horizon.

Hamlets and villages and larger settlements are mostly confined to the flat coastal areas and the valleys. What little cropland Norway possesses is found mainly in the south, while in the central and northern districts grazing is an important activity in the brief summer when the landscape is green and free of snow. As in Alaska, the most important settlements, including the fishing ports, are scattered along the outer coast where there are good harbours. Nowhere in the world except Alaska do salmon inhabit such wild and picturesque country. Finnmark has the most northerly salmon rivers in the world.

The salmon rivers

Norway has over 200,000 lakes and rivers that harbour a large variety of fish. Salmon is the most valuable freshwater species.

It is difficult to say how many productive salmon rivers there are in Norway. This fish may be discovered spawning in a shallow creek only a few yards wide as well as a broad river. Magnus Berg lists 138 salmon rivers in the three northern counties of Troms, Nordland and Finnmark, but the species is found in many other streams in this part of the country. Knut and Eyvind Dahl published a summary of salmon catches from 1880 to 1942 for 150 rivers. The definition of a salmon river in Norway is a body of water where the fish regularly enter and spawn, and of these there are between 150 and 170, not counting numerous streams with small stocks of salmon.

Many of the salmon rivers drain watersheds which depend partly on rainwater, resulting in a heavy flow while the winter snows are melting, after which a dry or wet summer determines the volume that will be available to fish. Rivers that derive their flow from normal mountain snow will fluctuate according to the size of the snow pack during the previous winter and the flow will not decline as early as those which are fed from lower-lying watersheds. The ice usually disappears in the rivers in the months of June through September and only a few lakes have drifting ice.

Most of the rivers are short and marked by fierce rapids and deep gorges. They derive some water from glaciers and fluctuate according to summer temperatures. As elsewhere, the salmon like a good depth of water for their upstream journey and if the river's level drops below their expectations, they refuse to ascend any farther.

Many Norwegian rivers, however, derive most of their water from lakes and other impoundments and are not greatly subjected to variations in flow. In the final analysis, the breezes of the Gulf Stream, whims of the winds, depth of the snow pack and rate of its melt in the mountains, rate of glacial erosion, and the amount of precipitation that falls in the valleys, determine how much water will be in the river during the relatively short season when the fish are running, and also how fast it will flow.

Traits of Norwegian salmon

Salmon (called *Laks* in Scandinavia and German-speaking lands) generally begin to arrive in the Norwegian rivers in April or May and the runs continue until late summer or early autumn, and then cease. The heaviest fish as a rule appear early in May or June. Smaller fish (grilse) are rarely seen before about June 24, but form the bulk of the late-summer runs in many streams. The fishing season is now limited to May 1 to August 4 at sea, including fjords, and to August 31 for rods. In the outer coastal area and many fjords the season is usually over by mid-July.[1]

The fish normally spawn in October and November, occasionally as early as September, and in scattered localities as late as January.[2] It is June before the alevin appear in the north, and they develop quite slowly because of the scarcity of food.

Most of the parr migrating as smolts from these Arctic waters are three, four or five winters old. In southern Norway, growth is faster but differences between rivers are found (Table 9). Once they leave the river, the shoals of young salmon move rapidly out of the fjords into the ocean.

Table 9

Age composition of salmon smolts in Norway

District	*Age at migration (winters)* 2 (%)	3 (%)	4 (%)	5 (%)	*total* (%)
Kristiansand	18	68	13	1	100
Trondheim	6·5	67	26	0·5	100
East Finnmark	2·5	47	43·5	7	100

Source: Knut Dahl, *Salmon and Trout: A Handbook.*

Norwegian salmon may stay in the ocean up to five winters before returning to home waters. Their size is in some proportion to the length of their absence because they eat gluttonously in the depths of the sea. Hence Norwegian rivers tend to produce unusual numbers of heavy salmon. Table 10 shows the age-weight composition of a typical catch from a northern fjord.

Nearly all the salmon running up the Norwegian rivers are in their pre-spawning phase; they feed no more. Where do they spend their growing period?

Knut Dahl and Sven Sømme inaugurated a series of studies in 1935, halted during the war, designed to trace the oceanic travels of the fish. They reported interesting and sometimes astonishing results. The Norwegian salmon seemingly wandered much farther and faster than had been imagined. The majority of those recovered were within 50 to 100 miles from their home rivers, but one was picked up in the Drammen River in Drammensfjord, 660 miles from Titran, and another was found in Russia, at the mouth of the River Wyg emptying into the White Sea, 1,500 miles from Titran.

Norwegian salmon tend to migrate mostly in a northerly and easterly direction but some individuals cross the North Sea and others journey around the south coast into the Skaggerak. None, however, has been found in the Baltic Sea, or in the Greenland fishery.

Table 10

Age-weight relationship of 659 salmon caught in Tanafjord East Finnmark

Number of winters in sea	1	2	3	4	5
Numbers of fish	13	315	210	119	2
Average weight (pounds)	4·2	7·0	13·9	24·6	41·2
Percentage of total fish	2·0	47·7	31·9	18·1	0·3

Source: Magnus Berg, *Salmon and Salmon Fishing*, 1963.

Impressive feats of endurance were exhibited by Norwegian migrants. The fish that traversed the stormy sea from Titran to the River Wyg in the Kola Peninsula moved at a steady pace of 30 miles per day for 52 days, and the one that journeyed from Titran to Drammensfjord covered 660 miles in 11 days, or 60 miles per day.[3]

Occasionally a Russian, Scottish or English fish pays a call on a Norwegian fjord and Norwegian salmon are discovered in a Scottish, English or Russian river. However, Dahl and Sømme believed that the dominant migration patterns of Norwegian salmon indicate that there are important feeding areas off western Finnmark and northern Troms. Perhaps these are the staging areas, as Menzies calls them, where the fish fill up their bellies before setting their built-in compasses for home waters. In fact, salmon caught off the outer coastal islands of Norway sometimes have food in their stomachs, but in the rivers their bellies are invariably empty when killed.

The spawning act seems to be more lethal to males than females but different kinds of rivers produce different effects. 'Spawning can hardly be as great a hardship in short and slow rivers as in long and rapid ones', says Magnus Berg. 'There is also ground to suppose that the time of entering the river may have some importance. . . . In northern Norway investigations show that much of the male salmon population spawns twice and conditions are therefore different from those in the south.'[4] From an examination of thousands of scales which reveal the life history of the fish, Dahl concluded that about one out of twenty Norwegian salmon spawn twice and only one in a thousand thrice, and that certain rivers may be more favourable than others for the recuperation of kelts.

The river fishery

Fishing for salmon and trout probably began as soon as human beings arrived in Scandinavia, perhaps 7,000 or 8,000 years ago. Primitive man used fish spears made of bones; many such spears have been found dating from the Stone Age. The Lapps set traps of osier into which salmon were lured at the mouths of rivers, or used seines like those still employed in Europe and North America. *Snorres Edda*, a compilation of Norse mythology written by the Icelander Snorre Sturleson in the thirteenth century, describes the fishing methods of the god Tor and other deities when the mischievous Loke jumped into the foss and transformed himself into a salmon. They clearly attempted to capture him with a net used as a seine.

'River fisheries for salmon', says Knut Dahl, are 'probably as ancient as the Norwegians themselves. . . . The famous Sele fishery —a seine fishery—at the mouth of the Figgen River on Jaederen is an instance.' A runic inscription unearthed at the Sele farm in Klepp tells us that half the seine fishing belonged to this establishment in pre-Viking times and 'the wording . . . appears to show that the fishing method was the same as at present even in those remote days',[5] perhaps as far back as the third century A.D.

So esteemed were Norway's inland fisheries that when King

Haakon I in 950 decided to fix the boundaries between the maritime and interior provinces, he set the lines of demarcation at the farthest limits of salmon migration. In time the Norwegians developed a thriving commerce in salmon with foreign countries. Taxes on salmon and herring catches eventually became one of the principal sources of Crown revenues. The clergy too extracted its tithe, so that the fisheries helped to endow and maintain many a religious house. Fishing rights were vested in riparian owners; even fishing in navigable waters was restricted to owners of adjoining lands. As might be expected, disputes and lawsuits, especially over weirs and impoundments, were numerous. Knut Dahl says that the famous weir on the Sands River in Ryfylke, for example, was the subject of contests and lawsuits as far back as the thirteenth century.

In a country where very little cultivable land is available fish were always an important source of food. Local people took as many salmon as they could out of the rivers, using every device they could think of. Knut Dahl says that in the Trondheim district he met old people who remembered that whenever the inhabitants of a farm in the Lower Gula area fancied some salmon, they brought out their boat and seine and fished until their needs were satisfied. In the autumn men, women and children would club together and empty every pool of the small rivers which flowed through the valleys. The catches were divided equally among the participants, a custom that existed for centuries. This traditional practice of looting the streams died hard even after restrictive legislation was passed.

The first salmon law was promulgated in 1850. It set a close period from September 14 to February 14, instituted a weekly closure of 24 hours (which did not apply to fixed gear), restricted meshes of nets to 1½ inches or larger, and not only forbade the sale of salmon or sea-trout of less than eight inches during the fishing season, but of any size in the close period. This was one of the most enlightened salmon laws in Europe. However, it took a long time to become effective.

The 'lords' rivers'

For hundreds of years the salmon stocks were prized by landowners primarily as a local food supply and to some extent as a source of income. Then a few eccentric English visitors, carrying fishing rods in their portmanteaux, discovered the possibilities of glorious sport in the wild country of northern Norway.

'The generation that followed the close of the Napoleonic Wars pioneered in pursuit of sport like explorers seeking the sources of the Nile,' says C. V. Hancock, writing in *Trout and Salmon* (March 1964). 'Not content with the remote fringes of the British Isles, they crossed the North Sea and pushed up far northern fjords in times and conditions when such journeys were arduous adventures.' One of the first was Sir Hyde Parker, eighth baronet, who fished several rivers from 1828 to 1840, particularly the Alta, and brought back jubilant reports to his friends. He had previously tried some of the streams in Sweden. Parker is known to have fished the Namsen in Trøndelag, where in 1837 William Belton landed 1,172 pounds of salmon in 30 days! The Alta was destined to become a pre-eminent 'lords' river', exploited mainly by the Duke of Roxburghe and Duke of Westminster.

Englishmen were fishing the Tana River in 1838 and in 1845 were dancing their flies on the Rauma River which drains a large portion of the Dovre mountain plateau. In 1850 they were on the Arøy which flows into Sognefjord. The Driva was opened up about the same time. The foreigners came back year after year and thus opened the eyes of astonished local farmers to the value of their salmon waters. Rivers were leased in part or whole. Sir Henry Pottinger and William Curtis leased nine miles of the Stjørdal in 1858 for 30 specie dollars a year (equivalent to 30 American dollars). Sir Henry's friends returned every summer and one of them, Major Charles Wingfield, held the lease up to the time of his death.[6]

The expeditions into Norway in those days demanded not only fortitude but time and money. It was a saying of Sir Hyde Parker's that 'a man ought to earn his salmon as he earns his bears'. Anglers had to accept the primitive accommodations the Norwegian farmers had to offer. At times they slept in barns. Later, some of them built their own lodges equipped with the kind of amenities Victorian families of wealth enjoyed at home, such as stoves, warm water and baths. They built groynes in the rivers to make holding places for fish and dug out cellars which the farmers filled with ice in winter to preserve the catch.

The 'lords' crossed the sea in chartered vessels or their own yachts, which they would moor at the nearest port. They had to buy their own carrioles, the carriage of the country, bring along their own harness, and sometimes be their own coachmen. They generally knew little or no Norwegian and the farmers, storekeepers and gillies spoke little or no English, but this was usually no bar to communication. The books they wrote about their fishing experiences have a rare flavour, such as William Belton's *Two Summers in Norway* (1840) and Llewellyn Lloyd's *Field Sports of the North of Europe* and its sequel, *Scandinavian Adventures*, and are comparable to those produced by Englishmen who pioneered the ascent of Mont Blanc and other massive Alpine peaks. The chief difference, of course, is that some men lost their lives in the Alps, but on the Norwegian rivers men only lost their tempers in fighting the salmon.

In the autumn of 1963 I visited the Stjørdal, one of the famous 'lords' rivers', emptying into Trondheimfjord. The sturdy lodge built by the British in the nineteenth century was intact. The river was now owned by a timber company. Bedrooms were spacious and the sitting-room had a large fireplace. All the chambers were comfortably furnished in heavy Victorian style. On the bookshelves reposed the novels of popular authors of the period like Charles Dickens, Charles Reade, Richard Blackmore, Mrs. Humphrey Ward and Wilkie Collins. Along the pine-panelled stairway hung crayon sketches on wood of prize salmon catches. One which attracted my attention was a pink-silver beauty, weighing 35 pounds. It was caught by the Prince of Wales on July 11, 1906.

The pioneers, often standing in water up to their armpits, fished from the banks, which they considered the noble way, but on fast rivers like the Alta, Tana, Pasvik, Maals and Rossa, only fishing from boats was possible. They used heavy rods, weighing up to 19 pounds, and brought with them the traditional flies, colourful creations made with the plumage of exotic birds.[7]

Sigurd Skaun in his book, *Salmon and Lords on the Stjørdal*, reminisces about the brilliant casters of the old days such as Major Wingfield who used the spey cast or underhand cast, which is best for a river with such difficult banks as the Stjørdal, or Major Cates who would cast his Thorndyke fly, the most successful on this stream, right across the fairly broad river.

George Arkwright and Percival Hambro first came to the Stjørdal in 1859, and Wingfield in 1860, accompanied by John Arkwright and Sir Ivor Guest, his brother Montague Guest, and George Gillett. That season's record was set by George Arkwright, who caught 75 salmon weighing 934 pounds. The next year the group included

Sir Henry Pottinger, Augustus Stewart and Percival Hambro. In 1863 Hambro and Stewart brought their wives, accompanied by a Miss St. Quentin. These ladies were probably the first who came expressly to fish a Norwegian river, and they proved to be as ardent and sometimes as successful fishers as men.

There were eccentrics among these anglers, temperamental gentlemen like Lord Barclay Paget. 'One day', says Sigurd Skaun, 'he was casting in Hesthølen. A salmon took the fly but, as often happens, the fish found its way around a rock and there it stood fast and could not be moved either up or down. Then the lord flew into a rage, threw the rod at Bes, his gaffman, and, trembling with fury, poked his mailed fist up to Bes' honest face.

'Bes felt himself getting angry but nevertheless took the rod and gradually was able to coax the salmon away from the rock. Then he called the lord who landed the salmon. Bes gaffed, bowed deeply to the lord and left.

'Then the lord became exceedingly unhappy. Bes did not know a word of English and the lord knew only one word of Norwegian. He used it. He ran after the angry gaffman, waved with a handkerchief, and cried: "Skaal, Bes!" Thus they continued down the road, Bes in front, the lord behind, unhappy and waving his handkerchief.

'Finally they met another gillie, Nils Renaa. "Good Lord, Nils!" cried the lord. "I have offended Bes. But tell him, for Christ's sake, that I wasn't angry at *him* but at the *salmon*."'[8]

The largest fish ever caught on the Stjørdal was a 49-pounder taken by Captain Harry L. Townshend in 1903. Captain Eaton is remembered for his feat in hooking 10 salmon in one day in July 1923, and with his wife landing 140 salmon and 24 grilse weighing 2,248 pounds during that month. Among the passionate anglers on this river was Lord Hill, so crippled by gout that his feet bent under him and he had to drive to and from his boat, but this did not deter him from fishing in wet weather or dry. Nils Renaa recalled seeing him engage in a titanic two-hour struggle with a 40-pound salmon which covered a considerable stretch of water before it was finally brought ashore below Gudaa station.

The British bestowed loving care on the rivers. Lord Marlborough bought up all the nets on the Stjørdal and burned them, including the deadly wedge nets near the mouth. The channels were kept clear and pools unobstructed.

'Their manners were impeccable', an old Norwegian woman, whose husband had been a gillie early in the century, said to me. 'They were generous and friendly and they strengthened the sense of cleanliness in all the farmhouses around here. Their visits brought a great deal of money to the people of Trøndelag. Just think, they paid something like 23,000 crowns each year for the fishing right in Stjørdalselven!'

What kind of a river is the Stjørdal? Originating across the border in Sweden as the Tevla, between Størlifjellet and Stenfjellet, it meanders in a north-westerly direction through a narrow forested valley. Although shallow, the current is furious. At the falls in Meraaker, Tevla meets a river coming from the south-west, the Torsbjørka, whose source is on the eastern side of Skarven. In its upper portion Torsbjørka absorbs the flow of several lesser creeks as well as seepage from marsh areas. Up there it is wide and flows calmly but below Løvlivolden it thunders through the forest. Below the steep slopes of Mannfjeldet, Midtifjeldet and Fronnfjeldet there are swarms of creeks rushing into it, and at the confluence with Tevla, Torsbjørka has become a mighty river. Both upper branches harbour trout but no salmon.

At its outlet the Stjørdal is wide, coursing along terraced land with sandy and clay banks and hog-back formations, all the way up to the mouth of its largest tributary, the Forra in Hegre. There it narrows considerably yet the valley floor hardly has room for the river, the railroad and the country road.

At high water the Stjørdal may be negotiated in smaller boats as far as Bjerkan, while larger boats can go to Bergsøren unless the water is very low. During summer downpours the river swells quickly but recedes just as quickly. In winter there are often violent and dangerous ice movements.

Over the centuries the Stjørdal has changed its course in whimsical fashion. Its meanderings have played havoc with farms, settlements, cemeteries. River pools were silted up and new ones formed. Evjenhølen, for example, disappeared as Nyraasa, or New Cut as the Englishmen called it, was formed. In the nineteenth century the river broke through a long tongue of land between Yati and Berg in Laanke.

Once the river's outlet was at Thyna, but a slide gave it another direction. Between Aunet and Hjelet in Laanke there is a deep incline towards Fugla–from here came the material which filled the channel at Hell and formed the so-called Hellesleir and part of Ora and possibly also Faeristaleret.

Because many Britons fished the Stjørdal, some of the pools have English names such as Brandy and Onions, Upper John and Lower John (after John Volden), Round Hole, Neck of Hell, Purgatory, Ladies' Pool, Pott's Hole (after Sir Henry Pottinger), Whirl Pool, Telegraph Pool, etc. The river is accessible to salmon for about 33 miles and spawning areas are found everywhere except in the lowest seven to eight miles. Between Trondheimfjord and Hegra fortress the water is too deep and low for salmon fishing but conditions are ideal between Hegra and Gudaa waterfall, a stretch of 18 miles.

The British fishermen are a romantic tradition in Norway. They belong mainly to the Victorian and Edwardian age that is dead. They discovered and developed the art of fly fishing in Arctic waters and advertised it to the world. The angling records they set will not be easily toppled. Norwegian river folk still talk about their achievements. 'Do you know Lord Phillips?' the mayor of Gunndalsøra, on the Driva River, asked the English journalist Nicholas Evans in the summer of 1965. It was fifty years since Lord Phillips used his fishing hut beside the Driva.

Courteous, skilful, tireless, Sir Hyde Parker was typical of the early Victorian angler who found Norway's misty rivers the best of fishing grounds. He fished until he was an old man, and in Llewellyn Lloyd's second book he is quoted as lamenting the good old days: 'In Norway every man is now a fisherman, and many of the waters are hired, so that it is difficult to get a cast to yourself; and I consider the game nearly up, at least for an old one like myself, and not worth going the distance. There are few flogging rivers, all dragging, which levels all, and skill avails nothing.'

Aristocrats of other countries found sport and solace from worldly cares in the blue-green waters of Norway. Thus, Nicholas Denisoff, Finance Minister of the last Czar of Russia, has held the waters of the River Arøy for forty-five years. He holds the world's record for a salmon caught on a fly–68½ pounds.

As two world wars and high taxes greatly reduced the number of aristocrats who could afford to purchase or lease Norwegian rivers, their ranks were filled by American tycoons, Norwegian and Swedish millionaires, foreign princes, local angling clubs and business organizations such as air lines, travel agencies, shipping companies, even newspapers that offer subscribers an opportunity to fish the 'lords' rivers' as circulation builders!

In the first decade of the twentieth century, 80 rivers were leased wholly or in part to sportsmen, with rentals totalling 300,000 kroner. In 1951 rentals aggregated 450,000 kroner; ten years later they had more than doubled: some 94 rivers were leased for a total of 1,150,000 kroner. In 1964 one river, the Alta, was leased to an American millionaire for 250,000 kroner ($35,000) for the period June 24 to July 24.

Commercial fishing

Unlike most countries where *Salmo salar* is found, Norway's stocks have markedly increased in recent decades. According to official statistics, which, it is believed, considerably underestimate the actual catch,[9] the yield from 1890 to 1950 was around 1,000 tons per year and since then has jumped to almost 2,000 (Figure 14). Salmon fetches the highest price of any freshwater or marine species but because of the small tonnage landed the total monetary returns are far below those of less valuable but much more prolific fishes like cod, herring or saithe. The returns to fishermen are based on size composition of the catch: salmon weighing between 3 and 6 kilograms fetch twice as much as those under 3 kilograms, while 6 kilogram fish are worth four times as much as those under 3 kilograms. A large portion of the Norwegian catch is exported.

Salmon are netted principally in the fjords and along the outer coasts, and by drifters in the sea. Fish caught in the fjords usually are heading for an adjacent river while those taken on the outer coast may belong to different streams. In a typical year 60 per cent of the catch may be landed in the Norwegian sea, 20 per cent in the North Sea, and nearly all the rest in the Barents Sea. A small number are caught in the Kattegat and Skaggerak.[10]

By far the most important gear is the bag net. The first contraption of this kind was set up at the mouth of the Haa River at Jaederen in the 1820s. By 1875 there were only 200 in operation. From then on they increased rapidly until a peak of 9,000 was reached in 1903. In recent years about 7,300 bag nets have been in operation.

Popular in Scotland, Sweden and other countries, the bag net is a self-fishing gear which traps the journeying salmon. No watchman

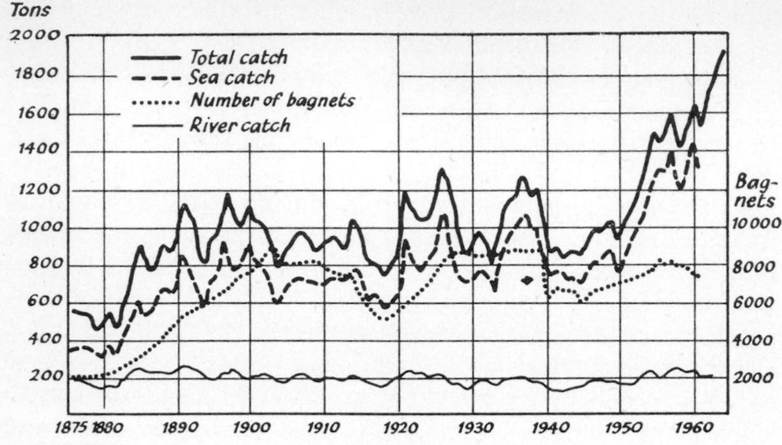

Figure 14

The salmon fisheries of Norway 1875–1961 and the annual number of bag nets used.

is required. The fish, in excellent condition, are collected periodically.

In the past century salmon fishing has tended to move to the outer coast from the rivers and fjords; about 85 per cent of the total Norwegian harvest is now taken in the sea and the rest in the rivers. The river catch, in fact, has remained virtually stationary at 200–250 tons since 1953. The net and rod catches (including a small proportion of sea-trout) on Norway's leading rivers in 1962–a typical year–were as follows (in kilograms):

Tana	35,696
Driva	11,958
Lagen	10,985
Laerdal	10,727
Alta	8,989
Namsen with	
Bjora and Sandola	8,329
Surna with Rinna	7,782
Orkla	7,107
Gaula (South Trøndelag)	7,107
Laks	6,451

Rauma	6,319
Vossa with Teigdal	5,363
Komag	4,941
Tengs	4,578
Vefsna	4,000

In some localities, as in parts of Finnmark, salmon is caught in spring by trolling from a motor-boat, usually as a recreational activity. Although attempts have been made to develop trolling on a commercial basis, the yields are too small to be profitable. A peculiar drift-net fishery existed early in the twentieth century in Drammensfjord, Gulafjord, and a few other places. Two men in an open boat operated a net 150 feet long, 20 feet deep, and with a mesh of five knots to the foot. As many as 10 nets were joined together and the fishermen drifted with them through the night. In 1908 there were about 200 such drifters in operation, but their total catch was relatively small. Improved nylon nets made drifting more profitable, so that a veritable fleet of drifters now (1966) operates every June and July along the coast, from Finnmark to south Norway seeking salmon. Their catch is about equal to the total bag-net catch along the outer coast, but drifters take smaller fish than bag-nets.[11]

Drifters are large, gasoline-powered vessels which stay within the 12-mile territorial limit. Nets are shot as the boat steams slowly downwind; then the engines are stopped, the sail hoisted, and the boat swings around to face upwind. Through the night, and regardless of weather, the vessel drifts, the fishing lantern slung from the mast swaying to and fro. The shoals of salmon moving up towards the surface strike the nets, which may be thousands of feet long, and are inextricably coiled in the mesh. After several hours of drifting, the nets are hauled aboard, the fish removed, and the boat races to port to land its cargo.

Drift nets catch not only 'clean' fish but kelts that are practically worthless in the market and immature salmon with years of growth ahead of them. Besides levying an unnecessary toll on the growing stock, they inflict serious injuries on fish wily enough to disentangle themselves from the mesh. Thus in the Alta River, where nets are not used, almost half the salmon caught in one season recently had bruises due to net marks which would have prevented many of them from spawning and probably proved fatal.

Despite the outcry of commercial fishery operators and rodsmen, drift-netting is being extended southward along the Norwegian coast. Under the new salmon law, enacted in 1964, the drift-net fishery may be prohibited in local areas or anywhere inside the 12-mile limit.

'In the past year [1966],' says Magnus Berg, 'a new problem has arisen as fishermen discovered some of the feeding grounds of the Norwegian salmon in international waters off the coast of Norway.'

Management of the fishery

It is a curious fact that whatever management can be imposed on an anadromous species must deal only with the juvenile, pre-spawning and spawning phases of its life. Within these limits we can maintain the stocks by safeguarding and improving the riverine environment and protecting them from their chief predator: man. The success or failure of any conservation programme, however, is at least partially determined by what happens to the fish during their lengthy stay in the ocean.

A salmon conservation programme should be designed to ensure the maximum harvest of the runs yet permit adequate breeding stock to escape and produce another generation. This goal can be pursued in various ways, primarily by (1) providing protection for the fish through biologically sound regulations, adequately enforced; (2) safeguarding their environment, as in the prevention or control of pollution; and (3) keeping the rivers navigable by migrant fishes, that is, free from man-made obstructions, or by providing ladders over dams and waterfalls. If these are the ends of a conservation programme, their attainment depends also upon the vigour of enforcement of the laws, the willingness of private landowners and the government to make suitable investments in river-improvement facilities, to launch a programme of artificial breeding, and to undertake research to provide scientific information which management needs. In the final analysis, it is public appreciation of the fisheries which will determine the success or failure of the conservation programme. Where public support is lacking, the fishery will diminish or disappear. Where the conservation spirit is strong, the species will prosper if habitat has not deteriorated too badly.

Much credit for improving the Norwegian salmon fishery must be given to those lawmakers who as long ago as 1850 promulgated the first salmon law. As amended periodically down to 1964, it sets forth the following regulations:

Fishing or killing salmon is prohibited during the protected period, August 26–April 14, inclusive. It is forbidden to use, set out, or leave gear suitable for fishing salmon and sea-trout in the fishing areas. Other gear may not be used for catching salmon or sea-trout.

Fishing with rod or hand-line is allowed until and including September 5. It is also permitted to fish with seine or ordinary nets for sea-trout at a distance of more than 400 metres (1,300 feet) from the outlet of a river where salmon or sea-trout go up during the period August 26–September 25 inclusive.

No one may fish at a salmon ladder, or in a similar structure, or increase or diminish the water flow or impede or try to impede the fish from entering or passing through the ladder. The distance above or below the ladder where no fishing is permitted is to be determined by His Majesty.

In places where vessels are run, the fishing gear moorings (buoys, poles, and the like) can be ordered removed if this seems desirable. If such an order is not obeyed, removal may be arranged by the police at the expense of the owner.

If the setting out of fishing gear on state lands in Finnmark can be supposed to impede the salmon's access to watercourses to a great extent, His Majesty may forbid the use of such gear.

Fees (from leasing or licensing fishing rights on state-owned lands) may be used to make possible or facilitate the running of the fish in the watercourse by building of ladders and similar structures in order to improve the fisheries in the watercourse.

It is forbidden to offer for sale, to sell, buy or receive salmon from September 1 and including April 14. Excepted from this prohibition are (a) fish which can be proved to have come from abroad, (b) prepared or frozen fish which can be proved to have been caught during a legal period, (c) fish which can be proved to have been fished with special dispensation from the regulations, except when the throwing out of fish is required, or caught with rod or hand-line in a period when fishing is allowed with this gear–but only . . . within five days of the end of the legal fishing period.

It is at all times forbidden to take immature salmon as well as salmon or sea-trout less than 20 centimetres . . . and to offer for sale or give away salmon or sea-trout of less than 30 cm. This prohibition does not apply to artificially produced young.

A close period from Friday, 6 p.m. to Monday, 6 p.m. is established for gear set out to catch salmon or sea-trout or arranged in such a way that their movements can be prevented. . . . Nor may the fish be caught by hand in this period. This prohibition is not applicable to seines or ordinary nets used to catch sea-trout in the ocean at a greater distance than 400 metres from the outlet of a river in which salmon or sea-trout go up; nor is it applicable to rod or hand-lines.

Net gear may not be used for salmon or sea-trout fishing with meshes of a size smaller than 5·8 cm. between the knots, counted from the midpoint of one knot to the midpoint of the other when the gear is wet. . . . If the gear is a dip net, or is put up above or at a waterfall, the mesh shall be at least 6·5 cm. This regulation is not applicable to a net used as auxiliary gear in fishing with hooks.

It is forbidden to arrange two or more gears in such a fashion that the mesh size is thereby diminished or to cover the nets with material or any other kind of artifice in order to circumvent the regulations concerning the mesh size.

Detailed regulations are given for the use of osier baskets, steel-wire traps, wooden traps and similar gear intended for salmon or sea-trout fishing so that an adequate escapement of fish may be possible. Thus:

Where salmon or sea-trout is fished by means of damming up a lake from a stream, channel or a similar watercourse, or from part of a waterfall, the fence which prevents the fish from turning off downstream must either consist of net gear with mesh of no less than 5·8 cm. or be equipped with such poles as are prescribed (in the regulations).

In weirs and similar gear where the fish is led in by the current, as well as at the gear suspended above or at waterfalls, its bottom shall, unless it be meshed gear, consist of horizontally placed poles (lattice-work) with openings of at least 50 cm. length and 6·5 cm. width.

In the river, or river tributary, where salmon runs, fishing gear may not be set up so that any part of the same–including lead arms or nets, as well as rocks or other natural impediments to the movement of the fish connected with them–is closer to the middle line of the current than one-eighth of the river's or tributary's width at medium water level. Instead of one-eighth, one-sixth shall apply to gear set up from opposite sides of the river at a shorter distance from each other than 100 metres, counted along the course of the current.

These regulations do not apply to dip nets, hooked gear, drift nets, seines which immediately after being put out are pulled up again, nor to gear in or at falls which were legally set up before this law went into effect.

In that part of the river which . . . is protected, rocks or other objects may not be placed which may be supposed to diminish the ability or will of the fish to pass by the fishing gear. It is also forbidden to deepen the course which leads into the gear either from below or from above, so that this becomes deeper than the protected part of the channel.

It is forbidden to use drift nets or seines within a distance of 100 metres (325 feet) from any gear with lead net or lead arm put out in a river.

In a fjord or bay no stationary meshed gear intended for salmon or sea-trout fishing may be set out at a greater distance from land than one-fourth of the width of the bay or fjord at ordinary low tide in midsummer.

The use of drift nets may be prohibited in fjords and both seines and drift nets in watercourses where there is salmon.

In using seines or drift nets in such a watercourse or at its mouth, there must elapse at least one hour between each time the gear passes one and the same place, and it may not extend over more than two-thirds of the width of the watercourse at medium water level.

In some watercourses where there is salmon, the placing of hooked gear with which salmon or sea-trout young can be caught, shall be prohibited. (The use of leisters and similar tools, except as auxiliary tools, is prohibited.)

The use of hooked gear, or certain kinds of such, shall be prohibited, in or for a stretch below rapids and falls, either natural or artificial, which makes it difficult or prevents the salmon from going farther up the watercourse.

The use of any gear except ordinary nets shall be forbidden in lakes where there is salmon.

In saltwater streams, straits or narrow fjords which form the main route of the salmon to watercourses, the regulations of salmon fishing in the ocean shall be in effect even as concerns seines, ordinary nets that are used in catching sea-trout.

It is forbidden to dam up rivers for the purpose of fishing, and to employ any objects for the purpose of frightening the fish.

In the following instances the salmon shall, as far as possible, if undamaged, be thrown back into the water: when caught during protected periods; when it is immature; when caught with a net that is smaller than the required mesh and the fish is no longer than 55 cm. from the tip of the nose to middle spines of the tail fin.

Whoever violates any of the regulations of the present law or a regulation issued in keeping with these regulations will be punished with fines.

Illegally used gear as well as illegal fish offered for sale, sold or bought or its value can be confiscated.

His Majesty can extend or limit the yearly protective period; shorten the weekly close period; lengthen the same to 4 days for hooked gear and gear set out by the open sea, and to 5 days for the respective gear at waterfalls. He can annul or limit most of the regulations previously mentioned.

Meshed gear must be marked with the owner's name or mark.

Anyone who fishes for salmon or sea-trout is obligated to furnish statistical data. Failure to do so, or giving false information, is punishable by fines.

His Majesty is enabled to require the use of grates at intake and outlet points of industrial plants to prevent damage to the salmon.

Since 1933 a fee has to be paid, 5 kroner per 100 kilograms, for the right to export salmon. This money goes into a fund used for improving the salmon and sea-trout fisheries. Failure to comply with this regulation subjects the guilty party to distraining.

An amendment of 1950 forbade fishing for salmon or sea-trout with purse seines in the sea, and when this gear is used the net may not extend more than 200 metres into the sea from the shore, and only one-fourth of the width of the fjord or bay. His Majesty can outlaw the use of engine-driven vessels to cast off and pull in seines when these fish for salmon or sea-trout. Line fishing for these species is now forbidden.

Article I of the 1964 law declares that the aim is to clear the way for optimum gain of salmon and inland fisheries for the benefit of the community and the riparian owners. It provides for a Fishery Commission to see that the act is executed and its aims and objectives are met. Ownership of the fisheries in the river goes with title to the land, and is a fundamental right established in the Norwegian Constitution. The new law compels the owner to improve his section of the stream in line with plans for the whole river and provides for the expropriation of his holdings if he fails to comply.

One of the major changes introduced by the 1964 Act is the curtailment of the fishing season. Also, all persons 16 years of age and over must now pay a fee for fishing salmon and other freshwater species. Together with the long-established export tax on fish, these revenues are expected to finance the government's salmon conservation programme, estimated by Fishery Inspector Joakim Harstad as costing 23 million kroner, which includes the laddering of waterfalls and construction of additional salmon and trout hatcheries. Many stocking establishments will be built by the hydro-electric boards as compensation for crippling or destroying salmon rivers.[12]

The best rivers

W. L. Calderwood remarked in 1930 that 'Norway is a splendid place for angling if one goes to certain rivers in which a fair stock has been preserved for the angler, but in many parts of Norway the stock has been reduced to a minimum by unwise fishing.'[13]

During the past half-century the fishing effort has generally decreased on the rivers and numerous nets and traps have been moved to the outer coast. In north Norway nearly 90 per cent of the salmon harvest is taken in the sea, mostly in bag nets.

When a river is used mainly by rodsmen the escapement is normally enhanced: that is, more fish reach the spawning grounds to produce another generation. As an example we may take the River Repparfjord (Figure 15), which was almost depopulated when it was leased by the state in 1932 to the West Finnmark Hunting and Fishing Association. Seine and net fishing were thereupon forbidden and only rods permitted. In the first years of their lease members of the association took a paltry 100 to 200 kilograms of salmon annually, but in recent years they have caught 2,400 to 4,000 kilograms. Since angling accounts for almost all of the river's harvest, this watercourse, once regarded as almost worthless, now produces a large and valuable supply of fish yearly. 'This instance is in no way unique', says Magnus Berg. 'We have many rivers that show a similar development. Such a change in the manner of fishing often has a better effect than protection because angling associations who are allowed to lease a stream will effectively supervise it.'[14]

While some rivers declined in fertility, others have been substantially improved. For centuries the salmon may have been confined to a small part of a watercourse where redd material and pools for the fry were available, yet upstream, usually above high and impassable waterfalls, there were much better nursery grounds. In order to encourage the fish to use these upper waters, ladders were built over the falls. About 100 ladders have been installed in the three northern counties–Troms, Nordland and Finnmark–since World War II. Fifty streams are scheduled to be laddered in southern Norway with proceeds from fees for fishing licences inaugurated in 1965. Also, since the climate has somewhat ameliorated in the past fifty years and glaciers receded, the salmon have ascended some rivers where they were never found in the last century.

The laddering 'programme, reduction of netting in the river and better supervision, largely account for the doubling of catches in Norway since World War II.

According to Magnus Berg in his authoritative book, *The Salmon Rivers of North Norway* (1964), the most productive salmon rivers in the north are the following (in terms of average annual yield in recent years):

	(*kilograms*)		(*kilograms*)
Tana	35,400	Skjomen	2,390
Alta	6,270	Repparfjord	2,365
Vefsna	2,850	Salt	2,360
Komag	3,325	Beiar	1,720
Maals	3,200	Neiden	1,655
Nordrei	2,900	Røssaga	1,447
Laks and Porsinger	2,770	Skall	1,120
		Grense-Jakob	1,060

Let us glance at some of the most renowned rivers. The Tana, which forms part of the boundary between Norway and Finland, is the largest salmon producer in the country, even though it has been overfished, legally and illegally. Starting in south Finnmark, the Tana accumulates the flow of numerous rivers before emptying into Tanafjord, an inlet of the Barents Sea. The lonely river traverses a barren and wild area. Scrub birch is the only tree one may see for scores of miles; endless vistas of sand and mud and few human habitations greet the eye. The cuckoo is one of the few birds whose call intrudes upon the eternal silence. The Tana is 2½ miles wide at the mouth, but in places narrows to 300 yards. The main stem of the river is 190 miles long and some of the tributaries are major streams in themselves.

The Tana breeds superb fish. Here the largest specimen of *Salmo salar*, 79 pounds, was caught with a spinner in 1928 at Storfossen by Henrik Henriksen, postmaster of Polmak. Here some of the heaviest

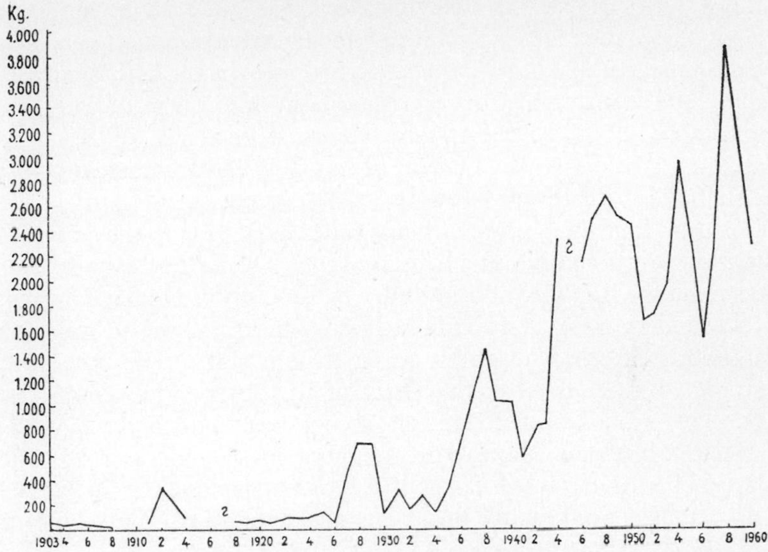

Figure 15

Salmon catches in the Repparfjord River.

catches, resulting from concentrated angling, have been recorded. The walls of the fishing hut at Leyvick show that between June 23 and July 26, 1873, during the period of the midnight sun, three rods hooked 156 fish weighing 2,676 pounds while from July 9 to August 10, 1874, three rods took 274 fish aggregating 4,746 pounds. A single day's record was made on July 16, 1874, when 29 salmon weighing 401 pounds were landed by one angler.[15]

The yield on the Finnish side of the river is almost equal to the Norwegian. Probably less than 10 per cent of the Tana's total catch is landed by rod.

The Alta is a much shorter but more famous river in sporting annals. It drains a network of lakes on the Finnmark plateau, emptying into the Arctic through Altafjord. Salmon can ascend 26 miles of the Alta, which is replenished by spring snow melt, so that the water is warmer than the ocean, making it easier for the fish to find its mouth. The stream bed consists of large pebbles and gravel and in the upper portions large boulders. Late in May or early June the ice usually disappears and the salmon, sensing this, swim up from the sea. You can see the husky fish leap from the river as you drive along the Arctic highway and watch the fly fishermen cast their lines from long, narrow boats punted by two men in the turbulent current. The largest salmon are usually caught from the middle of June to the middle of July. Early in August a good run of sea-trout appears. Whitefish, pike, burbot, perch, stickleback and grayling are also found in this river.

Tales about the capture of giant fishes hark back to the sixteenth century when records began to be kept. The largest salmon ever taken on the Alta was a 60-pounder by the Earl of Dudley in 1951; 50-pounders are not uncommon. Here men fish all night, and even around the clock, with gillies on eight-hour shifts. The best catch ever made is credited to the Duke of Roxburghe, 39 salmon and grilse in one night in 1860, and the second best to the Duke of Westminster, 33 salmon in one night weighing 792 pounds, in 1926. The Duke of Roxburghe still fishes the Alta, and on one trip he landed 201 salmon. Almost 9,000 kilograms of salmon were caught by rods on the Alta in 1962. There are no nets in the river.

The Vefsna in Nordland county is a good example of a stream that has been vastly improved by laddering numerous rapids. The first ladder was built in the 1870s; twelve are now in place, thereby extending the spawning area from 8 to 90 miles. Salmon are seen at the first ladder at Forsfjord (about 16 feet high) at the end of May. Slowly they cross the network of foaming rapids, past the 50-foot ladder at Laksfors and the 16-foot ladder at Fellingfors to reach the upper stretches by mid-July. The ascent is easier now than it was a half-century ago. Big salmon are found in the lower parts of the river while some of the upper tributaries yield only small fish.

The Vefsna has produced salmon up to 67 pounds, and the largest female ever hooked in Norway, a 52-pounder, was landed here in 1928. It was ready to spawn for the third time.

Like other waterways in the north, the Vefsna is affected by Norway's expanding hydro-electric programme. Formerly only the upper reaches of streams were usurped by power dams and the lower, where the salmon are mainly found, remained unmolested. Nor was it customary to divert one stream into another to generate electricity. Now the flow of some watercourses is being tapped almost down to the sea, so that little spawning territory is left. Rivers whose fisheries are imperilled by existing or proposed hydro-electric projects are Røssaga (where the government is building a series of dams), Nea, Hundala, Rana, Heller, Maals, and Pasvik (which flows through Russia and Finland), and others in south Norway. Good spawning and feeding areas on Røssaga's main stem have shrunk, yet with its tributary, the Leir, it still provides 1 to 1½ tons of salmon a year.[16]

The Komag, emptying into North Varangerfjord, remains one of the best salmon streams in Norway. Here cessation of net fishing and rigid supervision resulted in a spectacular increase in the catch–from only about 150 kilograms in 1933 to almost 5,000 kilograms in 1962. Salmon are so abundant that local fishermen sometimes use two flies and kill two fish simultaneously! The wild Komag valley has a unique appeal. Vegetation is sparse. Only a few bushes here and there and hardly a dwelling break the monotony of the landscape. At the river's mouth sits Komagvaer, a spruce hamlet of fifty people.

The Maals is the largest and most productive salmon river in Troms. Bestriding the 69th parallel above the Arctic Circle, it harbours the famous Malang waterfall, 70 feet high, which was laddered in 1910 to enable the fish to make their way 25 miles upstream to reach Divielva and other tributaries possessing excellent spawning gravels. Some of the most expensive salmon fishing in Norway is available below the roaring foss, draped by snow-clad hills even in summer. Salmon take the huge ladder in their stride. Arriving the last days of May, they seem to rest a long time before venturing into the whirlpool, and normally do not go up until the middle of July. Since the Malangfoss was laddered, the stock of fish has multiplied greatly.[17] The best fishing is at the edge of the roaring maelstrom, where at times thousands of salmon gather, and the gillies must pull at their oars constantly to keep from being sucked into the whirling waters. The pool is fished day and night during the summer.

No Norwegian river surpasses the Driva in the sportsman's book. It drains the Driva valley in Nordmøre, the northernmost province of the fjord country. Salmon may be found over a distance of forty miles, from the fjord to Oppdal waterfall which lies at an altitude of 1,790 feet. The turbulent water flows through a series of gorges and drops hundreds of feet over boulder-strewn falls, fed by snow that is melting in the summer sun. In 1964, according to Nicholas Evans, 5,000 salmon were taken on rod and line in a hectic period of eight weeks.[18] The river is owned by various farmers, but some of the water has been held by British families for generations.

As renowned as the Driva is the River Laerdal in the west. It flows into Sognefjord. An aristocrat among rivers, it has seen probably more kings, princes and blue-bloods fish from its banks than any other stream in Europe. Many of the pools are named after British fishermen. The Laerdal holds salmon for about thirteen miles, between the fjord and Sjurhaug waterfall. 'It is to my mind', says T. T. Phelps, who fished the river nearly every year from 1900 to 1939, 'exactly what a river should be. . . . It is wide enough in nearly every pool to make casting worthwhile. Nearly all the fishing is from rock-strewn banks. There is no boat fishing. . . . The fish are curiously punctual in their arrival. . . . It is within the bounds of possibility to catch a fifty-pound salmon or a twenty-pound sea-trout. . . . Although it is vain to attempt comparisons of scenery, I put the Laerdal among the three most lovely valleys in that glorious country.'[19]

The rivers we have described are but a few of the many which have been well maintained, restored, or improved. But there are others which have been despoiled by poaching and overfishing, such as the Sørfjord, Fiskerfjord and Alsvag in Nordland county and Auster and Signaldal in Finnmark.

Few salmon are seen any more on the Pasvik, largest river in north Norway, owing to the construction of a power dam at Boris Glub on the Russian side. Two fish ladders and important spawning beds were flooded out and now the salmon have been restricted to about half a mile of the waterway.[20]

Until the British initiated sport fishing, the Norwegian farmers regarded the fish in their rivers as a source of food and sometimes income. Gradually many city folk discovered the pleasures of angling and in time the farmers imitated them. They found that there was not only sport in catching fish with the rod, but this method promoted conservation while netting could seriously depopulate a river.

Farmers formed associations to safeguard their fishing interests, and they are spreading to many parts of Norway. Angling clubs arose and attained large memberships. The Oslo Sportsfiskere, formed in 1932, has about 3,000 members. In remote areas, as in Finnmark, where the lands are mostly held by the Crown, the government has leased some rivers to sportsmen's groups who enforce the regulations and are responsible for building salmon ladders, improving spawning grounds, and planting fry (which may be bred in their own hatcheries). To finance these activities, they are allowed to charge a fee for fishing cards.

Table 11 shows the leading angling rivers in Norway as of the year 1962. No later data are available at the time of writing. The top producers, so far as sportsmen are concerned, are the Driva, Laerdal, Alta, Surna (with Rinna), Namsen, Orkla, Komag, Førde, Laks, Gaula, Vossa, Saltdal, Elvegard and Vefsna.

In the more accessible rivers farmers have either established fishing lodges of their own or leased their waters to hotels or business organizations. Anglers come from far and near and thus create a thriving recreation industry which the Norwegian River Owners' Association and the government are actively promoting. The value of a salmon caught by rod is much greater than what the commercial fisherman can get for it. With salmon angling carrying enormous prestige, returns from well-stocked rivers have risen steadily.

Fishing on the Maals River costs as much as $250 per day, while the rod fee at Gammelholen pool on the Driva is $300 a week. Denisoff charges $250 a day to fish the Arøy. Rauma, Mandal, Vefsna, Stjørdal and other good rivers may be fished for lesser fees. Since the demand for beats is growing, it is often difficult to hire a river or a boat. The Norway Travel Association in its guide, *Angling in Norway*, lists 96 rivers where salmon angling may be obtained, sometimes for a few dollars a day.

'In North Norway there is rod fishing for the man on the street,' Magnus Berg says. 'In Finnmark fishing licenses may be bought for most of the rivers, whilst in Nordland and Troms many rivers are privately owned and other people may not be able to get permission to fish.' In most of the far northern streams only rod fishing is permitted.

Future of Norway's salmon

In recent years Norway has produced about as much Atlantic salmon as any nation. However, although it is in a healthy state compared with other European countries, Norway's salmon resource is faced with adverse forces. The threat of overfishing is always present, not only by drifters whose nets scoop up shoals of immature as well as mature fish in the ocean, but by nets and traps operating in excessive numbers and during close periods. The discovery of the salmon's

Table 11
Rod catches on leading Norwegian angling rivers, 1962

River	*Rod catch* (*kilograms*)	*Per cent of total catch*
Driva	10,088	84
Laerdal	9,944	93
Alta	8,989	100
Surna with Rinna	7,782	100
Namsen with Sandola and Bjora	7,226	87
Orkla	6,266	87
Komag	4,941	100
Førde	3,840	100
Laks	3,819	59
Gaula	3,463	93
Vossa with Teigdal	3,200	60
Saltdal	3,000	100
Elvegard (*Elvenes*)	3,000	100
Vefsna	2,850	71
Aurland	2,780	94
Bondal	2,780	100
Nord	2,520	100
Tengs	2,300	50
Suldalslagen	2,061	100
Repparfjord	1,983	100
Myrkreid	1,935	100
Gaula	1,916	27
Maals	1,843	99
Arsta	1,760	100

Source: Fiskerinspecktørens Aarsmelding om Ferskvannsfisket for Arene 1951–1962.

feeding grounds may set off an international fishery in Norwegian waters similar to that in the Baltic Sea.

A major concern is the plan to harness more rivers to serve the integrated power pool of Norway, Sweden and Finland. Ninety-nine per cent of Norway's population now enjoys the boon of low-cost electricity and average consumption *per capita* is the highest in the world, twice the level of the United States. Yet only about one-fifth of Norway's hydro-electric potential has been developed. With many industries dependent on cheap power and with domestic consumption rising, development will continue to expand and this will mean, as in Scotland and the United States, continual encroachment on productive salmon rivers.

Mill dams and timber floating also disturb the salmon's ascent. Magnus Berg points out that channels made for soil drainage and other watershed disturbances have already damaged fish environments and destroyed valuable stretches of rivers.

In the final analysis the strongest bulwark of the fishery is sound legislation well enforced and conservation consciousness by private owners of salmon water backed up by angling associations. This helped to bring about Norway's salmon upsurge in the present century.

Yet complaints pour in of failures to comply with the fishery law. Commander S. J. Carr says in *Angling in Norway*, published by the Norway Travel Association, 'One must be honest and state that there can be disappointments regarding the fishing in Norway. Netting, both legal and illegal, is rife and this more than any other factor is spoiling the rod fishing on many rivers. . . . Nobody is blind to the fact that . . . several fjords and rivers are almost jammed with fishing nets of many types. The law decrees that all stationary nets must be closed from Friday to Monday. . . . However, the law is often disregarded. Owing to the vast distances involved, and the remoteness of many rivers, it is a costly matter to organize efficient supervision, although inspection by aircraft has produced results during recent years.'[21]

One visitor observed that there were so many traps on the shore of the Vossa on the way from Bergen to Bulken that train travellers lost count of them. No bailiffs, river-keepers, or any form of control seemed to exist. Commander Carr reported that on the Driva 'excessive netting in the fjord and river mout his bad enough, but in addition, there are also salmon traps every 300 or 400 metres throughout the length of the river. . . . These are supposed to be closed on Friday, Saturday, and Sunday every week, but in fact are in use the entire time.'[22] In contrast is the River Orkla which had been a victim of overnetting but throw nets were banned in 1939 and seining at the river's mouth ceased in 1948. Since then it has been a good river for fly fishing. We may note that traps on the Vossa and Driva Rivers have been in use for hundreds of years, and if they are to be removed, the owners will have to be compensated. This is a costly procedure.

British anglers who have fished in Norway in recent years, like Arthur Oglesby, report that 'more and more rivers are returning to their former glory'. Rod catches are good and large salmon are frequently taken.[23]

In many Norwegian rivers only rod fishing is permitted now, and this has generated a great rise in the yield, for the salmon are not easily overfished in the small shallow streams. If exposed to too much rod fishing they may become nervous and not take the bait, and thus a larger number of fishermen will be apt to catch a smaller quantity of fish. In some rivers the local angling club has banned the rods for twenty-four hours every week, but this only means that more fish than usual will bite when fishing resumes.

To sustain the spurt in Norway's salmon population, it will be necessary not only to maintain effective regulation but to limit the fishing to rods in many rivers, since the bulk of the catches are taken in the fjords or at sea. More intensive government assistance will also be needed.

Until now, government research and management efforts have centred largely in the marine field administered by the Department of Fisheries, since ocean fisheries form a vital segment of the nation's economy. Freshwater fisheries, which are the responsibility of the Department of Agriculture, have been largely ignored. In fact, scarcely a dozen persons on the Crown's payroll are concerned with freshwater fish, and budgets for this work are insignificant. Yet, as Magnus Berg points out, the newly-opened stretches of the Maals River alone produce 700,000 to 800,000 kroners' worth of salmon annually, or 'almost double the budget of the Fishery Division of the Department of Agriculture'. The fact is that local fishery boards and sportsmen's groups have been mainly responsible for the rehabilitation and extension of spawning areas in Norwegian salmon rivers.

An important aspect of Norway's salmon upsurge is the role played by research, a field in which it is pre-eminent in Europe. Scientific fishery studies started as far back as 1850. Fishery Inspector Landmark tagged many thousands of juvenile and adult salmon in the years 1883–1899. Dr. Knut Dahl began his work on the life history and migrations of the salmon in 1904. In the years 1935–1940 Dahl and his assistant, Sven Sømme, tagged thousands of salmon and the results provided valuable information on their migrations in the sea. He was succeeded by Leiv Rosseland, currently in charge of salmon research in the Ministry of Agriculture. Magnus Berg has greatly enlarged our knowledge of the salmon in northern Norway.

As pressures build up that threaten the freshwater species, the government will have to carry a larger share of the burden, not only in management and research efforts, but in artificial breeding as well. There are signs that it is prepared to do so. The partnership of government and private interests, guided by an enlightened conservation policy, should assure a bright future for Norway's resource.[24]

NOTES

1 Salmon ascend most of the northern rivers in June and the best fishing is usually at the end of June and first weeks of July. In rivers which have glacial water the season begins very late.

2 In north Norway some fish enter the rivers in August and September and do not spawn until the following autumn.

3 Knut Dahl and Sven Sømme, *Experiments in Salmon Marking in Norway, 1935*, pp. 13–16.

4 Magnus Berg, *Salmon and Salmon Fishing*, p. 24.

5 Knut Dahl, *Salmon and Trout: A Handbook*, pp. 43–44.

6 Sigurd Skaun, *Salmon and Lords on the Stjørdal.*

7 These flies, such as Silver Doctor and Jock Scott, are still sold in Norwegian tackle shops, although they have been long out of fashion on British rivers.

8 Sigurd Skaun, *op. cit.*, p. 55.

9 'There is no doubt', says Leiv Rosseland, chief of freshwater fishery research in the Ministry of Agriculture, 'that the figures are too low. For the salmon statistics are based on information directly obtained from the fishermen and one must be somewhat optimistic to believe that everyone reports all his catches. Control tests at fish merchants have shown that the figures given are too low. The clearest proof of this is the fact that in certain years as much salmon is exported as the total reported catch. It is impossible to say how much we should add to the statistics to arrive at the correct figures but as much as 50 per cent has been estimated. If this is anywhere near right the take of salmon and sea trout during the best years could be 2,000

tons, of which it is estimated that 10 per cent are sea trout.' ('Salmon and Salmon Fishing', in *Havet og Vare Fisker*.)

10 *Bulletin Statistique*, International Council for the Exploration of the Sea, XLII.

11 Personal communication from Magnus Berg, April 26, 1965.

12 Norway now has 90 salmon and trout hatcheries and 12 stocking establishments. The goal is 40 stocking establishments.

13 W. L. Calderwood, *Salmon and Sea Trout*, p. 115.

14 Magnus Berg, *Salmon and Salmon Fishing.*

15 A. E. Gathorne-Hardy, *The Salmon*, pp. 129–30.

16 Magnus Berg, *Nord-Norske Lakseelver*, p. 291.

17 *Ibid.*, p. 277.

18 Nicholas Evans, *Sunday Times* (London), August 8, 1965.

19 Quoted in *Angling in Norway*, 1962 ed., p. 21. See also the magnificent account of fishing on the Laerdal by Ernest Schweibert in *Esquire*, October, 1967, entitled 'Where Fishing is a Blood Sport'.

20 Magnus Berg, *Nord-Norske Laksecluer*, p. 249.

21 *Angling in Norway*, 1962 ed., p. 7.

22 *Ibid.*, p. 31.

23 Arthur Oglesby, 'Two Norwegian Rivers', *Trout and Salmon*, February 1967.

24 Leif Rosseland reported at the 1966 meeting of the International Council for the Exploration of the Sea that 'the salmon stock in Norway is at present at a rather high level. Apart from the probably good natural conditions prevailing, the reason for this may be the better control of illegal fishing, especially the weekly close time, increased artificial propagation and the construction of a large number of fishways. . . . The increase in the drift-net fishery, and perhaps even more . . . in the number of other gillnets is alarming. We fear that overfishing may take place if we do not find some way of controlling this fishery.'

6

Plight of the English and Welsh Salmon – I

The rivers of England and Wales are not as spectacular as many of those in Norway. They are not set among fjord coasts, or lofty glaciated mountains; nor do they plummet down gigantic waterfalls and reverberate like thunder in the narrow valleys. They are slender and bucolic for the most part. The typical English river, as Somerset Maugham says, winds 'its cheerful way round hills, through quietly busy towns and by nestling villages, pausing now in a noble reach and then running powerfully through a woodland valley. It is alive, varied, windswept.'

Each river has its special voice or music. The English rivers seem mostly to murmur rather than roar or rumble and sometimes to cackle or gabble as they meander across the undulating countryside, over moor or fen, heath and dale. At times their music is a lullaby, soft and sweet.

The typical English or Welsh river is in American terms a 'little river'.

The salmon rivers

We do not know how many English and Welsh rivers were accustomed to seeing the armies of salmon return every year to familiar habitats before man tampered with the waters and watersheds and made life difficult for these sensitive creatures. We know, however, that many streams have been deserted by this species in the past century or two, including some of the most productive, while others were greatly depopulated. There are no more than two score salmon streams left south of the Scottish border, not counting their tributaries.

The east coast of Scotland contains many salmon rivers but the east coast of England now has but few. After leaving the Tweed, we meet the still productive Coquet which rises in the Cheviot hills and traverses the entire county of Northumberland before emptying into the North Sea; and then the Tyne, Tees and Trent, which were once known for opulent salmon runs but are now virtually deserted, and in fact hardly recognizable as waters that could hold migratory fish. Figure 17 shows the major salmon rivers of the British Isles.

A few hundred miles below the Trent is the Thames, which issues from clear springs in the Cotswold hills, and after pursuing a bucolic and pastoral course of 218 miles interrupted by busy suburbs and the city of London, flows into the North Sea at the Nore, 60 miles below London. Pure and limpid–the Elizabethan poet Edmund Spenser called it 'silver-streaming Thames'–it once harboured 'fat and sweet salmons, daily taken in the stream, and that in such plenty . . . as no river in Europe is able to afford'.[1] Salmon used to spawn as far up river as Basildon, sixty-five miles above London. The Thames, incredibly polluted, is now devoid of migratory fish.

South of the Scottish border on the west coast we encounter a number of rivers which still hold salmon. A typical north-western stream is the lovely Eden. Born in the bleak Yorkshire Pennines near the source of two other prominent rivers, the Ribble and Lune, it flows down the soft-green Westmorland and Cumberland fells. This is a region of 'beautiful hedges, . . . woods patched brown with long straths of larch and green with Scots and Austrian pines, the sheltered oaks wrapped in rustly dead leaves and the sycamores in cloaks of yellow'.[2] In its 65-mile run the Eden passes many serene villages and castles like Armathwaite and Corby until it receives the flow of the Irthing, then turns west and, acquiring the waters of other small streams, reaches the city of Carlisle and shortly disappears into Solway Firth.

Not many miles from Eden's mouth is the Border Esk which comes down from Scotland and crosses the Solway marshes before it meets the shining Irish Sea. The salmon are believed to reach the Esk by feeling their way along the Scottish coast, sometimes followed by grey seals and other predators. The firth is lively with shore birds, some of whom feed on young salmon: black-headed gulls nest here in summer, herons live in the high moors above Corby Castle and Dolphinby in the upper Esk Valley, and cormorants perch and roost in the trees around the estuary.

The Ribble and Lune remain noteworthy salmon waters. I stood on an old stone bridge on the Ribble one cloudy autumn morning, watching the late-running fish moving upstream. One could see their tails above the grey waters as they ploughed onward. Occasionally a salmon would leap into the air, as if to show his splendid form. The thud of a woodman's axe from a nearby oak thicket broke the stillness, geese wheeled overhead while horses lazily nibbled the grass along the river-bank. Except for the water bailiff casually puffing his pipe, no human being could be seen. The nearby village seemed asleep.

Moving into the Midlands we meet the Wye which issues from the desolate bogs of Plinlimmon in Wales, only a few miles from the source of the Severn. The Wye follows a twisting 130-mile course through several counties, including the tumbled plains of Herefordshire and uplands of Monmouthshire. It is in part a wild mountain stream and in part meanders through an area filled with hop gardens, apple orchards and lush meadows, a region well farmed and much of it still pastoral. The classic stretch is south from Hereford to the sea (which it enters below Chepstow) where it becomes a broad and stately river. Tintern Abbey, which inspired Wordsworth's great poem, stands on the banks of the Wye, a melancholy ruin. The Wye has many tributaries.

The 200-mile Severn is, next to the Thames, the longest river in England. Like the Wye, it is an Anglo-Welsh waterway. Its lower reaches are the most impressive; it is slow-flowing and meanders widely, usurping the flow of smaller rivers like the Stour, the Teme and the Stratford Avon. It enters the cathedral city of Gloucester, one of the most splendid in England, and then dashes 15 miles to its estuary. Set in a lovely landscape, the Severn rouses many an angler to bait his hook, though its salmon runs have sorely diminished.

Some of the Midland streams are fairly broad and deep, others rather shallow. Arched by rude stone bridges, some dating from Saxon times, they may be smothered in cherry or apple blossoms in early summer for they traverse the most intense fruit-growing region of England. The market towns are usually unspoiled, like Evesham and Pershore, lined with red-brick Georgian houses, or like Tewkesbury with its picturesque tangle of narrow streets surrounding the tall twelfth-century Norman church. Many rural Midland inns hold leases on salmon beats and cater to anglers and their multifarious needs.

The Mersey, Wear, Yorkshire Don, Aire and Calder, Swale, Ouse, Nidd, Derwent and Wharfe were important English salmon rivers but are now mainly or totally out of production.

The British Field Sports Society lists almost a score of Welsh rivers where salmon may be caught by hook and line. In addition to the Severn and Wye, there are the Elwy, Lledr and Conway in Carnarvonshire; the Dee and Ceirog in Denbighshire; the Mawddach and Dovey in Merionethshire; the Teifi and Ystwyth in Cardiganshire; the Towy and Taf in Carmarthenshire; and the Usk in Breconshire. Some South Wales rivers have been ruined as fish habitat by gross pollution from mines, collieries and factories.

The River Dee, one of the longest in Britain, remains a major salmon stream. Its source is in the Merionethshire mountains, and it placidly follows a corkscrew path for over 100 miles in north-eastern Wales and England; for a distance it is used as an aqueduct to carry water to Liverpool to supply domestic and industrial needs. Its estuary is about twenty miles below Chester.

The Usk still flows through verdant country, at least until it reaches the industrialized fringes of Newport. Augustus Grimble, the indefatigable historian of British rivers, sixty years ago described its course as follows:

> The high, bleak, desolate hills of the Black Mountains which lie on the borders of Carmarthenshire and Breconshire have the honour of sending on its journey to the sea, this–one of the most famous–of English salmon rivers. The Henwen, with the Hydfer, and other small brooks soon combine to turn it into a respectable river as it reaches Trecastle, some eight miles from its source; from there it winds its way through the Forest of Brecon. . . . Before it reaches Llanspydded, some three miles above Brecon, it receives the waters of several other streams, the largest of which is the Yseir; . . . here the Usk turns to the south to pass through a finely wooded valley. . . . At Brecon it is joined by the Tarw and Honddhu . . . spanned by a substantial and beautiful old bridge with seven buttressed

---

9a. An electric fish diversion screen on the River Leven flowing from Lake Windermere, England, constructed to debar access to ascending salmon and sea-trout which would otherwise enter the tailrace of an electrical generating station.

9b. Some of the fish which died as a result of pollution in Stocks beck, a tributary of the River Ribble in Lancashire.

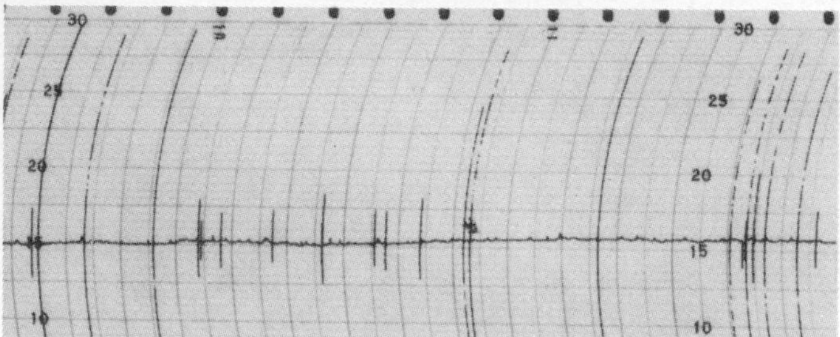

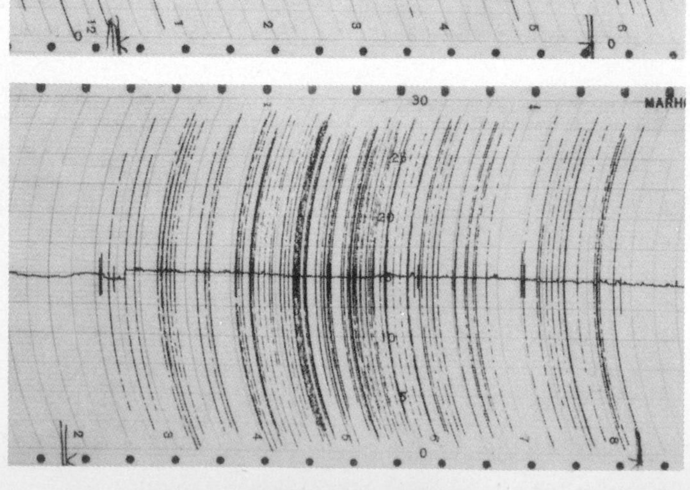

arches; it then wends its way towards Crickhowell through a valley of great beauty, and passing the Parks of Glanusk, Llangattock and Dan-y, it sweeps with a graceful curve by Ty Maur to reach Abergavenny,[3]

and thence to Usk, Newbridge, the Roman town of Caerleon, Newport and into the Bristol Channel, a run of 75 miles. Generally these Welsh waterways, like the Conway, remain unspoiled; they course through idyllic areas, redolent of England's distant past, when the landscape nearly everywhere was green and unmarred.

South England still boasts of many salmon rivers. The Exe, which gives its name to the cathedral city of Exeter, rises in Exmoor Forest in Somerset and is joined by the Barle at Dulverton, where it enters Devonshire. Gliding past many ancient villages and larger settlements, some of them little touched by time, it opens out at Exmouth into an estuary seven miles long. Equally renowned is the Dart, a quiet stream of some thirty miles, about half as long as the Exe, which ribbons the sombre Devon moors, famous for half-wild ponies. The Dart does not assume noticeable proportions until it is joined by the West Dart, after which, passing Totnes, it quickly hurls itself into the English Channel.

Chalk streams abound in this part of England. They harbour trout and coarse fish (carp, roach, pike, etc.) as well as salmon. The Frome is such a river, slow and deep in its lower stretches, peopled by ravens and hawks and wading and song birds of all kinds. Salmon were once so plentiful in the Frome that 'the officials of Wareham made a law that the apprentices of the town were not to be fed [this fish] more than three times a week'.[4]

Other south England waters where salmon are still caught in varying numbers are the Hampshire Avon, Stour, Taw and Torridge, Axe, Teign, Tavy, Camel and Fowey, Tamar and Plym.

10a. A fish-movement recording installation on the River Leven flowing from Lake Windermere, in which all fish are recorded in relation to their size and their movement linked to a number of natural variables such as air and water temperature, water level, barometric pressure, humidity, turbidity, dissolved oxygen, etc.

10b and 10c. A chart of the electronic recording of fish passing through the above station, which shows the traces indicating small fish and larger fish and the intensity of the run.

The salmon runs

Salmon enter British rivers at all seasons of the year. Those that arrive from December until March move upstream with greater deliberation than those coming up later. If the water is very cold in the winter or spring, fish may loiter in the deeper layers of the warmer estuary. Once they start their ascent they are not inclined to hurry, nor attempt to overcome obstacles such as weirs and falls. If a snowstorm intervenes they may turn around and go back down to the estuary. Forty-five degrees F. is believed to be good water temperature to lure fish upstream providing the river is in flood, running 18 inches or more above the normal winter level.

Salmon enter the rivers in schools but eventually disperse into smaller groups. At all times weather influences their movements. A mild winter will bring more 'spring fish' than a cold winter, and they will quickly leave the lower waters so that the middle and upper reaches have salmon as early as February or March. After a cold winter they are not expected upstream until April or May. Fish that arrive in summer or autumn have a different running pattern: a sudden rise in the river's level will send them upstream *en masse*. In summer the fish sensibly prefer to travel at night, when the water is cooler.

Autumn fish enter the rivers with their reproductive organs fully developed; hence they cannot dawdle. They are on the move as soon as they leave the estuary, attempting usually to reach the spawning gravels before it is too cold. Salmon that return in winter may delay their reproduction until the year following their arrival. Some biologists believe that the later a salmon reaches its home stream the nearer to the sea it spawns, but there is no proof of this theory.

For the most part, short west-coast British rivers have summer and autumn runs only, while east-coast streams may harbour spring and winter runs as well. These population patterns are not constant, however. At one time the Tweed was a predominantly 'autumn river' and now it is a spring river but still has an autumn run. In most British waters the largest runs come in summer and include, especially in Scotland, a sizeable proportion of grilse. Salmon returning after two years of ocean life may scale 9 to 12 pounds, and after three winters in the sea 18 to 25 pounds.

In the south of England young salmon grow rapidly and tend to migrate at one year of age. However, the vast majority of migrants from English and Welsh rivers are two years old; only a few stay longer in the rivers.

Considerable light has been thrown on the salmon's peregrinations after they leave English waters through the tagging of many thousands of smolts and some kelts. The opinion voiced by Menzies that the salmon spend their feeding years in northern sub-Arctic waters has been confirmed by the recovery off the west coast of Greenland of fish tagged in the Rivers Usk, Axe, Wye, Severn, Wear and Ribble. All but one of them were smolts when they left British waters. They had increased enormously in size and weight during the eighteen or twenty months that elapsed between release and recapture, despite journeys of 1,600 to 2,500 miles.[5]

There is an increasing interest in the kelts nowadays because the salmon is the most valuable fish found in European waters, and therefore in great demand. A spawned-out fish is but a pale version of its earlier self: thin, silvery, white-fleshed and long-toothed, with ragged fins and eroded scales. Many kelts, usually females, return to the river the following autumn to spawn again, others stay away about a year, and still others eighteen months. On returning, they are again fleshed out, dressed in gleaming silver coats, and move with agility. All the evidence, including their recapture in Greenland, suggests they are worth preserving and can contribute significantly to the fishery.

Salmon in the Middle Ages

We are relatively well informed about primitive man's use of the animals in his environment. The Mesolithic hunters knew the trails of the deer, watched the spring flights of the geese, the movements of mackerel and herring in the ocean, and counted on the return of the salmon to the rivers. There is some evidence that much later, in the Bronze Age, when population had increased in the British Isles, salmon and trout were taken on the hook and possibly also speared and netted.

The earliest-known historical allusion to *Salmo salar* in Britain is the remark of the Venerable Bede, writing in the early eighth century, that the island 'has the greatest plenty of salmon and eels'. This statement is corroborated by *Domesday Book*, the exhaustive survey of England's wealth made by William the Conqueror's agents in 1086 for the purpose of determining the power and resources of his feudatories and their vassals in every county. Scores of eel and a few salmon fisheries are listed on the coast and in the river valleys and fenland districts. For example, one thousand salmon yearly were rendered to the lord of the manor at Gloucester, and important salmon fisheries were reported in the counties of Devon, Hereford and Cheshire. At Tidenham on the River Wye a considerable quantity of salmon was supplied to the table of Archbishop Stigand and the religious establishment attached to the manor. Here the fish were caught in basket weirs and hackle weirs.[6]

Giraldus Cambriensis (Gerald the Welshman) in his *Description of Wales*, written in 1188, described salmon fishing on the River Teifi with little boats called coracles that are still in use on that very stream. Made of skins stretched on wooden frames and carried on men's shoulders, they were of very ancient vintage, for Julius Caesar used such craft in his invasion of Spain in the first century B.C. For fishing purposes, two coracles drifted downstream side by side; a small trammel net was held between them and when the fish struck the net was allowed to bunch up along the headline and then hauled aboard by the crew.

Information about salmon fisheries in England in the later Middle Ages is buried in numerous ecclesiastical and other archives that have not yet been investigated. (We are much better informed about Ireland's salmon fisheries, thanks to the diligent investigations of Dr. Arthur E. J. Went.)

In the fourteenth century Ranulph Higden, a monk of St. Werburgh's in Chester, noted in his encyclopedic tome, *Polychronicon*, written in Latin and translated into English by John of Trevisa, that England was 'rich in noble rivers with plenty of fish; there is great plenty of small fish, of salmon and eels. So that the churls in some places feed fish to sows.'[7] This plenitude remained for several centuries. As in France, some British towns incorporated the salmon in their municipal insignia. Peebles in Scotland had a standard emblazoned with the picture of a salmon and the motto, *One Up, Two Down.*

Just as the fisherman was regarded as a prominent citizen in his rural community, the fishmonger was an important personage in town and the Fishmongers Company ranked high among the merchant companies. It held a monopoly in the sale of fish. Each guild usually had a resplendent hall where meetings were held and business conducted. There was an annual feast for its patron saint. The guild participated in the financing and construction of the community's cathedral, established charitable institutions and schools, prepared and performed the miracle plays. In municipal parades its dignitaries marched in gorgeous liveries, displaying the banners of the trade in colourful pageantry.

In London fish were landed from very olden times, perhaps the ninth century, in the vicinity of Billingsgate Wharf where the market remains to this day and where a large portion of all the salmon caught in the British Isles is still sold at wholesale. In fact, the exact origin of the company is unknown, but a prototype existed long before Edward I granted its first charter in 1272. Later charters formally incorporated the company and laid down rules for its governance and regulation of trade.

Originally the right to fish in tidal and non-tidal waters was vested in the Crown but after 1215 the right to fish in tidal waters became public and no grants of fisheries after that date are recognized. In non-navigable waters the right remained with the manor or was conveyed to a buyer either with the land on the banks of the stream, or separately. *Domesday Book* records privately-held fisheries in tidal as well as non-tidal waters but this does not mean that at that early period there were 'several fisheries' where individuals had an exclusive right from which the public was barred. So valuable were fishing rights considered that Magna Charta, the great charter of British liberty which King John was forced by the barons to sign at Runnymede in 1215, stipulated that all fish weirs placed by the King or his agents in the Thames and Medway 'and throughout all England except the sea shore' shall be removed and free passage for migratory fish assured.

As in other countries, many of the best fisheries were owned by religious establishments.

Protective legislation

From the very beginning almost of English government the Crown adopted a protective attitude towards the inland fisheries. Legislation was usually concerned with salmon because it was the most valuable species found in British waters and also one of the easiest to catch. A riparian owner in the lower reaches of a river could–and sometimes did–trap an entire run, thus robbing upstream owners of their share of the harvest. The first act dealing specifically with salmon seems to have been that of 1285 (Edward I) which provided that in 'the waters of the Humber, Ouse, Trent, Dove, Aire, Derwent, Wharfe, Nid, Swale, Tees, Tyne, Eden, and all other waters [wherein salmon are found] they shall not be taken from the Nativity of Our Lady [September 8] until St. Martin's Day [November 12]. And likewise young salmon shall not be taken nor destroyed by nets, nor by other engines at mill pools, from the middle of April until the Nativity of St. John the Baptist [June 24].' Violators were to be punished by burning their nets and engines; a second offence risked imprisonment for three months and a third a year's incarceration. 'As their trespass increases, so shall the punishment', said the statute.

The statute of 1384 issued by Richard II confirmed and re-enacted the law of Edward I, extended the close season for all waters in Lancashire and various other rivers from Michaelmas Day (September 29) to February 1, and prohibited the use of nets called 'stalkers' and other gear to take salmon fry. A parallel enactment of Richard II made the Justices of the Peace of the counties responsible for enforcement of the salmon laws by appointing conservators to protect the fishery. These men continued to be responsible for appointing conservators until well into the nineteenth century.

A steady flow of statutes dealing with freshwater fisheries issued from the Crown in succeeding centuries. Usually they contained a preamble lamenting the decline of the fishery. They forbade the taking of salmon fry; imposed penalties for obstructing migration of fish; and established close seasons. One of the most stubborn problems were the fishing weirs and other obstructions that hindered or stopped fish movement. Statutes designed to curb this menace were promulgated by Henry IV, Henry V, and Henry VI in the fifteenth century. Edward IV reaffirmed these laws and ordered preceding ordinances relating to weirs to be enforced and a penalty of 100 marks imposed on every offender. Local courts of Admiralty were given jurisdiction over estuarial fisheries. By orders from the Crown and their own 'bye-laws' (regulations) they could regulate the size of meshes of nets and the use of particular fishing 'engines' and also set close times in the rivers and ports.[8]

These laws were reaffirmed by the Crown at different times in later centuries. We have been able to find little information on the manner of enforcing the numerous royal decrees relating to inland fisheries, but that they were frequently violated or simply ignored is revealed in Leonard Mascall's *Booke of Fishing* (1590):

It is a good thing to have plenty of fresh water fish, in rivers and ponds, and standing waters; and a great pleasure for man sometimes to take with his angle a dish of fish in those waters where fish is plenty and well preserved, not to use any other engine, but with the hook; and by such means as the laws of this realm doth permit and allow, not to use fire, handguns, crossbows, oils, ointments, powders, and pellets made to cast in the water to stun and poison the fish, nor yet to use all sorts of nets, and such as are devourers of fish, as bow nets, casting nets, small trammels, shove nets and draft nets; which are destroyers of fish before they are grown to any bigness. . . . I would wish no running waters should be let to any fisherman without order what mesh, what nets, he or they shall use to fish, and in what months of the year to refrain from fishing, upon pain to forfeit his lease and all such engines.

Mascall laments that England does not have 'more preservers, and less spoilers of fish out of season and in season; then we should have more plenty than we have through this realm'. He wishes that 'all stop nets, and drags with casting nets, were banished in all common rivers throughout this realm for three months: as in March, April and May, wherein they take fish out of season as well as others, with great spoils of spawn, both of great and small fish, for they use such nets with small mesh, that kills all fish afore they come to any growth'. Further, he tells us that water bailiffs appointed to guard the rivers shut their eyes to these illegal small-mesh nets, while the owners of fishing waters are equally indifferent, because the fishermen say that since they pay high rents they must take whatever they can so therein are 'none that cares for the preserving of the common wealth'. At the end of this gentle peroration he says, 'So I leave, wishing that careful men were put in office, and such as favours the common wealth, and all other put out that seeks for their own profit only. Then should we have within few years, much plenty of river fish.'[9]

In 1714 George I sought to halt depredations on salmon runs in the Severn, Dee, Wye, Teme, Wear, Tees, Ribble, Mersey, Don, Aire, Ouse, Swale, Calder, Wharfe, Eure, Derwent and Trent by enacting that in these waters 'if any person or persons whatsoever shall at any time hereafter lay or draw any kind of nets, engines, or devices, wilfully do or commit, or cause to be done or committed, any other act . . . whereby the spawn or small fry of salmon . . . or any salmon not being in length 18 inches or more from the eye to the extent of the middle of the tail, shall be taken and killed or destroyed or shall hereafter make, erect, or set any bank, dam, hedge, or stank, net or nets across the said rivers, or any part thereof, whereby the salmon therein may be taken, or hindered from passing or going up the said rivers to spawn', or shall fish in close season or with other nets than those allowed, he shall be fined five pounds–an enormous sum in those days–for every offence and the fish and nets confiscated. Justices were empowered to order obstructions to be demolished at the owner's expense. Although the law was not retroactive and did not apply to ancient weirs or locks, it was used occasionally to get rid of dams and weirs; sometimes, however, only after protracted legal proceedings.

The statute of 1714 also stipulated that no salmon under six pounds could be sent to London for sale from the 17 rivers named. Furthermore, as we learn from a notice in the government newspaper, the *London Gazette*, of November 4, 1706, salmon taken out of season and exposed for sale were to be destroyed as unfit to eat, 'as many lately have been, by the Rt. Hon. the Lord Mayor of the said city'. A reward was offered to any person who brought such unseasonable fish to the Lord Mayor, the amount to be paid by the Fishmongers Company 'according to what the Lord Mayor shall deem fit'.

Protection of wildlife, including fisheries, was advanced in Britain by the creation of extensive parks and game preserves by the King and great landowners. King Canute in the eleventh century was the first ruler to set aside large areas of forest land for his personal use. William the Conqueror greatly increased the number and extent of the royal forests. Windsor Forest, Epping Forest (which once covered the county of Essex) and New Forest in Hampshire were proclaimed royal preserves. The barons followed his example by establishing areas of unenclosed land where they could fully indulge in their favourite pastimes, riding and hunting, when they were not at war. Salmon and trout along with partridge, grouse, pheasant, hare, red deer and wild boar could only be taken by the royal family and such landowners as enjoyed the King's favour. Although protected, these game preserves were not managed in a modern sense for the purpose of increasing the crops of wildlife.

Gradually the right to hunt was extended until an owner of contiguous acreage could obtain this privilege on his land. In time the royal demesne and baronial parks were reduced in number and size so that they become relatively small enclaves amidst the agricultural and unenclosed land and common pasture. However, the existence of such extensive hunting areas during the industrial expansion and growth of towns in the eighteenth and nineteenth centuries undoubtedly served a beneficial purpose. 'The rich and powerful . . . were preserving habitats and that was of immense value', says Fraser Darling.[10]

Special laws were applied to the royal forests that made them inviolable. Under the Norman kings persons convicted of stealing game or fish received heavy fines, or were outlawed; they could even be mutilated or put to death, punishments that stopped all but the hardiest poachers. By the time of Henry II in the twelfth century greater leniency was shown to trespassers on royal or private preserves, although this offence was always regarded as quite serious in England, less so in Scotland.

Salmon as food

Fish was a very important item of the medieval diet since it was obligatory to abstain from meat on Fridays and during Lent. There was a dearth of meat before sheep-raising became common in England; where available, it was expensive. Thus a local supply of fish served to stave off food shortages when the harvests failed and meat was hard to find. Inland transport always influenced the markets.

Fresh fish was commonly available in most parts of the British Isles during the season while in winter salted or smoked fish was eaten. Salmon was preserved by salt-pickling in barrels topped with brine. Powdered salmon, preserved by dusting with crushed salt, was consumed in London in the fifteenth and sixteenth centuries, and smoked salmon, hard and salty and not the kind nowadays found on restaurant menus, was shipped to distant markets. 'Kippered salmon', really spawned-out fish, is recorded as eaten in the household of James V of Scotland.[11]

Salmon seems to have been a favourite in some noble menages, although not apparently the epicurean delight it became in France. In the north of England salmon was peasant's food. The earliest salmon recipe found, in the sixteenth-century *Noble Book of Cookery*, stipulates that the fish be cut in round pieces and roasted on a gridiron, using wine, minced onions, pepper, ginger and salt to add the proper seasoning. It was also customary to serve salmon grilled and unsauced, although we later hear of Hollandaise and Tartare sauces being used.

Some idea of the prevalence of salmon in the diet during the end of the seventeenth and first decade of the eighteenth centuries is revealed in the journals of Celia Fiennes, that redoubtable woman who sauntered on horseback through England and even ventured into the wilderness of Wales and Scotland. She ate salmon at Lord Clifford's house at Burlington, a fish that was over three-quarters of a yard long, 'very fresh and good', and cost but eighteenpence. She purchased a salmon in Scotland quite cheaply but carried it across the border to get it properly cooked. In Wales the miserable inhabitants had little meat, poor mutton, but were fairly well provided with fish. 'Very good salmon and eels and other fish I had at Hawarden', she notes.

When transportation improved and a means of preserving fish in ice was perfected salmon became the dish of the lower classes. In 1786 an ingenious Scottish fish merchant, George Dempster, conceived the idea of shipping salmon in ice from the River Tay to London, a distance of over 400 miles. So successful was his innovation that ice houses were soon built in all the chief salmon-fishing centres in Scotland and parts of Ireland. By 1817, over 700,000 pounds of iced salmon were reaching London annually from the Dee and Don, and by 1838 a regular boat service was taking fish from Edinburgh to the English capital where, arriving in prime condition, they could be preserved for ten days in cool weather and a week in summer.[12] With the spread of railways, freshwater fish found wide markets.

Salmon in abundance

Statistics on salmon catches are scarce before the 1860s but the evidence suggests that the English and Welsh rivers on the whole were well stocked until the advent of the Industrial Revolution.

Wales was especially renowned for its salmon. Giraldus Cambriensis reported in the late twelfth century that hordes of fish ran up the Teifi. In 1314 Edward II granted John de Hastings permission to erect a weir on the Teifi which was the largest in Wales; here, 250 years later, in the reign of Elizabeth I, 100 to 150 salmon were being taken daily. The weir was finally demolished in 1797.

According to the chronicle of the Priory of Finchdale of the Convent of Durham, the River Wear in North England abounded with salmon, grilse and trout in the Middle Ages, and its larder was well stocked with fish. In the year 1536 the monks purchased 756 salmon, probably to feed the poor as well as their own household. It was not unusual for this establishment to buy 550 fresh salmon from the Wear fisheries at one time.

We have noted the abundance of salmon in the Thames in the Elizabethan age. At the end of the Cromwellian era, the peripatetic Richard Franck observed in his *Northern Memoirs* that the most eminent rivers 'that accommodate the angler with the race of salmon are first, the Trent; next is the Severn; then the Ouse; and most illustrious of all is the Thames'.[13] Thomas Fuller, in the *Worthies of England* (1662), commented that 'there are plenty of [salmon] in this country, though not in such abundance as in Scotland'.

Celia Fiennes gives us glimpses of the salmon fisheries on the Severn, the Yorkshire Derwent, the Lune where 'there are great weirs or falls of water made for salmon fishing' and where nets are hung near the bridge at Lancaster town and great quantities are caught, and on the Kent at Kendall, where a barrier at the falls, partly man-made, enables the fishermen to spear the salmon as they try to leap over the obstruction. Riding along the ridge on the banks of the Eden just inside the Scottish border, she could see people 'with boats fishing for salmon and trout which made my journey very pleasing'.[14] On the River Swale she observed artificial as well as natural weirs convenient 'for catching salmon by spear when they leap over these bays'; on the Exe she found similar devices to trap fish above the bridge at Exeter.[15]

Daniel Defoe, who was a tradesman first and roving journalist second, took note of the freshwater fisheries in his *Tour through England and Wales*, published in 1724. For instance, at Totnes on the River Dart in Devon, located about seven miles from the sea, he saw a trap which lured the fish into an enclosure when the tide was up and left them stranded in a foot or eighteen inches of water when it receded. A hoop or shove net at the end of a pole was put into the water and fixed in place while a dog drove all the fish into the mesh. During his stay, Defoe saw scores of salmon caught daily. They sold for twopence apiece, while 'for such fish not at all bigger, and not so fresh, I have seen 6 shillings 6 pence each given at a London fish-market, whither they are sometimes brought from Chichester by land carriage'.[16]

Thomas Bewick, the celebrated wood engraver, recalled that when he was a boy in the 1760s, 'I was frequently sent by my parents to the fishermen at Eltringham Ford to purchase a salmon. I was always told not to pay two penny a pound, and I commonly paid only a penny, and sometimes three halfpence.' Bewick remembered that in his youth 'an article had been always inserted in every indenture of apprenticeship in Newcastle that the apprentices were not to be forced to eat salmon above twice a week, and the same bargain was made with common servants'.[17]

Midland salmon rivers were amply stocked. Thus, Martin's *Natural History of England*, published in 1785, notes that the Mersey 'greatly abounds with salmon, which in spring strive to ascend the arm of the sea, and with difficulty evade the nets of the fishermen before they reach Warrington Bridge, where the river becomes narrower. . . . The towns of Warrington, Manchester and Stockport are well supplied; and their overplus is either sent to London by stages, or carried on horseback to Birmingham, and other inland towns.'[18] Alas, the Mersey, like the Thames, no longer contains any salmon.

The north of England also yielded bumper crops of fish. The naturalist Pennant, writing in 1775, said that on the River Tees at Dinstall the netsmen worked day and night. The rental of 450 pounds yearly paid to the Dean and Chapter of the Cathedral was an indication of the fishery's great value. Pennant calculated that at the going price of eight shillings for a dozen salmon, the fishermen would have to catch 13,500 fish merely to pay the annual rental.

All told, it seems that most English streams were relatively unimpaired at the opening of the nineteenth century. The 'Driffield Angler' in his book of that title published in 1806 listed as prime salmon rivers some of those which had been in high repute in Tudor and Elizabethan days: the Thames, Severn, Mersey, Trent, Medway,

Exe, Usk and Wye. Salmon netting was then practised in the estuaries and at the mouths of rivers with a great variety of gear, handled by boatmen or from the banks, while upstream fish were caught by means of weirs or locks. There was relatively little rod fishing.

Impact of the Industrial Revolution

The turning point in the history of the English and Welsh salmon was the onset of the Industrial Revolution. The first true factory in England was built at Derby in 1718–22, a silk mill driven by water power from the Derwent, an excellent salmon stream. Fifty years later Matthew Boulton, who financed Watt's successful experiments with the steam engine, opened his Soho factory in the unravished countryside near Birmingham. Arkwright's first spinning mill was set up at Cromford, and later Jedediah Strutt built a cotton mill at Belper, both on the Derwent. Coalbrookdale, in Shropshire, then a romantically beautiful town, was chosen by the Darby family for their iron works because here a rapid stream entered the broad waterway of the Severn.

Growth of the cotton, iron and steel and other metallurgical industries, of coal and coke production, and of chemical and allied manufacturing, filled the lovely dales of the central and northern counties and green Welsh valleys with a multitude of blast furnaces and foundries, with smelters and forging mills, with hideous industrial towns. The mills and foundries worked incessantly, pouring their smoke and gases into the air, glowing with crimson light at night, producing the steel needed for the railroads and bridges that were changing the land. Cities arose on the banks of pastoral rivers, their streets lined with unsanitary brick houses and hovels back to back, dimly lighted, unpaved, ugly with grime and smoke. Manchester usurped the River Irwell; Liverpool sprawled on the Mersey estuary; Leeds straddled the Aire; Sheffield was situated at the confluence of the Sheaf and Don; Newcastle on the Tyne. South Wales, south Yorkshire and Tyneside acquired enclaves of bleak industrial settlements which spread inexorably, poisoning the rivers, fringed by verdant shrubs and trees and carpets of wild flowers, once so pure people used to drink from them.

The moist western side of the Pennines became the centre of the cotton textile industry. Here the little mills once turned by mountain streams were soon abandoned, and great factories arose in their stead. On the east side of the mountains, where sheep-grazing and wool-gathering were ancient forms of agriculture, dreary cities like Bradford, Leeds and Huddersfield arose. Here yarn was spun and cloth woven in dismal factories, usually located on a pellucid brook or river.

South Wales became the nation's metallurgical centre. At the end of the eighteenth century Swansea, on the River Tawe, and its environs had a copper smelter and tinplating works; coalmines had been worked in the neighbourhood for centuries. Merthyr Tydfil, not far away, boasted of thirteen blast furnaces.

It was customary nearly everywhere to pour refuse and wastes from factories, mills and mines as well as untreated sewage into the nearest waterway, heedless of the consequences to water or fish. Capitalists brooked no interference with the divine law of *laissez faire*. They made their money and left their muck, as someone said. Moreover, it was believed that flowing water washes everything, purifies everything, as it may have done when there was very little pollution to purify.

England initiated the Industrial Revolution and set the pace, and also showed the world how to wreck prized rivers. 'There is nothing more beautiful', said the late H. D. Turing, the great crusader against pollution, 'than one of our clear English streams, flowing through lush meadows and pastures by tree-lined banks and past quiet hamlets to the sea, unless it be one of our Welsh or Scottish mountain streams, dancing and tumbling over the rocks to a music which is one of Nature's purest songs.'[19] Before the Industrial Revolution, when England was sparsely populated, much animal and vegetable refuse was deposited on the land to form manure, and the liquid waste flowed into the river where it was actually beneficial, for the resulting salts fertilized the bed of the stream, thus increasing insect life and food for fish. Industry was then on a small scale, largely associated with agriculture, and its wastes could not do noticeable harm, however small or large the stream.

When small towns and villages, like Newcastle, Manchester and Birmingham, bourgeoned into cities, human wastes, created at an ever-increasing rate, had to be disposed of more or less in one place. It was easiest and cheapest to run liquids into a pipe or ditch connected with a stream. As towns acquired piped water supplies for drinking and other purposes, the solid wastes, including untreated sewage, were also flushed into sewers where they could be carried off into the river by liquid wastes. When sewage and effluents reached the stream, after being in the sewers a considerable length of time, they were in an advanced stage of decay. A large mass of bacteria which absorbed all the oxygen they could obtain had already formed. The low oxygen content of the water drove away fish, killed insect life, and partly or entirely destroyed the normal weed growth in the waters which also needs oxygen. Thus, for considerable distances below the sewage outfall, the river was usually dead and could only recover when pollution decreased and eventually disappeared. But in many waters the self-purification process was too slow or ineffective, and the fish populations dwindled or even disappeared. Salmon, a species that needs water with large concentrations of dissolved oxygen, was especially affected by impure or slowly purifying rivers.

The dead reaches of the rivers are usually deserted by anadromous fish. In these waters there is not enough oxygen to keep pace with the demands of both organic life and the sewage they harbour; part of the organic matter that is not wholly purified then sinks to the bottom to form a layer of sludge or mud in which nothing will grow. Instead, bacteria attack this mass and generate gases that are carried downstream for several miles, forming as it were an impenetrable blockade for fish until rendered harmless by chemical reaction with some other substance. In the industrialized regions of England, Wales and Scotland, many salmon streams were impaired or ruined in this fashion.

'To see the effect of pollution at its worst,' said Turing, 'one must as a rule go to the estuaries and tidal waters.' It was generally supposed that the sea, or the mixture of fresh and salt water in the lower tidal sections, would break up the heavy flow of untreated sewage and factory wastes coming downstream. But the material was often too formidable for sea water to handle it, so that many estuaries became nothing more than open sewers, like the rivers above them. Walls of sludge, dark, dreary and smelly, were wafted downstream; the tides would wash them out to sea, where they would be partly oxidized, and then bring them back, until, moving back and forth, they finally disappeared. Sometimes they formed bars at the river's entrance and had to be dredged and taken far out to sea.

Heavy pollution makes it difficult for the hardiest fish to reach their upstream destination; to tiny seaward travellers it may be lethal. For the salmon, the crucial period is during the transformation from parr to smolt. Smolts do not go directly to sea but hang around the estuaries to acclimatize themselves. At this point they are extremely vulnerable to shortages of oxygen and to harmful substances like acids in the water. Hence if they meet a zone of pollution they may perish *en masse*. In some cases they are stupefied and sucked into salt water unwillingly, so that the sudden change of environment kills them, or they are decimated by gulls while gasping for air at the surface. If the smolts did not select a time of flood to make their dash to the sea, said Turing, there would be years when in a contaminated estuary scarcely any salmon runs would appear. 'In years which have a dry spring this probably happens and may account for those inexplicable years when the salmon crop seems to fail almost entirely.'[20]

It was typical of the early Victorian age that 200,000 people lived in hideous slums in Manchester, without a single public garden, and that sewage from its dwellings and factories was dumped into the pristine Irwell. In time little or no natural water normally entered this river, from its cradle in the moors to its grave in Manchester Ship Canal. Fish could not live because there were no insects, no weeds or life of any kind except sewage fungus, chemical effluents and dirt that were not disposable elsewhere. And the Irwell was only one of many wrecked rivers in the industrialized parts of the British Isles.

In 1877, Archibald Young in his summary of the British salmon industry presented the following list of English and Welsh salmon rivers seriously affected by pollution–some of them have never recovered:

River	*Kind of pollution*
Axe	Sewerage
Camel	China clay, mines
Dart	Chemicals, mines, paper works, wool washings

11. The powerful but futile leaping of salmon at a vertical obstruction which debars them from reaching the spawning grounds. This weir on the River Ribble has now been opened up and makes available 30 miles of river for the first time in 160 years, an example of what can be done.

Dee	Oil and alkali works, petroleum, paper works, wool washings
Dovey	Mines
Eden	Sewage, tan, mines
Exe	Sewage, paper works
Fowey	China clay works, mines
Kent	Manufactures
Ogmore	Coal, tan, sewage
Rhymney	Ruined by pollutions
Ribble	Sewage, factories, chemicals
Severn	Sewage, mines, tan, dye works
Stour	Sewage
Tamar and Plym	Mines and clay works
Taw and Torridge	Sewage
Tees	Mines, sewage
Teifi	Debris from slate quarries, mines
Teign	Mines
Towy	Mines, chemicals
Trent	Sewage, factories
Tyne	Chemicals, mines, coal washings

---

12. Aerial view of part of the Bala Lake Works in Wales of the Dee and Clwyd River Authority, showing the control sluices (centre), the new channels, weirs, and fish passes of the Afon Tryweryn (top right) and the improved outlet channel of the River Dee from Bala Lake (top left to bottom right). By means of these works, the discharges down the River Dee from both Bala Lake and the Afon Tryweryn have been brought under a substantial measure of control, resulting in a major reduction in the frequency and size of flood flows into the upper Dee, and the increase of the minimum flow in the Dee to more than double its natural drought flow. This increases the amount of water which can be abstracted from the river for public supply, and as the principal abstractions are near the tidal limit, the benefits of the increased minimum flow are available to fisheries over virtually the whole length of the river, and this benefit has been evidenced by the increasing salmon catches since the control works became operational in 1956.

The subsequent development of Llyn Celyn on the Afon Tryweryn by Liverpool Corporation permits even greater regulation of the river, and the minimum flow is now about six times that of the natural drought flow. The loss of natural spawning ground at Llyn Celyn has been made good by the provision of a fish trap and a modern salmon hatchery.

Usk	Tinplate works, iron works, lime, ashes, coal washings, sewage
Wear	Ruined by mines
Wye	Mines, tin works, sewage
Yorkshire rivers	Tan, lime, factories, sewage

Restraint in the use of the natural environment was almost unknown in Britain (as in the United States) during the nineteenth century. If the countryside was desecrated by ugly cities swarming with workers dwelling in miserable slums; if foundries and mills night and day poured plumes of suffocating smoke into the air and flushed their wastes into the nearest body of water; if rivers ran black or yellow with dirt and chemical refuse–this was regarded as only the concomitant of progress. Industrialists could destroy the environment with impunity. In fact, they rarely gave the matter any thought despite the shrill protests of such writers as Charles Dickens, John Ruskin, Thomas Carlyle, William Morris and others. The sense of pride in natural beauty which animated pre-industrial England was too often buried in the immeasurable lust for profits.

Weirs, canals, overfishing

High on the list of factors that contributed to the serious reduction of migratory fish populations in England and Wales was the construction of weirs or dams to divert water for millraces, or provide water supplies for household uses or industrial operations. Sometimes these barriers stretched across the entire width of a river without any gaps or passes to enable fish to get by, in open violation of long-standing laws. The Royal Commission on Freshwater Fisheries, created in 1861, learned that the Ouse, Wharfe, Ure, Derwent and other Yorkshire rivers were studded with weirs while the Severn, Dee, Cumberland, Derwent, Lune, Taw, Torridge and Test were 'also conspicuous for the deterioration of their fisheries since weirs have come into general use'.[21] As we have noted, the Act of 1714 named seventeen rivers on which it was expressly forbidden to construct impediments to fish passage. In 1868 every one of them was either partly or substantially blockaded by weirs or damaged by pollution (Table 12). The Mersey, Yorkshire Don, Aire and Calder were totally inaccessible to salmon.

Canalization was also an appreciable factor in destroying fish runs.

Table 12
Status of English salmon rivers in 1868

River	Length (miles)	Area of catchment basin (sq. miles)	Area still accessible (sq. miles)	Area closed by weirs (sq. miles)	Area closed by weirs and pollution (sq. miles)
Severn	178	4,437	2,037	2,400	0
Dee	93	850	400	450	0
Wye	148	1,655	880	775	0
Wear (Durham)	70	455	35	0	420
Tees	95	744	444	300	0
Ribble	61	501	251	250	0
Mersey	68	1,706	0	0	1,706
Don (Yorkshire)	68	721	0	0	721
Aire and Calder	134	802	0	0	802
Ouse	59				
Swale	71	1,905	700	1,205	0
Wharfe	75				
Ure and Nidd	61				
Derwent	72	928	360	568	0
Trent	167	3,543	1,500	2,043	0
		18,247	6,607	7,991	3,649

By converting a river into a navigable waterway spawning beds were destroyed, 'the salmon's nest became a pike pond, and the capabilities of the river, as a salmon-producing stream, were enormously lowered'. Yet in 1869, when the Inspector of Salmon Fisheries made this remark, England's canal-building era was long past, few canals were being used for transportation, and navigation locks throughout the country were mostly neglected and in a mouldering state.

Take, for example, the Thames. It has a catchment basin of 5,162 square miles. In 1868 the main stream had 61 mills on it and the fourteen tributaries 299 mills. It was navigable nominally from the estuary to Lechlade, but practically not beyond Oxford. Many of the locks and weirs were old and in ruinous condition. In fact, the weirs were no longer much used for water power and were scarcely more than auxiliaries to steam. Above Oxford the navigation locks were in utter decay, the channel was unnavigable, and traffic had disappeared. Below Oxford navigation was maintained to some extent.[22]

According to Frank Buckland, the last salmon was caught on the Thames in the 1820s and bought by George IV, then living at Virginia Water, for a guinea a pound. William Yarrell in his *History of British Fishes* says that the last salmon was taken in June 1833. (Shad disappeared about the same time as the salmon.) The conclusion of a commission which looked into this matter was that the major causes of the loss of the Thames salmon stocks were: (1) deposition of sewage; (2) discharges from gasworks; (3) poisonous drainage from mines; (4) non-observance by netters of close seasons; (5) obstructions caused by weirs and stake nets; and (6) navigation by steamers.[23]

The rise in the value of salmon, induced by growing demand, encouraged heavier fishing efforts. New and more efficient nets were employed in the estuaries, and increasing manpower was enlisted. Scottish-type stake nets were imported into the north, as on the Solway Firth, around Morecambe Bay, at the mouth of the Trent, and in the Lune estuary. 'Putchers' and 'putts' were traditionally employed in the Severn estuary and at the mouths of the Usk and Rhymney Rivers. Putchers are conical wicker baskets 24 inches in diameter at the mouth and tapering to a point, placed in three, four or five parallel rows. For instance, at Goldcliffe, near the mouth of the Usk, there was a fishery consisting of 1,200 putchers with their mouths turned upstream to catch fish dropping back to the sea on the ebb tide, and close by another set of 900 facing downstream to trap the salmon on their ascent in flood tide. Putts work in a similar way but are larger and more complicated in construction. In 1860 it was estimated that over 11,000 putts and putchers were operating in the Severn estuary. Easily erected and removed, they were catching fish with total disregard of close times.

At Swansea, Lynmouth and other places it was customary to enclose an area on the shore with brushwood or wickerwork to trap the fish and leave them stranded at the fall of the tide, later to be picked up and taken to market. In many places 'raise nets' (or 'baulk nets') were anchored on the beaches; these worked with the tides and cut off retreating fish.

On the Usk there was a type of fishing called 'stopping' which consisted of mooring a boat where the salmon were supposedly running and letting down a large U-shaped net which flared out underneath and could be quickly raised whenever a fish struck. It was not uncommon to see twenty boats moored close to each other across the stream, forming almost as formidable a barrier as a stone weir.

Commercial salmon fishing was, in fact, conducted by every conceivable means, and often without regard to the law. On the River Ribble, prior to 1861, the estuary was hard-fished by draught nets and stake nets, but there was no getting above tidewater. On the Hampshire Avon, pure as of yore, one fixed hang net worked night and day outside Christchurch harbour and another, 200 yards long, was frequently stretched across the river. Since there were also fishing dams at Knapp's Mill, a half-mile above tidewater, and at Winkton farther upstream, few salmon managed to reach the spawning beds of the upper waters. It is understandable that by 1860 the salmon runs had dropped to a very low level on the Avon.[24]

The Devon Axe was another stream in poor condition, suffering mostly from overfishing. 'Mackerel seines' worked at the mouth and snared nearly every salmon that came up the river. Those which escaped were brought to a standstill at Axminster Weir, where merciless netters awaited them. The same melancholy tale was reported from other waterways. The Wye salmon were subjected to a 90-mile barrage of nets almost to the headwaters. Moreover, kelts were incessantly poached from the upper reaches while up to two hundred persons fished for parr between Monmouth and Hereford. Hotels in the neighbourhood were filled with visitors who came for the express purpose of eating that rare delicacy, Wye 'whitebait'. Worse still, organized bands of masked poachers frequently raided the unprotected spawning beds of the upper Wye.

Overfishing was flagrant on the incredibly productive Tyne. At its mouth during the height of the runs one could see, as the night approached, said the Inspector of Salmon Fisheries in 1869, 'hundreds of lights glimmering in every direction from literally hundreds of boats engaged in fishing. . . . Nets tied together floating along with the tide barred the passage of the harbour in every direction, it was impossible to reach the harbour without steaming through the nets. I found the more distant [stake] nets usually anchored in defiance of all law, and the same men constantly fishing with three or even four nets, but with only one licence.'[25] Kelts were nabbed in their passage to the sea while parr were scooped up by the thousands as they were detained at the mill weirs and fed to pigs or used as fertilizer. In the year 1872 the salmon catch on the Tyne reached almost 130,000.

Poaching was a traditional practice by country people, and was usually regarded as a sport, especially in Scotland. Writers like Sir Walter Scott,[26] William Scrope and Thomas Tody Stoddart, all widely read, cast an aura of romance over the spectacles of 'burning the river' and 'sunning the river' but these practices resulted in despoliation of salmon stocks, especially in the Tweed. In defence of poaching Scrope proclaimed that a salmon is like a bird of passage that must be taken during its brief sojourn in the river or be wasted.

In addition to chemicals, various and sundry tools were used to stupefy, maim or kill the husky fish. The leister, with three or five barbed hooks, was a favourite with 'sportsmen'. Fastened to a pole 16 feet long, it was used to propel the boat as well as nail the fish. Three men were involved, one sitting at the head of the little craft, another in the stern, and a third in the centre to kill the fish and trim the torch, for the operation was usually conducted at night. Many boats were wont to prowl a fruitful stretch of water, the torches casting an eerie glow over the operation, like monstrous fire-flies in the darkness. Spectators watched from the banks, having had the foresight to bring carts to carry away the loot, for scores of fish might be killed in a single night. Fish that managed to wriggle free from the leisters left a trail of blood which attracted the eels who attacked them and ate their flesh. Organized gang-type poaching was difficult to suppress until adequate protective staffs became available on the rivers. Pitched battles in which a bailiff or a river pirate met his death were not unknown.

A myriad of gear was used to take fish illegally in addition to the leisters: splash nets which entangled the salmon; shove nets that scooped them up from under the banks or rocks; nets that caught fish as they leaped out of the water; and fine seines with which the pools could be dragged at night from the banks or from a flat-bottomed skiff with outriggers managed by a single person. A barbarous custom, countenanced in some localities by local people, was raking the waters with a weighted triangle. In parts of Ireland, said Gathorne-Hardy, ' "sportsmen" may be seen in rows manipulating a bunch of weighted triangles through a shoal of salmon–sometimes with a prawn or minnow attached to them as a colourable pretext for the proceeding'.[27]

The variety of devices and extent of fish looting in Great Britain were dramatized at the International Fisheries Exhibition held in London in 1883. One of the most prominent exhibits consisted of weapons taken from poachers. There were 240 leisters or spears seized along the Welsh Usk and Ebbw alone. There were pitchforks, scythes and numerous rakehooks, one of which, taken on the Derwent, was worked by a rope between two men, with an oyster shell at the end that attracted the fish. There were lamps of many types, from the most primitive lanterns to an elaborate naphtha torch with a metal case which could be rapidly lighted up, darkened, or extinguished. Illegal fishing had become an art to which technology contributed many refinements.

The lamentable results

By the middle of the nineteenth century it was apparent that many of the richest salmon rivers had noticeably declined: among others, the Mersey, Calder, Tees, Trent, Wye, Yorkshire Don and Tweed (a binational stream), the Afon Lwyd, Ebbw and Tawe. There are virtually no statistics for this early period but on the Thames we have the diary of the holder of the fishings at Maidenhead, recording the sad diminution of his business. In 1801 he netted 66 salmon weighing 1,124 pounds; in 1804, 62 weighing 943 pounds; in 1812 18 totalling 224 pounds; and in 1821 only two totalling 31 pounds. By then it was virtually useless to seek the fish in this river.

The general downhill trend was to some extent documented by the Inspector of Salmon Fisheries in his report for 1869. English and Welsh rivers drained 46,000 square miles of land more or less adapted to salmonid migrants, and 12,000 not adapted to them. Large sections of productive waterways were by then ruined. For instance, the Severn below Stourport was useless as a breeding stream, and only half of this long river was still accessible to salmon. The Wye was in a parlous condition. Although the main stream was open, all important tributaries were closed by weirs. 'If we turn to the case of the Tyne, the smallest of the [major] rivers but immeasurably the most productive at the present in salmon, the whole of the South Tyne and Derwent, its most important tributaries, are inaccessible to salmon.' And so it went.

'Of the six largest rivers of the kingdom physically adapted to the salmon, draining above 24,000 square miles, not one-third of the whole, produce salmon at all, and of this 7,450 square miles less than 3,000 square miles are accessible to fish.' Put in another way, 'Out of 36,000 square miles of country which ought to be productive of this most valuable fish only one-fourth, or a little over 9,000 square miles, produces salmon at all.' He concluded: 'It is surely fair to say that it is the existence of weirs which has operated against the improvement of other rivers, by preventing the cultivation of the 27,000 square miles of country which I have shown to be inaccessible to salmon.'[28]

NOTES

1 Henry B. Wheatley, in *London Past and Present*, Vol. III, p. 365.
2 Eric Hardy, 'That Other Eden', *Salmon and Trout Magazine*, September 1955, p. 178.
3 Augustus Grimble, *The Salmon Rivers of England and Wales*, p. 116.
4 *Ibid.*, p. 116. The fish were undoubtedly kelts.
5 Paul M. Hansen, 'Report on Recaptures in Greenland Waters of Salmon Tagged in Rivers in America and Europe'.
6 Reginald Lennard, *Rural England, 1086–1135*, pp. 248–52.
7 W. O. Hassell, *How They Lived, 55 B.C.–1485*, p. 52.
8 Stuart A. and Hubert Stuart Moore, *The History and Law of Fisheries*, p. 176.
9 Leonard Mascall, *A Booke of Fishing*, London, 1884, pp. 31–32, 44.
10 Fraser Darling, *A Treasury of English Wildlife*, p. 133.
11 Charles S. Cutting, *Fish Saving*, p. 84.
12 R. J. Mitchell, *A History of the English People*, pp. 215–16.
13 Richard Franck, *Northern Memoirs*, p. 297.
14 *The Journeys of Celia Fiennes*, p. 203.
15 *Ibid.*, p. 218.
16 Daniel Defoe, *A Tour through England and Wales*, Vol. I, pp. 224–5.
17 In Francis Day, *Salmonidae of Britain and Ireland*, p. 113.
18 *Ibid.*, p. 117.
19 H. D. Turing, *Pollution*, 3rd Report on Behalf of the British Field Sports Society, p. 20. Much of the material on pollution in this chapter is taken from these reports and Turing's book, *River Pollution*.
20 H. D. Turing, *River Pollution*, p. 26. For an excellent discussion of the effects of pollution on fish see F. T. K. Pentelow, *River Purification*.
21 'The Salmon Fisheries of England and Wales in 1861', *Trout and Salmon*, November 1964.

22 Thomas Ashworth, *The Salmon Fisheries of England*, 1868.
23 Macdonald Hastings, 'The Last Thames Salmon'.
24 Augustus Grimble, *The Salmon Rivers of England and Wales*, pp. 13–14. The Avon has been partially restored since Grimble's day.
25 *Report of the Inspectors of Salmon Fisheries (England and Wales) for 1869*.
26 A. E. Gathorne-Hardy said, 'I hardly know of any sort of poaching which he (Scott) does not describe and countenance, except the serious practice of spearing salmon on horseback described in *Guy Mannering*.' (*The Salmon*, p. 164.)
27 *Ibid*., p. 163.
28 *Eighth Annual Report of the Inspectors of Salmon Fisheries (England and Wales)*, pp. 69–71.

7

Plight of the English and Welsh Salmon–II

By the middle of the nineteenth century there was a widespread feeling in England that the salmon resource, dear to the nation, was in parlous condition and perhaps in danger of extinction. Many publicists took up the cause of conservation. Among them Charles Dickens was probably the most vehement and eloquent. In an article in his sprightly weekly, *All the Year Round*, of July 20, 1861, he summarized the state of the salmon in his customary hyperbolic style:

> The cry of 'Salmon in Danger!' is now resounding throughout the length and breadth of the land. A few years, a little more over-population, a few more tons of factory poisons, a few fresh poaching devices . . . and the salmon will be gone–he will become extinct.
>
> Shall we not step in [he cried] between wanton destruction . . . and so ward off the obloquy which will be attached to our age when the historians of the nineteen-sixties will be forced to record that: 'The inhabitants of the last century destroyed the salmon, and did much to injure the other species of fish now so rare in this country'?

A combination of evils had 'thinned the salmon's ranks like a charge of British grape-shot sent into a Chinese fort'. Parliament had a duty to step in, 'like a policeman into a riot'.

'In the rivers Ribble and Hodder,' said Dickens, 'I am informed, on good authority, the young salmon were caught by the thousands on the way to the sea in "shackle nets" and sold to be *eaten* at 8d. a pound. Ye foolish fishers, ye are eating banknotes at 8d. a pound.'

On Devonshire rivers fry were being taken and sold as sardines!

What was needed were rules 'as strict as those in Newgate Prison' to be applied during the close season. 'We have our laws regarding the close season, but are they as stringent as the regulations which governed Newgate Gaol?' 'Is the pollution problem solved? Are we completely happy about the nets which still operate?'[1]

The legislative counter-attack

The campaign for parliamentary action resulted in the formation of a Royal Commission of Inquiry in 1860. It found the salmon fisheries generally in a state of depression, due to: (1) 'defective regulation of close seasons'; (2) excessive use of fixed 'engines'; (3) obstruction to the free passage of fish; (4) illegal fishing–'destruction of unseasonable fish, spawning fish, spent fish, young or fry'; (5) lack of an organized system of management of the rivers and fisheries 'affording the means of efficient protection against poaching and other destructive and illegal practices'; (6) poisoning of waters by 'the efflux from mines'; (7) 'pollution of waters by manufacturers, gas works, and other nuisances'; and (8) 'confusion and uncertainty of the law and difficulty of enforcing its penalties against offenders'.[2]

Parliament acted promptly by passing the Salmon Fisheries Act of 1861 which codified all previous salmon legislation relating to England and Wales–Scotland was to have counterpart but not identical laws–and took a few steps forward. A uniform close season was fixed (September 1 to February 1 for nets and November 1 to February 1 for rod fishermen), thus eliminating the diversity of seasons set by local magistrates for each district which opened the door to fraud and poaching. The Home Office was entrusted with supervision of the salmon fisheries and authorized to appoint two inspectors, a responsibility that was transferred to the Board of Trade in 1896 and to the Board of Agriculture and Fisheries in 1903.

For the first time the discharge of waste waters into rivers was regulated although clauses were incorporated into the Act which clearly restricted the efficiency–in fact, usually nullified–the law. Enforcement of the anti-pollution measures remained with persons appointed by the ineffectual Justices of the Peace, and worst of all, no funds were provided for their work.

Further advances in the direction of conservation were made by the Salmon Fisheries Act of 1865 which set up Boards of Conservators with jurisdiction over an entire river or group of rivers. No boards could be created for rivers which contained only trout or other freshwater fish. For the first time a licensing system was introduced in England and Wales for both netting and rod fishing.[3] Under this act fishery districts were established and boards of conservators constituted for each; by 1894 there were 53 boards covering three-quarters of England and Wales. In 1888 the duty of nominating local government representatives to the boards was transferred from the Justices of the Peace to the County Councils.

A vital aspect of the 1861 Act was the effort to control the use of fishing weirs and mill dams designed partly to trap fish and partly to supply water for milling. With few exceptions, the only structures of this type that were 'henceforth legal for taking salmon and sea trout were those which had been in use in the open season of 1861 by virtue of an ancient right. All future weirs were required to have a free gap, not less than one-tenth of the width of the river, to allow the fish to escape, while mill dams could not be used for fishing purposes unless they had approved passes that were in good condition, with a constant flow of water to attract migrant fish. If an owner failed to provide a fish pass he forfeited the right to use his mill dam for fishing purposes.'[4]

Stationary nets were banned in England and Wales, with exceptions in certain places.

The 1861 and 1865 Acts, though weak, helped to arrest the decline of the salmon fisheries in England and Wales. Appointment of an energetic Inspector was an important move. Frank Buckland, who held the post from 1867 to his death in 1880, travelled across the length and breadth of the country inspecting weirs and dams and devising fish passes for many of them. He was also a prominent fish culturist, imbued with the need for breeding fish to replenish depleted streams. Perhaps his greatest contribution, however, was the message he disseminated that the inland fisheries were of great value and important to the national welfare.

Buckland was followed by the renowned scientist, Thomas Henry Huxley, to whom the post was given, in the words of Cyril Bibby, his recent biographer, as 'a piece of scientific pluralism'. Sir William Harcourt, the Home Secretary, in offering the position, admitted: 'It is not a grand place, nor as good in its emoluments as I could desire, for it is worth only £700 per annum . . . [but] salmon have the good taste to addict themselves to healthy and picturesque localities . . . [and] I do not see why you should not inspect the fish as well as Newton governed the Mint.'[5] It does not seem that Huxley, during the five years of his tenure, found much time for the fish amid multifarious scientific and educational pursuits. Newton did a much better job for the Mint. Huxley's successors were more effective.

In 1865 a Royal Commission was formed to inquire into the problems of river pollution. Its first reports, dealing with the Thames, Lea, Aire and Calder, revealed to the nation the appalling unsanitary methods of getting rid of urban sewage and wastes. Later reports described conditions on most of the rivers in the industrial regions of England and Wales. As a result of this work, the Rivers Pollution Act of 1876 was passed, a pioneer attempt to deal with a complex and refractory problem which, ninety years later, is far from solved.

The Act placed 'an absolute prohibition on the deposition of solid matter in streams so as to cause pollution, either by itself or in combination with other similar acts, or so as to cause interference with the proper flow'. It summarily forbade 'the discharge of sewage into streams, the only exception being effluents discharged by a channel in existence when the law passed and then only if the best practicable means were used to purify the effluent'.[6] Less stringent requirements were placed on industrial discharges. The law had a fatal weakness in that it did not apply to tidal waters unless they were declared a 'stream' within the meaning of the Act by the Minister of Health. Subsequently six estuaries were so designated but their condition was not appreciably improved.

The procedure for enforcing this anti-pollution measure was cumbersome since the only remedy against a polluter was to obtain an order from the court directing that the evil should be abated. Failure to comply could be punished by a penalty that involved further proceedings. It is generally agreed that the Rivers Pollution Act of 1876 was a failure. The condition of English and Welsh waterways, on the whole, continued to deteriorate.

It was fifty years before the next major piece of fisheries legislation was enacted for England and Wales. The Salmon and Freshwater Fisheries Act of 1923 consolidated all the earlier laws and added important new features. For instance, the builder of any dam that created an obstruction to fish migration was required to install a fish ladder which had to meet the approval of the Minister of

Agriculture and Fisheries. This provision also applied to any alterations in existing dams.

Section 8 of the 1923 Act 'made it an offence to pollute waters so as to make them harmful to fish', excepting those methods employed by prescriptive right or in use at the time the Act was passed, 'provided that the best practical means within reasonable cost were used to prevent such discharges doing injury to fisheries'. Another provision stipulated that those planning to build sewers or other works for discharging noxious matter into a stream must notify the Fishery Boards or the Minister of Agriculture and Fisheries who, however, could not give or withhold consent but only call attention to defects in the plans and warn potential offenders of the danger of harming fish-bearing waters. Despite these escape clauses, the 1923 measure greatly strengthened the hands of the Fishery Boards in fighting river contamination.

The next milestone in controlling and regulating England's inland fisheries was the River Boards Act of 1948. For the first time each river system was placed under an authority responsible for unified control of salmon, trout, and other freshwater fisheries, land drainage and for prevention of water pollution. Thirty-two river boards were created, embracing England and Wales except the Thames and Lea watersheds and the environs of London, all of which were covered by other legislation.

A very important aspect of the 1948 law was the power conferred upon the boards to obtain by 'precept' (levies) on their counties and county borough councils funds to carry out their work, thus adding considerably to the revenues obtained from fishing licences. For the first time in the history of English fishery administration, responsible authorities could find the means to hire adequate protective personnel and undertake capital improvements (such as fish ladders and hatcheries).

Three years later came the Rivers Pollution Act of 1951 empowering river boards to draft by-laws (regulations) that set standards with which effluents must comply. It now became an offence to cause or knowingly permit any poisonous matter to enter a stream. Outfalls for the discharge of sewage required approval of the river boards. Violation of this Act was punishable only with fines up to £100, but the hands of local government bodies were strengthened in the unending battle against pollution.

The 1961 revision of the Rivers Pollution Act further bolstered the river boards' authority to prevent new poisons from entering the non-tidal portions of rivers since it became unlawful to make a 'pre-1951' discharge of 'trade wastes' or storage effluents without obtaining the prior consent of the boards. The Clean Rivers Act of 1961 conferred upon the boards similar powers over the estuaries and tidal waters.

Because of growing water-use conflicts, the Water Resources Act of 1963 was passed by Parliament. It transferred all the functions exercised by the river boards to river authorities, including jurisdiction over fisheries, pollution control, land drainage, and for the first time use of water for agriculture. Local authorities now appoint slightly more than half the members of the river authorities and the rest are selected by the Minister of Agriculture, Fisheries and Food and the Minister of Housing and Local Government to represent local fishery, land drainage, and water supply interests.

Arresting the tide of depletion

While England was struggling to develop a code of laws and administrative machinery to cope with management of the multiple resources of its rivers, what was happening to the salmon resource? The Inspectors of Salmon Fisheries for England and Wales in their report for 1887 remarked:

> On the whole, I am satisfied that the general quantity of salmon taken still continues to be maintained; but, in saying this, I would not be understood to mean that the future of these fisheries is by any means secure. The provisions of the Salmon Fisheries Acts of 1861 and 1865 caused a great and rapid improvement in the stock and in the capture of salmon. The improvement has been maintained in the Districts in which those provisions have continued to be carried out and observed, and in which no seriously destructive element, such as pollution of the water, or an unduly capricious mode of fishing, has existed.

As the twentieth century opened the general trend was believed to be more encouraging than fifty years earlier but many important rivers, such as the Ribble, Severn and Tyne, were gravely damaged. Others, like the Mersey, were defunct.

The general situation around World War I was summarized by J. Arthur Hutton, who had done yeoman work as a member of the

Wye River Fishery Board to restore that much-abused stream: 'Not a single river in this country is producing the quantity of valuable food it could and should do, and this is simply the result of mismanagement.' Among the reasons he listed for the grave decline in fecundity of rivers were pollution, the diversion and storage of stream flow for diverse purposes, inadequate regulation of fishing, and an excessive number of government agencies meddling with the fisheries. 'There is a crying need for one central authority which shall have full powers to deal with and prevent pollution', he said. Netting should be stopped in the upper waters of rivers and ultimately confined to tidewater and the sea coast, and even there it should be strictly controlled to permit an adequate number of fish to reach their spawning grounds. Hutton believed that an expanded hatchery programme would to some extent counteract the loss of wild stocks.

Attempts to produce salmon artificially had begun in England in 1868 at Troutdale in Cumberland. Because of the failure of the water supply, this operation was moved to Scotland but other small hatcheries arose, usually rearing salmon to the fry stage, after which they were deposited in suitable streams. Exalted hopes were raised by this technique of restocking barren waters but they proved to be largely illusory. Artificial production was probably helpful on some British rivers, such as the Tay in Scotland and a few in Ireland, but the enthusiasm died down considerably as it became obvious that this was not a panacea for saving every threatened salmon stream.

Ribble: example of a deteriorated river

The Ribble is a classic example of the exigencies faced by a glorious salmon river in the industrial age. Its main stem forms the boundary between industrialized east and west Lancashire, cradle of the cotton industry, and verdant, rural north Lancashire and Yorkshire. The valley of the Ribble constitutes an undulating green belt which in summer attracts crowds of people from the dreary cities, searching for clean air, blue skies, country paths for walking, a stream to fish, and peace and quiet.

Centuries ago the 56-mile Ribble with its much shorter tributaries, the Hodder on the right bank and Calder on the left, yielded amazing quantities of salmon. The earliest record, dating from the sixteenth century, indicates the existence of huge spring runs and a long fishing season. It was not uncommon then for an owner to report catches of the order of 1,390 salmon in one day, 600 the next, and 200 the third, all from one pool.

In 1784 the owners of Brockholes mill upstream erected a solid stone fishing weir across the Ribble which became an impenetrable barrier to further migration. After lengthy court action, it was demolished in 1811. But there were other obstructions. At Low Moor, near Clitheroe, a dam was built in 1782 to provide power for a cotton mill. It had a fish pass that was open 180 days a year, only when the mill was closed or there was enough water for both the mill and fish. Gradually the pass fell into disrepair and a bailiff was stationed to scoop up the salmon and ladle them over the dam.[7] Above this point there were two more dams with gentle slopes which the fish could negotiate.

Despite all the difficulties, the Ribble remained an excellent fishing stream. In 1834 one of the property owners wrote that salmon 'are speared and netted . . . by day and night; they are caught with fly; they are taken with switch hooks [large hooks fixed to the end of staves] or with a triple hook fixed to the end of a running line and a salmon rod; if the river becomes low, parties of idle fellows go up each side of it in search of them, and, by stoning the deeps, or dragging a horse's skull or large bone of any kind through them they compel the fish to "side" and then they fall an easy prey when the pool is of small extent.' No protection was afforded the spawning stock. Typically a single gang killed 400 fish in one season near the source of the Ribble and sold the roe alone for £20.

Between 1860 and 1867 the ancient weir at Settle was rebuilt as a massive six-foot embankment without a pass, thus stopping the ascent of fish at this point. Although the barrier was declared illegal by the law of 1873, no effort was made to remove it. Perhaps, as A. T. R. Houghton, historian of the Ribble fisheries, says, the upper proprietors, who were more interested in trout, did not really want salmon in their waters knowing that they would be the object of vigilant poachers, first the navvies who were building a railroad in the valley, and when they had gone, the irresponsible quarry workers.

From 1867, when 15,000 salmon were caught, the fisheries went downhill at a dizzy pace. Only 34 fish were taken in the year 1900!

The main causes were incredible pollution and intensive netting in tidal and non-tidal waters below the barrier.

The Chief Inspector of the Ribble Joint Committee, after touring the north-east portion of the watershed, declared that manufacturers in this district could be divided into two classes: 'Those who had done nothing at all (to abate pollution) and those who had done as little as possible.' He had inspected four paper plants, six dye and calico printing mills, one alkali plant, one dye works, one bleaching plant, three collieries and two tanneries. All contributed their refuse to the nearest watercourse. He also visited every community in a 200-square-mile area of the Calder watershed and reported that of 16 local authorities only two intercepted and treated their sewage. The rest dumped it into flowing waters. The situation was far worse on the Darwen (a tributary of the Ribble) as that river had to deal with the wastes of fourteen paper mills, one paper-staining mill, two dye works, a tar distillery, and many cotton mills. It was not necessary to take water samples because at Blackburn one was greeted with an odour of 'sewage forming inky cascades down the river banks'.

Proprietors who went to court in an attempt to abate these nuisances lost the first two test cases. Thenceforth the polluters felt they could maltreat the rivers without restraint, and 'it became a recognized practice for owners of mill lodges to open their sluices at week-ends and clear out the sludge which had settled during the week'.[8]

Yet somehow the Ribble fisheries were at least temporarily revived. Stronger anti-pollution legislation enabled the Ribble Joint Committee and its successor, the Lancashire River Board, to persuade factory owners and communities on the three major streams of the watershed to build modern disposal plants and facilities, at a cost of many millions of pounds, and a scheme of regular inspection was devised to make sure they were working properly.

The turning point came with the 1923 Salmon and Freshwater Fisheries Act. One of its first results was the opening of the fish pass at Clitheroe–where the bailiff who lived close by used to ferry the salmon by hand over the impoundment–thereby adding about twenty miles of water which had been partly or totally closed for a century. The Fishery Board's regulations were stiffened. All netting above the Naze was outlawed, thus freeing about five miles of the estuary, and the drift nets were limited to six. An increase in rod licence fees enabled the Board to acquire enough revenue to employ a head bailiff and provide him and his assistants with a means of rapid transportation to apprehend poachers. Natural runs of salmon were supplemented with planted ova.

Total salmon catches increased steadily, reaching a peak of almost 2,000 in 1948 and 1950 (Table 13).

Yet, such are the tribulations of industrialized rivers that in the 1950s the salmon catches once more began to decline, partly due to re-emerging pollution. In its 1960 report the Lancashire River Board said that 'the outlook for the future . . . is now gradually becoming clear. River conditions, chemically, are slowly improving and a better environment for fish is developing. A vast amount of work and investigation has been undertaken to secure cleaner conditions in the estuary and finances have been expended on the problems . . . to enable the Board to acquire legislative control over the conditions of these streams.'[9] Considerable improvement in the harvests have occurred in the last few years. After dropping to a new low of 218 in 1961, the catch bounded to 1,200 fish in 1963 and slipped to 859 in 1964.

Resuscitation of the Wye

In contrast to the Ribble, the Wye was restored to reasonable levels of productivity by prudent management after many trials and tribulations. The upper Wye is a small and magnificent angler's river, with the water cascading from pool to pool, sometimes in a trickle and at others in full-bodied strength. Lower down the river becomes a wide and fast-flowing stream.

Until the late nineteenth century the river was netted all the way to Whitney, ninety miles from the sea, and illegal fishing was common. Parr were stolen by the bushels while adult fish were speared in low water or gaffed on the spawning beds. Even kelts were freely taken. Nobody in particular was charged with enforcing the Salmon Acts.

As elsewhere, the close season varied from county to county, and where the river was the boundary, said H. A. Herbert, historian of the Wye, 'fishermen could operate on one side during the close period and laugh at their neighbours while doing so'.[10]

With the salmon runs in grave danger, the Wye Preservation

Table 13
Salmon catches in River Ribble, 1900–1964
(*numbers of fish*)

Date	*Rods*	*Nets*	*Total*
1900	34		34
1932	18	891	909
1933	19	447	466
1934	37	416	453
1935	39	806	845
1936	49	592	641
1937	40	791	831
1938	141	556	697
1939	73	770	803
1940	68	1,079	1,156
1941	53	1,204	1,257
1942	157	1,619	1,776
1943	176	1,028	1,204
1944	163	610	773
1945	92	481	573
1946	83	932	1,015
1947	46	774	820
1948	217	1,770	1,987
1949	99	1,229	1,328
1950	257	1,714	1,971
1951	48	1,204	1,252
1952	101	1,166	1,267
1953	87	291	378
1954	227	641	868
1955	51	346	397
1956	82	106	188
1957	88	360	448
1958	288	358	646
1959	33	476	509
1960	87	441	528
1961	72	146	218
1962	143	523	666
1963	208	992	1,200
1964	114	745	859

Sources: *Report of Committee on Salmon and Freshwater Fisheries*, May 1961, London, and 'Report of the Lancashire Rivers Board', 1965.

Society was formed by the landed proprietors in 1862 and thus began the long struggle to resuscitate the river. In 1865 a board of conservators was created, and ten years later the Wye Fisheries Association was established to obtain control of net fishings and protect spawning beds.

The attempt to introduce conservation practices, however, ran afoul of the interests of proprietors on the upper, lower and middle river. It was to the benefit of the upper owners to curtail fishing lower down, but the latter resented any attempt at reducing their netting privileges, even though they were yearly declining in value. It was largely due to the Duke of Beaufort and John Hotchkiss, chairman of the Wye Fisheries Association, that the netsmen were eventually greatly reduced in numbers. Hotchkiss' policy was to lease netting rights as they came on the market. First he persuaded the owners above Hereford to stop netting their waters. Then in turn he purchased for the association the netting privileges on the middle stretches until he controlled almost the entire river. Heavy freshwater fishing had in fact so depleted the river that netting rights had become almost valueless. The association recouped its expenditures by selling fishing tickets and sub-leasing its rights to rod fishermen.[11] In 1901 the Duke of Beaufort sold his rights on the lower river to the Crown and the fisheries were taken over by the Association.

There was a gradual decline of the runs until about 1890; then it became catastrophic. In 1892 the sons of Alexander Miller, who had become wealthy netting the lower Wye, harvested 12,000 fish; by 1900–1 they were getting barely 3,000 and very few, says H. A. Herbert, escaped to spawn. In the years 1902–4 all the nets were removed from tidal waters and little commercial fishing was conducted in the river as a whole. As a result, considerable numbers of salmon began to show themselves in the higher stretches and riparian owners awoke rather suddenly to the fact that their rod fishings were acquiring considerable value. Indeed, in 1904–5 a spring run was established in the Wye. In 1909 all netting above Brockweir Bridge was banned, and in 1924 the Conservators borrowed money and purchased the remaining netting rights, and then limited this kind of fishing to the wide and turbulent tideway, to a point above Tintern Abbey at Brockway Bridge. (So tremendous is the rise and fall of the waters that the netsmen must catch their fish largely during neap tide, a space of three hours.)

In a relatively short time the Wye acquired a reputation as a splendid sportsmen's river. By the 1930s rod catches were exceeding the harvest of the nets and this situation has continued (Table 14). The potentialities of this river are illustrated by the renowned angler Robert Pashley, who set a record not only for the Wye but for all English rivers perhaps. He hooked 9,800 salmon with the fly in a lifetime of fishing the Wye, 1906 to 1951. For 41 successive seasons he took over 100 fish. His best years were 1936, when he killed 678 salmon; 1926, 535; 1933, 461; and 1946, 379.

Collective angling rents jumped from £1,000 in 1900 to £8,000 in 1912. In 1949, according to J. A. Hutton, gross rentals were about £10,000. Adding money spent by anglers for house rent, servants, car and horse hire, and other amenities, the total annual income from the fisheries must have been about £50,000.[12]

Table 14
Annual salmon catches in River Wye
1906–1964
(*numbers of fish*)

Year	*Rods* (*Ave.*)	*Nets* (*Ave.*)	*Total* (*Ave.*)
1906/1910	1,507	2,910	4,417
1911/1915	2,294	4,055	6,349
1916/1920	2,556	2,878	5,434
1921/1925	3,175	3,888	7,063
1926/1930	3,606	4,104	7,710
1931/1935	3,790	3,182	6,972
1936/1940	2,664	1,092	4,566
1941/1945	1,950	1,049	2,999
1946/1950	2,821	1,312	4,133
1951/1955	4,106	1,265	5,371
1956/1960	2,791	1,520	4,311
1961/1964	3,346	798	4,144

Source: Wye River Board, Annual Report for 1964.

Today the Wye is England's pre-eminent angling river. As Table 15 shows, the Wye is in a class by itself. In the four years 1961–64, the rods took an average of 3,353 fish and nets only 798 on the Wye, a ratio of over four to one. Fishing rights on a single mile of both banks of the river were recently sold for £20,000 ($56,000).

The Wye has become the playground for sportsmen from the industrial areas ranging from Wigan to Swansea. So great is the demand for angling that coarse fishing privileges, not long ago despised and ignored, are now almost as valuable over considerable stretches of the river as salmon fishing rights. In 1964 the Wye River Board sold 16,381 coarse fishing licences, 15,965 trout licences, and 3,291 salmon licences; 18 per cent of its licence revenue came from coarse fishermen, 35 per cent from trout fishermen, and 47 per cent from salmon fishermen.

Upsurge of sports fishing

Angling is an ancient tradition in Britain, although its origins are lost in the mists of time. The earliest book on fishing in the English language, *Treatise on Fishing with an Angle*, ascribed to Dame Juliana Berners, or Barnes, was printed in 1486, but the manuscript had been in circulation for perhaps a century, and the techniques discussed suggest that the sport was already well developed. Dame Juliana describes several methods of catching salmon, using worms as bait. The fly was apparently unknown and tackle was hardly strong enough to give all but the most skilful angler any hope of success.

Several angling treatises published in the reign of Elizabeth I, notably Leonard Mascall's *A Booke of Fishing* (1590), do not seem to have advanced the art beyond Juliana's methods. A description of a salmon rod and recipe for dressing a fly is first found in Thomas Barker's *Art of Angling* (1657). He talks of worm fishing and trolling for salmon in the river, presumably the Thames, using gudgeon as bait. Four years earlier Izaak Walton had published his *Compleat Angler* (1653), and was the first writer in England to mention the marking of salmon in order to learn if they returned to the river. He gives no details but speaks of 'ribbons' tied to the tail, which must refer to kelts. However, it is hard to believe the ribbons were kept in place during the kelts' absence from the river.

Fairly modern techniques of casting with an artificial fly, at least in the rivers of Ulster where he was accustomed to fish, are described by Robert Venables in *The Experienc'd Angler or Angling Improved* (1662).

The first true book on salmon fishing was written by Richard Franck who served in Cromwell's army and made an angling tour of Scotland in the 1650s. His garrulous *Northern Memoirs*, imitative of *The Compleat Angler*, was not published until 1694.

We may well ask, who pursued this sport in the days before there were angling clubs, when transportation was difficult and salmon beats often difficult of access? Before the industrial age the land-owning class seems to have monopolized field sports. Chasing the deer or wild boar was the perennial pastime of kings and aristocrats. In the eighteenth century angling was the recreation of country gentlemen like Sir Roger de Coverley, and was practised with the kind of tackle and rods we know. Will Wimble, the fictitious character invented by Addison and Steele, 'makes a May fly to a miracle' and furnishes his neighbourhood with angling rods. In *Rural Sports* (1713) John Gay tells us how flies were made:

> Oft have I seen a skilful angler try
> The various colours of the treach'rous fly;
> When he with faultless pain hath skim'd the brook,
> And the coy fish rejects the skipping hook,
> He shakes the boughs that on the margin grow,
> Which o'er the streams a waving forest throw;
> When if an insect falls (his certain guide)
> He gently takes him from one whirling tide;
> Examines well his form with anxious eyes,
> His gaudy colours, wings, horns and size.
> Then round his hook a proper fur he winds,
> And in the back a speckled feather binds
> So just the properties in ev'ry part,
> That even Nature's hand revives in art.

A unique memento of earlier times is the Anglers' Arms Inn at Weldon Bridge in Northumberland. Here in Regency and early Victorian days came by gig or stage-coach a coterie of anglers from Newcastle-on-Tyne to fish the Coquet. The group included Robert Roxby, Thomas Doubleday and Thomas Bewick the engraver. On their way to Newcastle or Edinburgh stage-coach passengers would stop to watch the fishermen with their huge, clumsy rods playing the salmon from the stream bank, and perhaps carouse with them afterwards, singing fishing songs over a glass of ale or wine. Robert Roxby was something of a poet and some of his songs acclaiming the inn and the river are worthy of mention, such as:

Then, hey! for fam'd Weldon, to anglers the dearest,
 Old Weldon, whose cellars and streams never fail;
There we'll talk of our triumphs, and boast of our slaughter,
 How 'we hook'd him, and play'd him, and killed him so fine';
And the battles, so gloriously finish'd in water,
 Again and again we'll fight over in wine.

Weldon Arms Inn is still going strong and attracts fishermen who work the Coquet up to Rothbury and down to Felton. 'The old mill race near by is no longer a mill, and the mill race is dry. Saplings have grown on the banks since those early days, but the river, clear and fresh from the hills, still gurgles and murmurs with the glad music of Nature beneath the arches, over which thunder the coaches and cars of this modern age.'[13]

The industrial era resulted in the democratization of salmon and trout fishing. Bankers, manufacturers, tradesmen, politicians, diplomats, writers and scholars among others found delight in dancing a fly on a serene stretch of water, far from the madding crowd, dusty office, lecture room or laboratory. Sometimes they were accompanied by wives and children. Kings, princes and nobility took up the rod. The royal family in the Victorian era owned six miles of the River Dee in Scotland and leased fifteen miles more. King George V as Prince of Wales had sought the salmon on cold Norwegian rivers. Prime Ministers Gladstone and Neville Chamberlain found respite from the cares of office on purling rivers and recorded their experiences in diaries and memoirs, some of which are eminently readable. Writers and scholars like Charles Kingsley and Andrew Lang eulogized the sport of salmon fishing.

Riparian owners formed associations to protect their interests and to work with the boards of conservators (and later the river boards) to improve their fishings. They regulated the use of members' waters, established fees for tickets, determined the close seasons and type of permissible gear and bait as well as minimum sizes of fish that could be taken. (There are no bag limits for salmon on British rivers.) For example, the United Usk Fishery Association permitted angling only with an artificial fly, prohibited the use of the gaff as an auxiliary to the rod and line, closed the river on Sundays, banished dogs, allowed coracles on the water only where salmon were not caught, and forbade anglers to sell their fish. Violation of these rules and any kind of conduct unbecoming a gentleman resulted in forfeiture of one's ticket.[14]

Some landowners fished themselves, others leased this privilege. Augustus Grimble, in his exhaustive account of the rivers of England and Wales, published in the first decade of the twentieth century, gives us glimpses of the manner in which property owners handled their fishings. Dipping into his volume at random, we learn that Colonel Fife Cookson of Lee Hall who owned two miles of both banks of the North Tyne never permitted strangers to fish his waters, employed nets (and not gaffs) to land his catches until the kelts had departed, and was accustomed to net and preserve 'fish that are off colour and not worth eating'. Angling was limited by him to the fly only, the longest being 2/0 Limerick, since he considered most of the standard patterns too deadly.

To some contemporary fishermen like Major John Ashley-Cooper, the leisurely Edwardian age was the halcyon era. Then people travelled not in fast motor-cars but in pony-drawn wagonettes or carts to streamside, accompanied by their gillies, and 'were out simply to enjoy themselves, with a code of behaviour involving far greater mutual consideration than is usual nowadays. The size of the bag was a comparatively secondary consideration.' Few or no rod-caught fish were ever sold. They were given to friends or dependents. Fishing waters were much more extensive than they are today; the sport was in fact practised under ideal conditions.

From the end of the Edwardian age to World War II little major change occurred. There were some improvements in tackle, the greased-line method became popular. Bait fishing became widespread on slow rivers like the lower Tweed and lower Wye but it was still generally frowned upon. Meanwhile expenses, such as gillies' wages, cost of gear, and boats, were rising. The number of anglers gradually increased.

Spreading wealth has brought salmon and trout fishing into the ken of a much larger group of persons. Although not exactly the pastime of the common man, it is a great prestige symbol. As a consequence, desirable stretches of water are selling for fantastic prices. Some £30,000 ($84,000) was paid for four miles of one bank and 1½ miles of another on the River Taw in Devon, a second-class stream, while a mere 1,000 yards of one bank of the Lune brought £30,000. Good beats now rent for as much as £1,000 ($2,800) for a fortnight's use of a single rod.

The upsurge in sports fishing is reflected in aggregate revenues from licence fees, reported by the river boards of England and Wales, which jumped from about $200,000 in 1949 to $530,000 in 1959. 'The army of anglers grows each year', says Ian Wood, editor of *Trout and Salmon*. 'There is now too little water available though much salmon fishing can still be had at reasonable cost on club, association or hotel waters throughout the country. But any stretches that are rented to individuals are now very highly priced. This tends to make those who have paid so highly for their privilege fish hard and sell their fish.'[15] Anglers fish longer hours and succeed each other in rapid rotation. Owners now want large bags in order to increase the value of their fishing, or to profit by selling their catch, and therefore permit the use of whatever bait promises success. Tenants want heavy fish to help pay their rent. Thus much sport fishing is now really commercial. A stretch of water that can show a series of good catches obviously acquires great capital value.

'It is a regrettable fact', says John Ashley-Cooper, 'that commercial fishing and bait fishing go hand in hand. This fact can be seen on almost any salmon river today. It is, of course, largely due to the vast improvement in bait tackle. . . . The onus of providing this extra financial benefit is loaded onto the salmon and on to his rate of reproduction. . . . He has hazards enough already, both natural and man-made.'[16]

Table 15 shows rod catches on English and Welsh rivers in recent years.

Rivers dirty and clean

'Pollution, water extraction, hydro-electric schemes and commercial netting combine to make the future of our salmon angling anything but bright', says Ian Wood. 'Commercial netting goes on round our coasts and in the estuaries to such an extent that one wonders how the stocks have carried on at all. Then recently great damage was

Table 15
Rod catches of salmon in principal English and Welsh rivers
1950–1964
(*numbers of fish*)

River	*1950*	*1951*	*1952*	*1953*	*1954*	*19*
Avon (Hampshire)	449	333	186	311	865	1,1
Axe (Devon)	10	17	23	28	67	
Conway	721	628	731	595	584	9
Dart	471	401	179	185	374	2
Dee	1,205	1,760	1,216	553	994	1,0
Eden	1,335	1,546	1,565	1,210	1,771	1,9
Esk (Yorkshire)	129	157	89	169	185	1
Exe	700	1,027	386	1,045	1,484	1,4
Frome	162	310	194	267	571	4
Lune	596	286	367	531	630	4
Ribble	257	48	101	87	227	
Severn	462	542	557	455	763	1,0
Stour (Dorset)	37	28	8	13	80	1
Tamar and Plym	525	716	179	390	1,007	4
Taw and Torridge	571	526	425	626	1,559	1,5
Teifi	NA	NA	545[a]	384[a]	840[a]	8
Teign	130	120	45	26	43	1
Towy	920	NA	1,175[b]	1,403[b]	2,050[b]	1,5
Usk	718	879	1,367	835	1,635	1,0
Welsh rivers	386	465	269	430	458	4
Wye	3,441	4,116	4,523	3,071	4,774	4,
Total	13,225	13,905	14,130	12,614	21,061	19,

[a] Include catches on Rivers Nevern and Aeron.
[b] Include catches in Eastern and Western Cleddau.

1956	1957	1958	1959	1960	1961	1962	1963	1964
977	460	506	413	566	424	676	799	569
63	22	50	71	24	20	31	21	11
,159	1,171	1,302	523	731	542	919	793	1,047
262	314	336	275	360	150	178	321	291
517	1,260	1,261	841	1,526	1,156	1,036	1,315	1,057
,489	2,094	1,874	1,799	1,619	1,535	1,682	1,615	1,435
607	333	437	58	593	249	542	339	219
,108	936	691	1,144	1,167	663	521	1,521	935
303	358	337	464	258	318	470	692	362
477	652	755	360	560	635	838	1,035	866
82	88	280	33	87	72	143	208	114
707	796	1,070	1,014	754	768	743	751	417
102	42	22	70	74	37	71	88	71
753	690	834	361	523	227	383	735	430
744	1,062	1,094	1,019	1,000	723	812	1,303	814
325	159	304	128	227	232	515	896	557
88	103	40	109	189	90	58	134	90
917[b]	421	734	228	679	470	1,177	1,638	950
781	469	899	565	374	327	923	895	775
049	837	1,512	439	837	476	1,305	1,298	1,040
082	2,735	3,619	2,845	2,677	2,056	3,158	4,505	3,657
592	15,002	17,957	12,759	14,825	11,170	16,181	20,902	15,707

ces: *Report of Committee on Salmon and Freshwater Fisheries*, May 1961, supplemented
ata supplied by Ministry of Agriculture, Fisheries and Food for the years 1960–64.

done through drift netting in the open seas [off the coast of Scotland] when parts of sea routes of the salmon were discovered. This has been stopped temporarily at least, by legislation.'

Water pollution remains probably the most serious obstacle to the rebuilding of the salmon stocks in England and Wales. 'To see the effect of pollution at its worst,' said Turing in 1952, 'one must as a rule go to the estuaries and tidal waters.' Existing laws seemed to be unable to prevent many of these outlets of rivers from becoming little better than open sewers.

For example, the joint estuary of those beautiful Devonshire streams, the Taw and Torridge, received the effluent, mostly raw, of about 20 large sewers emptying into tidal waters. The Usk estuary was 'so bad that at times there appears to be a complete pollution barrier and the river is only saved from extinction . . . by the very strong tides, which break the barrier so that fish can get up'. Many pure rivers flowing down from the Welsh hills were so contaminated that the water discharged into the open sea poisoned shellfish and migratory fish alike.

When industrial effluents are added to domestic sewage a river has almost no chance of purifying itself. Such effects could be seen at their worst in South Wales, despite a century of anti-pollution legislation. Coal washings from mines and spent acid from steel mills in this region destroyed the best part of a dozen streams.[17]

In north-east England most of the rivers, which rise in limestone formations or flow through such outcrops in their upper reaches, are naturally prolific salmon and trout waters and where they are pure, remain among the best fishing streams. Others have been deserted by migratory fish.

The 80-mile long Tyne was once the most productive of English salmon streams. Its northern arm issues out of the Cheviot hills near the Scottish border, and its southern on the borders of Durham and Cumberland. Hard-fished in the nineteenth century, dirtied and poisoned, blockaded and dammed, the Tyne offered to Turing the most depressing example in the British Isles of how a river can be ruined.[18]

When Turing inspected the Tyne in the late 1940s he learned that about 30 million gallons of virtually raw sewage came into the tidal reaches daily, so that large sections of the waterway were robbed of oxygen. In fact, a bar of sewage sludge regularly formed at the mouth and had to be dredged periodically and taken out to sea. For this reason alone, it was almost impossible for adult salmon to go up-river or smolts to descend. Day after day hordes of dead young fish could be seen washing out with the tide, while few adults appeared seeking the mouth of the river. Only a thousand salmon were landed in the Tyne in 1964–compared with 130,000 in 1870–and these were taken almost entirely in or near the estuary. The loss of the Tyne is England's greatest single fishery disaster. Its magnitude in terms of a food supply and economic wealth is difficult to measure, but staggering.[19]

The Tees is another major victim of pollution. It rises in the bleak and featureless Pennine Mountains at 2,500 feet elevation, forms part of the border between the counties of Cumberland and Westmorland as it flows seaward, sometimes tumbling over many steep precipices to reach its estuary at Stockton, with the industrial city of Middlesbrough (founded in the early nineteenth century) at its mouth. A century ago a large part of this lively 95-mile watercourse was well stocked with anadromous fish, despite the many weirs that studded its serpentine route. On the high, barren fells rains quickly produced heavy run-off which raised water levels downstream so that fish coming from the sea could fairly easily negotiate these obstructions and wander as far as its tributary, the Lune. At that time some acids from the lead mines entered the waters and poisoned the fish but no serious losses were reported.

In 1867 about 10,000 salmon were netted in the Tees–rod fishing was then inconsequential. A dozen years later only one-fifth of this number were taken. For the next two to three decades the Board of Conservators worked to improve fish-passage facilities and the results became apparent in resurgence of the runs. Between 1905 and 1916 the salmon catch fluctuated between 7,000 and 9,000 annually; by World War II all the salmon had vanished, the fishery was gone, and the men who depended upon it for a living went elsewhere. What had happened?

Turing declared that the pollution of the estuary, particularly by refuse from coke ovens, made it impossible for fish to survive. The Tees is a turbulent river and were it not for the poisoned estuary, it 'could, with the assistance of modern treatment plant for its sewage, easily purify itself for all the needs of the population of its valley as well as providing a badly-needed supply of food in the shape of fish'. In short, lack of energy on the part of responsible authorities and indifference of the polluters destroyed a major fishery. In recent years very few salmon have been brave enough to enter the Tees. Anadromous fish can still go up the estuary on flood tides which ride over the polluted water and dilute it enough to be comparatively harmless. But smolts cannot get through the de-oxygenated lower areas safely.

Let us turn to that renowned Anglo-Welsh river, the Severn. A swift and bucolic waterway, it flows through a rather narrow valley. Five navigational weirs built in 1842 without efficient fish passes created an obstacle race for migratory fish. Above and below Shrewsbury there were eel weirs which were illegally used in the spring to trap salmon smolts going to sea. Intense netting in the estuary helped to eliminate much of the brood stock. Indeed, the Severn prospered or declined with the ability of the proprietors and Board of Conservators to control net fishing, remove weirs and fight pollution, an heroic task. The number of putts and putchers dropped from 11,200 in 1863 to less than half after they were licensed under the 1865 Act. In 1870 22,500 salmon were caught and in 1885, 20,000, averaging 12 pounds. In those days rodsmen were few and their luck was usually poor. The river was netted all the way up to the Welsh border.

Then the decline of the fishery began in earnest. Failure to provide an adequate escapement combined with other detrimental forces was reflected in persistent drops in the catches, although the Severn remained one of the most productive rivers in England. In 1900 the catch totalled 10,500. Recovery followed and a peak of 33,000 salmon was reached in 1910. From then on the returns slid rapidly–to an average of 17,000 annually in the 1920s, 8,600 in the 1930s, 4,400 in the 1940s, 3,600 in the 1950s, and 4,500 in the 1960s. Meanwhile the Severn had become a prominent sportsmen's river and in some years one-quarter of the catch was taken by the rods.

The Severn suffered not from gross, spectacular pollutions like the Tyne, Tees or Mersey (where salmon have long been extinct), but rather from many small-scale and almost wholly preventable damages to habitat. Picture-book villages on the upper reaches unconcernedly allowed sewage to escape into the mirror-like streams. A sugar mill emptied its washing-water tanks, containing fine-grained organic matter, into the Tern, and thus generated sewage fungus not only in the little tributary but the main stem as well. The Stour, which joins the Severn at Stourport, was the repository of acids from numerous Kidderminster factories. Destruction of spawners and smolts by poachers was fairly widespread.

The worst polluter on the Severn was the venerable and historic city of Gloucester which turned all its sewage untreated into the tidal river. The bar of foul matter could only be diluted slowly, and thus for days ebbed back and forth from Gloucester to Minsterworth, a distance of seven miles, suffocating thousands of fish in its passage.

What can we say about the Trent and its tributary the Tame (which drains the great industrial area north of Birmingham), the Irwell, the Yorkshire Don, the Churnet? As fish havens they are all defunct or nearly so.

Once the Churnet was an idyllic river whose flow, running through a wooded valley, was gin-clear, as fishermen say, with a bottom of clean gravel. When Turing sat on its banks in the 1940s not a fish moved nor an insect stirred on the surface of its dead waters. Its bed was covered with sewage and fungus, and there were no weeds all the way to Froghull, seven miles from its mouth. Where the Churnet joined the Dove, Izaak Walton's favourite stream, it poisoned that water too. Piscator would run away from it, were he able to return.

To have seen British river pollution at its worst some thirty years ago we should have gone to South Wales, an area resembling industrialized sections of Pennsylvania, the centre of steel and other metallurgical and heavy-machinery manufacturing, rich in coal deposits. Two materials, coal washing from the mines and spent acids from the foundries, killed the fish in a dozen rivers, including the Usk, which comes down from the lightly-vegetated Welsh hills in pristine purity. Hikers in the upper reaches did not hesitate to drink from its cool waters, but downstream the flows were poisonous, running blood-red with acid (which coated all the stones) or inky black with coal dust. The fact that fish still thrived in some of these murky watercourses was due to the strong tides which broke up the heavy cargoes of polluted matter and created oxygenated zones where they could breathe and move. 'The cure for both these pollutions is known,' said Turing, 'yet apparently no attempt was being made to install effective purification methods.'[20]

In contrast to the bleak picture we have drawn of renowned salmon rivers, we might mention a few which have either not retrogressed or produced increased catches in recent decades, thanks to the ability of proprietors and river boards to restore or maintain their purity, to facilitate fish migration by keeping them free of obstructions, and in some instances to bolster wild stocks with plantings of eggs or fry. In this category belong the Hampshire Avon, Conway, Eden, Lune, Welsh Dee, Tamar, Dart, Coquet, Dovey in Wales, and Taw and Torridge. All these are outside the main manufacturing districts of the country.

The melancholy results

What does it all add up to–the systematic impairment of fish habitats, the unrestrained harvesting of fish, the apathy of government, the flaunting of law by manufacturers who regard the rivers as created for their benefit and not necessarily to sustain fish life, the indifference of communities to the health of waterways on which they debouch? What has been the loss in terms of a food supply and source of sport and recreation? Table 16 shows the melancholy results.

It is clear that, despite the legislative bulwarks and other measures taken during the past century to protect and bolster the fishery in England and Wales, the nation has permitted the largest part of its salmon stocks to be frittered away. From Table 16 we can see that in the 1870s six rivers–the Tyne, Severn, Tees, Usk, Ribble and Dart together produced about 185,000 salmon yearly. Since the start of World War II all the principal English and Welsh rivers together have yielded only about 40,000 to 50,000 fish annually. We may thus conclude that the salmon stocks of England and Wales in the aggregate are now probably less than a fourth of what they were a century ago, and at that time they had already doubtless declined appreciably from the eighteenth-century levels.

An uncertain future

The salmon in Britain, as Wilson Stephens, editor of *The Field* observes, is 'the fulcrum of financial processes involving property values and a whole series of apparently unrelated trades and industries'. At the peak of the season, salmon may fetch £1 ($2.80) a pound. In the upper waters of good rivers, the right to fish with rod and line now sells at auction for £30,000 ($84,000) a mile, and far more on the best streams. Thousands of persons depend upon the salmon directly or indirectly for their livelihood.

Most salmon rivers flow through countryside where money spent by visiting fishermen at hotels, shops and garages is the mainstay of the local economy. In many areas, as Stephens points out, 'the salmon is the main, often the only, source of male employment, either for netsmen in the commercial fisheries or for gillies on rod-fished waters.' Salmon angling opportunities are a prime tourist attraction in some parts of England, and to a greater extent in Scotland, while the British fishing tackle industry is a considerable earner of much-needed foreign currencies. What is the future of this valuable resource?

In November 1956 a two-day conference was held by the British Salmon and Trout Association on the problems confronting the fishery. The consensus was that the main factors which restrict and imperil the runs are (1) overfishing; (2) obstructions in the rivers; (3) water abstraction for agricultural, domestic and manufacturing purposes; and (4) pollution.

Salmon can be easily overfished. 'If they are overfished,' said R. S. Fort, 'it is by the nets, not by the rods. On the average, between 60 and 70 per cent of the total catch of salmon in England and Wales is taken by professional netsmen in tidal waters where the fishing is public. In Scotland the net catch is 80 per cent of the total catch.'[21] Scotland's total production is considerably greater than England's.

Fort pointed out that the river boards and the Minister of Agriculture, Fisheries and Food have all the necessary powers not only to control fishing but the distribution of salmon. No fresh salmon may be bought or sold in the United Kingdom between August 31 and February 1 unless it is caught outside Great Britain and Ireland. The close season for nets must be not less than 153 days a year and, unless altered by local regulation, falls between August 31 and February 1. There is also a weekly closure between Saturday 6 a.m. and Monday 6 a.m. In addition, any river authority with ministerial consent can ban the use of nets entirely, or limit them to certain areas, and determine the size of net, its mesh and conditions under which it may be operated. Thus, once a man has purchased his licence with the names of his assistant endorsed on it, labelled it, and lettered and numbered his boat, he can start netting. He must be careful not to shoot or work his seine or draft net more than three-fourths of the width of the river or within 100 yards of any other net.

Table 16
Salmon catches (rods and nets) in principal English and Welsh rivers, 1870–1964 (selected years)

River	*1870*	*1880*	*1885*	*1890*	*1900*	*1905*	*1910*
Avon (Hampshire)	1,060	1,042	1,838	1,067	262	390	804
Axe (Devon)	NA	25	60	NA	NA	NA	NA
Conway	NA	NA	169	157	123	84	83
Dart	7,015	NA	NA	NA	1,397	2,787	3,547
Dee	NA	12,500[a]	NA	NA	NA	NA	NA
Eden	NA	NA	NA	NA	NA	NA	NA
Esk (Yorkshire)	NA	2,089	5,293	5,790	6,811	8,121	8,049
Exe	NA	NA	NA	1,886	1,754	2,239	3,895
Frome	NA	NA	NA	NA	7	NA	36
Lune	130	NA	NA	NA	NA	NA	NA
Ribble	6,990	3,971	4,323	331	NA	NA	NA
Severn	22,500	16,005	20,000	13,500	10,500	22,500	33,000
Stour (Dorset)	NA	NA	NA	NA	NA	NA	5
Tamar and Plym	NA	NA	NA	NA	NA	NA	NA
Taw and Torridge	NA	NA	NA	NA	NA	NA	NA
Tees	10,000[b]	NA	NA	NA	NA	9,190	7,311
Teifi	NA	NA	NA	NA	2,164	3,493	3,546
Teign	NA	130	NA	NA	464	519	971
Tyne	129,100[c]	27,460	20,870	9,327	14,272	18,807	17,341
Towy	NA	NA	NA	NA	NA	NA	NA
Usk	9,100[d]	NA	NA	NA	NA	NA	NA
Welsh rivers	NA	NA	NA	NA	NA	NA	NA
Wye	NA	NA	NA	NA	NA	3,025	6,048
Grand Total	185,895	63,222	52,553	32,058	37,754	71,155	84,636

[a] 1881. [b] 1867. [c] 1872. [d] 1873.

He may not anchor the net, only drift. When he lands a salmon he must report it to the river authority on the requisite form.

'You have only to visualize', said Fort, 'thirty boats fishing the night tide on a long estuary to realize the difficulty and expense of enforcing these regulations, day by day and night by night throughout the netting season.' And the enforcement staff is only a small part of the organization necessary to maintain a salmon fishery and

…20	*1925*	*1930*	*1935*	*1940*	*1945*	*1950*	*1960*	*1961*	*1962*	*1963*	*1964*
49	315	418	1,403	745	379	769	1,339	1,422	1,878	2,091	1,834
A	NA	NA	611	262	107	10	418	164	192	80	51
46	380	292	706	652	567	954	1,079	763	1,268	1,083	1,663
89	2,693	440	2,554	608	787	1,643	1,258	1,168	1,499	1,964	1,844
	NA	2,469	5,558	6,731	3,700	4,449	4,535	3,915	4,357	4,539	5,312
	NA	NA	NA	2,260	1,564	2,877	3,600	3,806	3,488	3,694	3,870
89	1,616	3,398	5,028	2,159	1,678	940	2,256	1,597	3,784	1,616	1,303
27	4,628	1,440	4,412	1,971	1,791	1,718	2,384	1,995	2,476	3,014	2,173
00	225	199	450	247	163	188	319	388	592	891	492
	NA	NA	3,204	3,817	1,713	2,593	3,171	2,707	4,793	4,097	4,533
	NA	NA	845	1,156	573	1,971	528	218	666	1,200	859
00	15,500	4,225	14,425	4,290	3,825	2,770	4,332	3,560	5,220	4,012	4,432
33	9	7	31	17	25	37	74	37	71	88	71
	NA	536	3,914	1,124	1,739	3,631	2,768	2,333	3,110	4,474	3,327
	NA	2,755	5,209	3,680	4,170	3,997	4,399	3,263	4,179	3,842	3,934
75	634	147	855	NA	NA	NA	3	8	38	23	23
3	5,029	1,872	5,352	1,659	1,212	NA	1,675	837	1,408	2,593	1,583
1	1,162	160	1,185	695	403	1,203	1,186	706	764	1,094	1,052
6	4,816	2,678	7,832	550	657	658	555	282	529	347	1,000
	710	331	2,634	1,147	1,317	2,120	1,037	724	1,426	2,005	1,475
3	3,710	1,779	4,948	2,019	1,814	1,810	1,455	1,165	2,326	2,172	2,374
	NA	NA	NA	94	206	901	1,042	755	1,585	1,465	1,207
5	7,337	2,868	10,311	3,376	2,852	5,257	3,694	2,520	4,152	5,371	4,534
6	48,845	26,014	81,467	39,259	31,242	40,496	43,107	34,333	49,801	51,757	48,947

es: *Report of Committee on Salmon and Freshwater Fisheries*, May 1961, supplemented ta supplied by Ministry of Agriculture, Fisheries and Food for the years 1960–64.

protect the runs until spawning is completed and the young smolts have safely escaped to the sea.

The river authority obtains 90 per cent of its income on an average salmon stream from rod fishermen and levies on riparian owners, and only 10 per cent from net fishermen, yet the latter take about 60 per cent of the annual harvest.

According to the Bledisloe Report (1961) some 2,000 persons were engaged in commercial fishing for salmon, sea-trout and eels in 1958 and about 850,000 anglers purchased licences to fish (of whom only a very small number sought salmon).[22] Most of the inshore fishermen who work the salmon nets spend the remaining seven months of the year in trawling, fishing for herring or shrimp, and the like.

Existing methods of catching salmon by netting in the estuaries–relatively few nets operate above tidewater–are regarded as 'antediluvian and extravagant' by Fort. There may be up to a hundred men in an estuary working fourteen hours a day in the season. At times they may make phenomenal catches but they also have blank days. They have no idea from one week to the next what their income may be. It would be more economical to eliminate the netters completely and install an efficient trap at one of the lower weirs on a salmon river through which all in-running fish would pass, and in this way two men working part time could replace all the netsmen. The river authorities have the power to do this very thing providing they compensate the netsmen out of the proceeds of whatever percentage of the fish taken they decide to market–permitting the remainder to escape and perpetuate the stocks.

This is the crux of the matter. Who can determine what proportion of the annual runs should be marketed and what proportion escape since there is no accurate knowledge of their size on any river? Replacing the nets with traps would for the first time provide data on which to base a sound management programme. But up to now only one or two river authorities have taken advantage of their powers to eliminate nets and go into the business of commercial fishing. So the threat of overfishing remains.

Growing demands for water is regarded as another and mounting peril to the anadromous fisheries of the United Kingdom. In fact, water abstraction may be more insidious even than pollution because its effect is indirect and hence more difficult to assess. Spawning areas must have plenty of water since otherwise the fry tend to crowd together and become vulnerable to large fish. There is evidence that whenever water is diverted into a pipeline to supply a town, industry or other user, fish life may suffer–for several reasons. There may be less flow to dilute the contaminants which are present downstream; floods which induce salmon to move upstream may be curtailed in volume; and in case of drought the flow may fall to disastrous levels and make it difficult for the fish, especially the young, to survive at all.

England, although a well-watered land, faces serious regional water shortages. Soaring demands arising from the growth of population, higher living standards (resulting in the installation of more sanitary facilities, water-using appliances, and the like), and rapid industrial development have taken many local government bodies by surprise.

In some areas underground water is not available for municipal supplies and surface waters have to be used. It was mainly in the Pennines that shortages first became serious and there it was found that fluctuations in the flow of streams made them unreliable as a source of regular water supplies and therefore reservoirs were constructed in the upland valleys to store water in times of flood, so that it could be used evenly throughout the year for domestic and industrial purposes. Sometimes these impoundments, located in sparsely inhabited areas, where the water is pure and fish life abundant, are a long distance from where it is used. About one-fourth of England's population is now supplied with water from such sources; for example, London depends on the Thames and Lea, Newcastle on the Tyne, Darlington and Middlesbrough on the Tees, York on the Ouse, Chester on the Dee, and Coventry on the Severn.[23]

Nearly every sizeable lowland river in England is now eyed by local authorities or industries as a prospective water tap. Critical situations are apparent in the heavily populated south-east, in East Anglia, and in the industrialized north-west. For example, in the Tees valley entire communities were without water in the summer and autumn of 1964 except what could be provided by tank trucks. In this area demands by a large chemical operation requiring large supplies of water aggravated the shortage. Here, as in other English valleys, no effort is being made to conserve the heavy winter flow and provide storage for summer use. In the counties of Kent and Essex water supplies are so inadequate that authorities have warned that rationing may become necessary.

Numerous schemes are being projected to augment water supplies by building reservoirs and damming headwaters of rivers. These impoundments would not only flood out spawning grounds, but alter the downstream flow in a manner that might be harmful to fish. There are also proposals which stagger the imagination, such as a barrage across the northern part of Morecambe Bay to form a lake and meet the water requirements of the north-west until the year 2000; an even more ambitious project to dam the Solway Firth; and the building of a fifteen-mile barrage across the River Wash to form a lake almost half the size of the Zuyder Zee. One cannot view these proposals with equanimity because they would certainly damage the already hard-pressed salmon fisheries.

Finally, what is the United Kingdom's record now on river pollution? River authorities are responsible for preventing the poisoning of watercourses and streams in their areas, and they have the power to prosecute offenders under the Rivers (Prevention of Pollution) Acts of 1951 and 1961 and the Salmon and Freshwater Fisheries Act of 1923. Pentelow said in 1958, 'The river boards have now been operating long enough to show that they are doing extremely valuable work. Armed with the new pollution powers, they have undoubtedly made great strides in the control of pollution, and that is of great assistance both to fisheries and to those who are seeking suitable water for domestic or industrial use. . . . Each annual report [of the river boards] includes an impressive list of new works installed for the better purification of waste waters, and wherever the effluent from these works discharges to non-tidal streams the river board imposes conditions designed to ensure that the discharge does not cause pollution.'[24] England has indeed come a long way in the past century in curbing the propensity of industries and local authorities to get rid of their wastes in the easiest possible way and thereby permit the health of streams to deteriorate and fish populations to decline or die out. 'It is most encouraging to see how successfully river boards, local authorities and industry have managed to agree . . . and how seldom a dispute has had to be referred to the Minister of Housing and Local Government for settlement.'

Looking over the map of the United Kingdom, Pentelow in 1958 saw bright spots but also areas where pollution was still rampant. There are many rivers in the Midlands, South Lancashire, the West Riding of Yorkshire, and the Forth and Clyde areas 'where no fish can live, the water is black, brown, grey, or even strikingly coloured, where the consistency may be that of thin mud and the odour likely to be a public nuisance'. These conditions are mostly a legacy from the nineteenth or early twentieth century, and one can only hope that river authorities which have adequate power will not permit any of these streams to get worse. However, the increasing use of pesticides in agriculture and chemical detergents in households complicates the pollution problem because residues entering the watercourses are difficult or almost impossible to dilute. They are known to have killed salmon and other fish in large numbers.

The picture is generally darker in the estuaries, where the river authorities have acquired jurisdiction only in very recent years. They have continued to decline. 'The explanation is', said Dr. B. A. Southgate in 1965, 'that the purifying capacity of an estuary is a great deal less than might have been supposed by considering the large volume of water it contains.' New pollutants which are difficult to dilute, such as detergents and pesticide residues, suggest that 'the net rate of passage to the sea of polluting matter discharged to an estuary may be so slow that a very high concentration accumulates in the central reaches. Also–what was not known before–the rate of supply of oxygen from the air through the surface of the water is surprisingly small.'[25]

A vivid example of a badly-polluted estuary is the Humber, formed by the confluence of the Yorkshire Ouse and the River Trent at Faxfleet in the East Riding of Yorkshire. It extends eastward for about twenty miles to Skitter Ness, and after about twenty miles enters the North Sea. A thorough investigation of the Humber by a group of Government scientists in 1949 found that since the beginning of the war the number of migratory fish in the Ouse had seriously decreased, and this was not due to fishing intensity but deterioration of the river itself. Indeed, for long periods the upper Humber above Hull contained so little dissolved oxygen that fish attempting to pass through it would be asphyxiated. Heavy dosages of filth were entering its upper end–sewage and trade wastes (factory effluents) from the towns situated on the banks of the river.

Anglers' fight on pollution

Backing up the war on pollution by agencies of government and private industry is a militant non-political and non-profit organization–the Anglers' Co-operative Association, unique in Europe. It was founded in 1948 by a London barrister and angler, the late John F. Eastwood, K.C., with the assistance of colleagues from the Fly Fishers Club, and Sir Roger Conant, Bt., C.V.O., present Chairman of the A.C.A. They were determined to fight polluters and pollution by asserting Common Law rights which say that a riparian owner is entitled to have the water passing his property in its natural state, unaltered in quality, temperature or volume. Any material change in the quality or temperature amounts to pollution, and any degression is an infringement of Common Law. Anti-pollution laws seemed to have been of no practical use to the victims of pollution.

Through its vigorous pursuit of the rights of owners the A.C.A. has forced the courts to rule that anyone–industry, local government, farmers–who use the rivers as the cheapest way of getting rid of wastes is breaking the law.

Linked up with the alteration in quality is the quantity of water which also must not be unduly impaired. As Charles Wade, Director of the A.C.A., says: 'Having a law is not enough–no single owner of fishing can fight a large industrial concern, or a local corporation, or City Council on his own. He would have neither the time nor the financial resources. As far as the individual angler was concerned the law was hardly worth the paper it was written on.'[26] Eastwood and his colleagues believed that if anglers would join the A.C.A. by paying a nominal subscription and if some members would promise to guarantee payment up to a certain amount if called upon, in the event of a case being lost, then actions could be fought. The idea was quite revolutionary and met with strong opposition from polluters, and also from some anglers who did not understand the legal system or suspected the aims of the organization.

Acting for proprietors, the A.C.A. can sue for damages as well as seek an injunction. Sometimes the mere threat of action is a sufficient deterrent, since it is now generally recognized that anyone who fouls the water of a riparian owner is infringing the right of property.

Since 1952 the Association has undertaken over 650 cases and scored many spectacular successes, both for individual proprietors and angling clubs whose fishing rights were impaired by illegal pollution. It has obtained damages of over £100,000 ($280,000) for fishermen who had their sport killed by factory and other effluent discharges that poisoned the waters. For example, it has helped to clean up the River Derwent, which was almost devoid of fish, by forcing the city of Derby to improve the waste-disposal system, and it has successfully fought such industrial giants as English Electric, Monsanto Chemicals, Imperial Chemical Industries, and British Celanese, as well as nationalized industries and small companies. It has stopped the pollution of many stretches of rivers in Great Britain and has not yet lost a case.

'Fighting pollution is an extremely expensive business', says Wade. 'To bring a polluter into the High Courts, and to secure an injunction against him, involves enormous cost and months of work.

There has to be a preliminary investigation, there are biologist's fees, analyst's fees, and the expense of retaining a reliable Counsel to conduct the case.' For example, the A.C.A. successfully sued the Consett Iron Company on behalf of a miners' club in Durham. The case went all the way to the Court of Appeal. If it had lost the verdict, the association would have been assessed £12,000 ($33,600) in court costs and probably gone out of business. Even the winning of a case and being granted costs can involve a considerable drain on the funds of the A.C.A. for all costs are not always retrievable. Polluters tend to exploit every loop-hole, and the A.C.A. must prepare its evidence with thoroughness if it is to stand a chance of bringing the polluter to heel. Engineers are sometimes employed to cost sewage disposal schemes and quite often this supplementary evidence is not called or needed, but it is very costly and must be at hand even if the presiding judge deems that particular outlay as irrecoverable from the defendants.

Today the A.C.A. has over 13,000 subscribing members and member clubs. There is a central office in London at 53 New Oxford Street, W.C.1, and branch offices throughout Great Britain. The Guarantee Fund now stands at over £40,000 ($112,000). Not one penny of it has yet been drawn upon.

As we look to the future, there is hope that the salmon runs of England and Wales, although they will in the aggregate never again approach the levels of even a century ago, may be able to hold their own in the face of all adverse forces–water pollution, water abstraction, the threat of building barrages to close up rivers, the heavy slaughter of British fish in Greenland waters, salmon disease in some rivers and other factors. Certainly those who have a vested interest in the fishery, as well as a large section of the public, are aware of the dangers. They are organized in potent organizations like the British Salmon and Trout Association. They have eloquent spokesmen in Parliament and on the river authorities. They are alert and determined to fight for survival of the stocks of this royal fish. The task will not be easy.

An up-to-date evaluation of the salmon resource in England is given in a personal communication of December 13, 1966 by J. D. Brayshaw, Fisheries and Pollution Inspector for the Avon and Dorset River Authority, one of the best informed men on the subject in the British Isles: 'Pollution, although still a serious matter is now almost certainly contained and I think we are past the nadir. . . . The other serious threats to salmon, now, are netting, disease (probably only transitory)[27] and water abstraction. The Greenland fishery is definitely the threat of the future. Water abstraction is obviously a potential threat but the new Water Resources Board is bent upon a policy of adapting water supply schemes so that they may, far from doing harm, actually serve to improve fisheries by regulating flows.'

Constructive aspects of the salmon problem which are coming to the fore are experimental work on the census of fisheries so as to provide data for better management, and the development of up-to-date rearing establishments. A step forward was taken at the end of 1966 with the announcement, at the annual meeting of the Salmon and Trout Association, of the creation of a Salmon Research Trust in England for which private funds will be solicited.

All this bodes well for the future. The tide of decline of English runs has been stemmed, if catch statistics of recent years are regarded as evidence. And all those who have vested interests in the valuable fisheries, including proprietors, anglers, and local and national government authorities, seem determined to make fishery conservation a living reality.

NOTES

1 Peter Leslie, 'Charles Dickens: Defender of the Salmon', *Trout and Salmon*, July 1963.
2 Francis Day, *Salmonidae of Britain and Ireland*, p. 120.
3 Scotland still requires no licence for taking salmon either by rod or net.
4 R. S. Fort and J. D. Brayshaw, *Fishery Management*, pp. 286–8.
5 Cyril Bibby, *T. H. Huxley*, p. 128.
6 F. T. K. Pentelow, *River Purification*, p. 10.
7 A. T. R. Houghton, *The Ribble Salmon Fisheries*, p. 51.
8 *Ibid*., p. 80.
9 Lancashire River Board, *Fishery Officer's Report for Year ended 31st March, 1960*, p. 4.
10 H. A. Herbert, *Tale of a Wye Fisherman*, p. 84.
11 *Ibid.*
12 J. Arthur Hutton, *Wye Salmon and Other Fish*, p. 143.
13 C. R. Denton, 'A Regency Angling Club', *The Field*, August 26, 1965.
14 Augustus Grimble, *op. cit*., p. 126.
15 Personal communication, December 30, 1963.
16 John Ashley-Cooper, *The Field*, November 21, 1963, p. 963.
17 H. D. Turing, *River Pollution*, p. 60. The Afon Lwyd in South Wales has been cleaned up and now supports a trout population.

18 Grimble reported that 'in 1867 the deadly hang nets made their appearance and for the following five or six years they captured vast numbers of fish; then their terribly destructive powers began to tell and from thenceforth they slowly, but surely, played havoc with the fish.' The catches slid rapidly. In the five years 1883 to 1887 all the nets in the river garnered only an average of 25,450 salmon per season, and from 1897 to 1907, 10,030. 'At that rate of decrease,' said Grimble, 'in another thirty years the Tyne will be a salmonless river.' His prediction was uncannily accurate.

19 In 1965 salmon and sea-trout were seen and caught above Hexham, and it was expected that the Northumbrian River Authority would step up the projected cleaning up of the stretch between Shields and Blaydon.

20 H. D. Turing, *River Pollution*, p. 62.

21 *Salmon and Trout Magazine*, January 1957, pp. 48–49.

22 *Report of Committee on Salmon and Freshwater Fisheries*, London, May 1961, p. 3.

23 F. T. K. Pentelow, 'A Survey of the Problems of Trade-Waste Waters', p. 3.

24 F. T. K. Pentelow, 'River Boards in Britain', *Nature*, June 7, 1958.

25 B. A. Southgate, 'Progress in the Control of River Pollution, 1948–65', pp. 7–8.

26 Personal communication, March 31, 1966.

27 In the autumn of 1967 the salmon disease, now called Ulcerative Dermal Necrosis or U.D.N. for short, was found in rivers in Lincolnshire, Cumberland, Lancashire, and in the Welsh Dee, Elwyd and Gwynedd. An account of the salmon disease U.D.N. is given on pp. 308–9. It is of interest to recall that nearly a century ago there was an outbreak of serious disease among salmon and the symptoms were very similar to those of the present epidemic. It appeared in 1877 in the Border Esk and Nith and soon spread to the Eden and other Solway rivers; then it spread to the Tweed and other Scottish rivers and to the Lune and southwards to many English and Welsh rivers including the Usk, Wye and Severn. The disease raged in individual rivers for between eight and twelve years but its virulence had greatly decreased by the 1890's. There were occasional outbreaks in the early 1900's but Hume Patterson had some difficulty in obtaining diseased fish then. He isolated a bacterium which he called *Bacillus salmonis pestis* and he showed that this would produce symptoms in sea-trout and opened the way for the fungus *Saprolegnia* to attack the skin.

8

Scotland's Salmon Wealth and its Problems

Scotland is a small country, about three-fifths the size of England, from which it is separated by the Cheviot hills, the Solway Firth and the lower reaches of the Rivers Liddel, Esk and Tweed. Physiographically it is divided into three divisions: the southern uplands, central lowlands, and northern Highlands which include the Hebrides, Orkney and Shetland islands. Numerous salmon rivers and lochs are found in all three areas.

The Highlands form an imposing land mass that occupies the northern half of Scotland, with the Great Glen (or Glen More), a natural trench running north-east to south-west, dividing the region into two parts. The Great Glen itself is occupied by long narrow lochs. To the west is a series of mountains resembling the Great Smokies of Tennessee, rising over 3,000 feet and drained by short, swift and steep rivers which empty into the sea lochs, really fjords, that penetrate the entire coastline of north-west Scotland. The irregularly-shaped offshore islands, separated from the mainland by deep sounds and kyles, are dissected by rivers and dotted with innumerable lochs. Salmon and sea-trout are found in some of the short streams of the Hebrides. The Grimersta, for example, although only a mile and a half long, but with numerous head lochs and burns, is one of the richest salmon rivers in Britain.

East of the Great Glen the Grampians rise to an altitude of 2,000 to 3,000 feet. Here the mountains are not so much a chain as a great elevated mass, with beautiful smaller glens and straths running through them, all the way from the Moray Firth on the east coast to the Firth of Clyde on the west. Near the seaboard, around Aberdeen, the terrain is low but inland the mountains gradually rise as you go north until you reach the Cairngorms. The tallest peak is

Ben Macdhui, almost 4,300 feet, whose summit overlooks a landscape of Highland corries and lochans and rushing streams. The Cairngorms, grey or red in appearance, house the headwaters of the renowned rivers Dee and Don which follow parallel courses until they tumble into the sea at Aberdeen. In the Monadhliath mountains which lie west of the Cairngorms and run parallel to the Great Glen are the headwaters of the Nairn, Findhorn and Spey, all famous salmon rivers which empty into the Moray Firth. The 118-mile Tay, longest in Scotland, traverses Loch Tay and a large part of the Highlands before it drops into the North Sea below Dundee. The Tay is still one of the richest salmon streams in Scotland, although its two main tributaries, the Tummel and Garry, have been dammed and diverted to generate electricity. In the Highlands the rivers cut through the mountains and most run out of or through lochs, so that migratory fish must traverse them in order to reach their spawning grounds. Figure 17 shows the major salmon rivers.

The landscape of the southern Highlands is wild and majestic. Driving from Inverness to Fort William, you follow Loch Ness and then Loch Lochy which leads into Loch Linnhe. The waters glisten in the sunshine of a late autumnal day. There is little traffic on the road that nestles close to the shore. Nothing stirs on the lakes. Stands of young spruce march straight up into the hills. Sheep are nibbling the brown dried grass. You know that salmon are in the lochs although you cannot see them, and fat spawners are mating in the river gravels. There is snow on the highest peaks, frost in the air, and as you near Loch Linnhe, where the ocean breeze freshens the wind, a cold drizzle sets in. At Fort William snow-covered Ben Nevis towers over the landscape and beyond are range upon range of purple mountains.

In contrast to the rugged Highlands are the central lowlands which form what geographers call a 'rift'. Here flow the impressive rivers Forth and Tay across undulating country. Here is the watershed of the 100-mile River Clyde which empties into the Firth of Clyde.

The southern uplands comprise a region that extends from a straight line running from Girvan to Dunbar to the English border. The terrain is about a thousand feet lower on the average than in the Highlands and this means that the rivers do not drop so steeply in their journey to the sea. The lochs are fewer, smaller and less elongated than in the north. In fact, you are on a plateau, an expanse of grassy moorland often tinted with heather, broken by rivers coursing through fertile valleys.

The romantic Tweed, almost 100 miles long, of which some 20 miles form the border with England, dominates a large part of the southern uplands. It drains the northern slopes of the Cheviot hills and the southern faces of the Lammermuir and Moorfoot hills, running in an easterly direction to meet the North Sea at Berwick, an English town famous as a salmon fishing centre.

Several major streams rise in the high plateau west of the Tweed Basin: the Clyde, descending from the central lowlands, and the Annan, Nith and Esk which follow parallel courses into the Solway Firth.

Biological characteristics and migrations

There are well-defined runs of salmon at regular seasons in Scottish waters. In rivers such as the Tay and Tweed fish seem to run during every month of the year regardless of weather. A large proportion of the catches in many streams are grilse. 'Along the shore between Rattray Head and Montrose,' says Menzies, 'grilse first appear about the middle of May. Occasionally very early fish may be caught in March and odd specimens in mid-April. Few enter the rivers before June.'[1] The full run is preceded by harbingers coming in ones and twos, at intervals of days or even weeks. On the east coast, where some netting stations depend largely on grilse, the main run may not start until May has passed. Then one battalion after another moves into the river. The migration reaches a peak in three or four weeks.

Salmon spawn from September to January in the rivers of Scotland. In good seasons, some Highland streams are thick with salmon in October and November.

Usually the females in the rivers of eastern Scotland die during the winter following spawning, but in the western streams a considerable proportion manage to survive and return to the sea and spawn again. Young male parr who have never been to sea always die after participating in the spawning act with adult fish, provided they have delivered their milt.

In cold Scottish waters, as in other northern rivers, parr usually grow only from April to October because they become passive when the water falls below about 45 degrees F. Most young salmon in

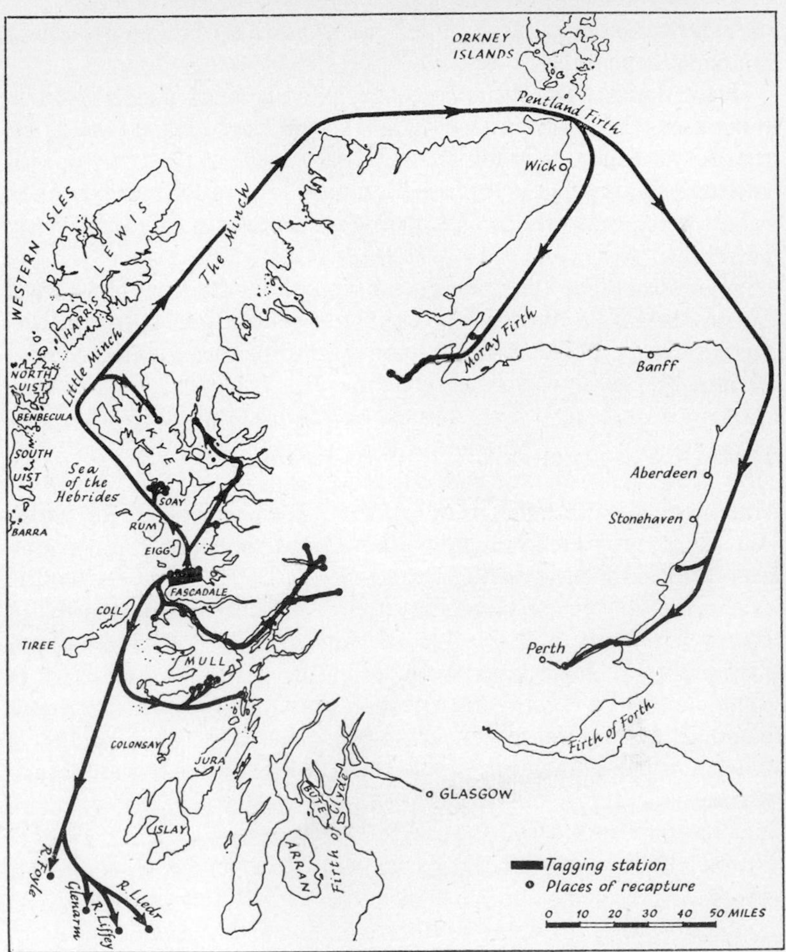

Figure 16
Migration of marked salmon, West Coast of Scotland.

Scotland migrate to the sea when they are two years old. Biologists have reported that the migration down the rivers is made individually, but shoals collect as they near the ocean. The smolts living farthest from the sea start first, and those dwelling downstream start later. When they reach the mouths of rivers they feed voraciously on crustaceans and shrimp.

Grilse may weigh from $1\frac{1}{2}$ to 10 pounds in Scotland and odd specimens will reach 14 pounds. The greater part of the runs, however, are fish four or five years old that spent two years in the river and two or perhaps three winters in the sea.

Heavy salmon weighing 30 to 40 pounds and more are fairly numerous in the rod and net catches, and specimens of 50 to 60 pounds are occasionally found.

Menzies found that on the average 5 per cent of the fish examined by him were kelts, but the ratio varied from 2 to 7 per cent among rivers.

Migrations of Scottish fish have been studied for several decades. In his Buckland Lectures for 1947 Menzies provided a summary–alluded to in Chapter I–of the results up to that time. He theorized that the general movement of Scottish salmon in search of food was northward and westward towards Arctic waters, although many individuals were recovered heading in other directions. For instance, some of the grilse marked at Ardnamurchan Point on the west coast were moving north either through the Minch or west of the Outer Hebrides, passed along the north coast and then went down the east coast to Montrose, 350 miles from the tagging station, or on to the Tay, some distance farther (Figure 16). Others headed south and were found in the Rivers Foyle and Glenarm in Northern Ireland, the Conway in Wales, and the Liffey in Eire. Fish tagged at Stoer Point and Loch Inchard on the north-west coast were recovered mainly in nearby waters but a few went as far as the Tweed (300 miles) and the Yorkshire coast (410 miles). One crossed the North Sea and was captured in Sognefjord in Norway.[2]

Menzies' theory about the migration pattern of Scottish fish was substantiated by the recoveries in west Greenland waters of fish, mainly smolts, tagged in Scottish rivers. One kelt had navigated 1,750 nautical miles from Inverness-shire to Fiskenaesset and the other 1,865 miles from the Blackwater River in Ross-shire to Eqaluk, Sukkertoppen. The smolts had been in the ocean 17 to 19 months and travelled from 1,420 miles (the River Tummel to Iqalikofjord in the Julianehaab district) to 2,135 miles (the River Conon in Ross-shire to Aqigsserniaq in the Egedesminde district).

Use and abundance

When the great ice sheet which embedded Scotland as thickly as it now does northern Greenland finally disappeared, the streams were populated by an invasion of salmon, trout, char and white fish from the Atlantic Ocean. The climate was still harsh and the land was clothed with almost impenetrable forests of Scotch pine. The earliest human inhabitants, dating from about 10,000 years ago, who were hunters and fishermen, huddled in caves along the sea-shore or on the margins of lochs. The later Neolithic peoples built pile dwellings or crannogs on bogs and marshes, or on lochs, a little distance from the shore. They netted or speared the abundant salmon and sea-trout.

During the Middle Ages the right of salmon fishing belonged to the Crown but the King could and did dispose of such rights to his subjects, sometimes without the right to the adjacent land. Unlike Ireland, England and Wales, there has never been any public right of fishing in Scotland along the coast or in the estuaries. Many of the coastal fisheries are still Crown property and are managed by the Crown Estates Office.

Because the salmon and sea-trout fisheries were valuable sources of revenue as well as food, they were well protected, at least by law. From the reign of Malcolm II came a long series of salmon acts. An edict of 1030 established a close season for taking salmon fry and old salmon between Assumption Day (about the end of August by medieval reckoning) and St. Martin's Day (November 12 in the medieval calendar), and from mid-April to St. John's Day (June 24). Violators were to have their gear burned. A second offence was punishable by six months in prison, a third by one year, and each succeeding conviction doubled the penalty.

The close season was frequently changed, to accord with what was then regarded as better protection of the spawners. In 1424, it was extended to St. Andrew's Day (end of November). There is reasonable doubt that these statutes were well obeyed or enforced because they were frequently revised (but without change of date) and the penalties made stiffer. Robert III in 1400 went so far as to decree that three convictions for slaughtering 'redd' fish in the forbidden time constituted a capital offence. We do not know if this extreme penalty was ever inflicted.[3]

Salmon were fished with seines in the Middle Ages, as in Norway and other countries, and sometimes with hook and line using natural bait. A considerable portion of the catches was made at weirs. There was almost no fishing for salmon on the shore, as there is now, and none in the open sea. In order to ensure an adequate escapement, weirs were subjected to regulation by the Crown, as we learn from a curious ordinance of 1212, which stipulated that 'a water course must be left open in the middle to the width that will permit a three-year-old hog to turn around freely'. A statute of 1318 forbade the erection of permanently fixed engines (nets or traps) of any size or form which would obstruct the ascent of the fish up a river or their return to the sea. Acts of 1424 and 1457 specifically forbade the erection of cruives and weirs which might impede the migration of smolts or adult salmon.

In 1489, during the reign of James IV, it was enacted that the sheriffs should destroy all illegal engines, and before the sixteenth century ended James VI had created a system whereby distinguished individuals were appointed conservators for all the major rivers of the kingdom with full powers to inflict penalties up to £200 (an enormous sum) or to imprison those who flouted the fishery code.[4] All the available evidence suggests that the rivers and lochs of Scotland continued generally to have an abundance of fish at least until the advent of industrialization.

Along with wool and hides, salted salmon was a staple of Scottish export in the medieval era. In the thirteenth century Aberdeen, Perth, Berwick and Glasgow were already centres of the salmon trade and many a family owed its wealth at least in part to this plentiful species. For instance, William Elphinstone, a Glasgow merchant of the fifteenth century, made a fortune by curing salmon and herring and exporting them to France, bringing back cargoes of brandy and salt. Curing and exporting fish continued, until the Union of 1707 with England, to be the chief foreign trade of Glasgow, where now the crowded River Clyde flows with the murk and filth of industrial wastes.

French, German and Italian merchants used to journey to Scotland to purchase fish and bring in exchange cloth, velvet, silks, spices and wine. The shipment of salmon to Flanders and France began at least as early as 1380. In fact, there is a Scottish decree of the fourteenth century stipulating that French merchants must pay for their salmon with silver and partly with wine.[5]

A considerable market for Scottish fish also existed in England, which even in the Middle Ages did not always produce enough to meet the demand, much of which came from religious establishments. However, the animosity between the two nations, expressed in sporadic outbursts of warfare along the border, sometimes made commerce difficult. Border rivers like the Solway Firth sometimes were the scene of riots between English and Scottish fishermen, as described by Sir Walter Scott in *Redgauntlet*.

In 1436 James I forbade the sale of salmon to Englishmen unless they paid cash on the barrel head, and invited his subjects to take their fish to Flemish ports, offering at the same time safe conduct to foreign merchants who came to trade in Scotland. Seven years earlier, as a measure of retaliation for the English occupation of Berwick and Roxburgh, the Scottish Parliament permitted fishing the year round on the Scottish portion of the Tweed. This situation lasted until the two kingdoms were united in 1603.

Many visitors have left records of the great riches of Scottish waters. The Spanish Ambassador Don Pedro de Ayala, who went as far as the Rivers Beauly and Spey in 1498, was astonished at the immense quantities of fish that were taken out of the rivers. Some twenty years later Taylor, 'the water poet', reported that single hauls on the Tweed yielded hundreds of fish. Richard Franck, who visited Scotland in the 1650s, described the plentiful catches at various fishing centres. At Stirling, he said, 'the Forth relieves the country with her great plenty of salmon, where the burgomasters as in many other parts of Scotland, are compelled to reinforce an ancient statute that commands all masters and others not to force or compel any servant, or an apprentice, to feed upon salmon more than thrice a week. . . . The abundance of salmon hereabouts is hardly to be credited.'[6] On the River Ericht he noted that the local people used neither net, rod, nor spear. The salmon jumped into a pot placed on a rock, presumably at a waterfall. At Inverness, he said, 'truly I stood amazed to see such companies of salmon'. Lochs in Sutherland were full of fish which were netted and barrelled up for shipment to France. On the Solway Firth men pursued the salmon on horseback, at full gallop, through the shallows left by the retreating tide. The guide who accompanied Franck's fictitious characters, Arnoldus and Theophilus, on their tour, took his leister along in case they should espy any salmon. 'This may be called salmon hunting', remarked Sir Walter Scott, who edited Franck's memoirs when they were republished in 1821, after being neglected for 130 years.

When Daniel Defoe rambled through Scotland in the early eighteenth century, he noted that at Kirkcudbright 'there is a fine salmon-fishing in this river [Dee]', and at Aberdeen, long a centre of the fishing industry, 'the rivers Dee and Don afford salmon in the greatest plenty that can be imagined, to the degree that in some of the summer months the servants won't eat them but twice a week'. An English officer, Captain Burt, writing from Inverness about the same time as Defoe made his journey, noted that the price of the fish there was a penny a pound and 'the meanest servants who are at board wages will not make a meal upon salmon if they can get anything else to eat'. (The probability is that they were being served tasteless kelts.) At Perth he saw prodigious quantities taken from the Tay, destined for shipment as salt fish to Edinburgh and other towns where there was no local supply, and also sent on coastwise smacks to London. At Aberdeen 'the quantity of salmon and perches . . . is a kind of prodigy; the profits are very considerable, the salmon being sent abroad into different parts of the world, particularly into England, France, the Baltic, and several other places'.[7]

The export of salmon to London remained an important item of commerce throughout the eighteenth century. The fishing industry was organized on capitalistic lines much as it is today. A proprietor let his fishing to a 'tacksman', who provided the cobles (shallow-draught boats) and nets and hired the crews. Aberdeen, for example, specialized in this type of enterprise which yielded high rents to the proprietors. Between 120 and 150 fishermen were employed in the season, each receiving £5 to £15 per annum. Skippers in charge of the boats earned a somewhat higher wage, £6 per annum, and were entitled to oatmeal, the traditional Scottish cereal, and seven shillings for 'sap money' or drink. Sometimes they received a *douceur* or 'sweetening' of a halfpenny for each fish they caught as an inducement to greater exertion. Most of the catch was sent to Billingsgate in London, but in summer salted fish were dispatched to the ancient markets of France and Flanders. Fish were cured at Macduff and other places; those that were pickled went to London and those salted to France and Spain.

On the River Deveron in Banffshire the tacksmen employed 80 to 100 men in salmon fishing and at Speymouth over 130 persons were engaged in fishing, coopering and other activities related to the salmon trade. The Duke of Gordon received £1,500 for the rental of five miles of the Spey. Workmen seem to have been well treated. There were allowances for extra-size catches; bread and beer were provided while working and a bottle of spirits to be shared among the crew of eight men and an overseer, all of whom worked twelve hours a day when the fish were running.[8]

At the end of the century George Dempster revolutionized salmon marketing by shipping fish in ice from the River Tay to London. Exports vastly increased. By 1838 there was a regular transport service from Edinburgh to Billingsgate market. The advent of railroads speeded up the transportation of fish and expanded the demand.

The prodigal wealth of Scottish rivers was nowhere more evident than in the Tweed. The naturalist Pennant stated that in his day a boatload of salmon, and sometimes nearly double that quantity, was often taken in a single tide, and in earlier days as many as 700 fish were swept by the waves into a single haul of the net. In 1802, according to the Reverend Richard Warner, 75 to 80 boats (presumably cobles) were constantly employed in fishing a few miles of the Tweed between January 10 and October 10 and that as much as 40,000 kits, each weighing 40 pounds–a total of 1,600,000 pounds–used to be dispatched from Berwick annually, but the volume had declined by the end of the century to around 8,000 kits (320,000 pounds). All the farmhouses in the Vale of the Tweed, said Richard Kerr in his *General View of the County of Berwick* (1809), depended upon the salmon for a considerable portion of their winter's food supply.

The Reverend James Hall in his *Travels in Scotland by an Unusual Route* (1805) noted that the Forth's salmon fishery was still productive but 'this species of food is generally too dear to be used by the common people. . . . Fisheries on the rivers, as well as the sea coasts of Scotland, are more and more becoming an object of concern.'[9]

Towards a crisis: overfishing

By the 1860s salmon in Scotland had become, according to Alexander Russel, a keen student of the industry, 'everywhere a costly luxury'. With the single exception of the Tay, 'the decline was universal and alarming, extending over almost every river and district, from the south-western Doon to the north-eastern Dee; although in one or two cases, such as the Spey and the rivers of Sutherland, where the fisheries are in the hands of one great proprietor, who had resorted to wise moderation, a great difference for the better was discernible'.[10]

We can trace the beginning of the resource's decline at least as far back as the spread of stake nets, bag nets and other fixed engines along the coasts. It was discovered that the fish do not move directly from the ocean into the rivers but nose their way along the shores in search of their natal stream. Therefore, ingenious nets were devised, really traps, to intercept them before they reached estuarial waters. Stake nets are said to have been first erected in 1788 in the Solway Firth, at a place called Newby, near the mouth of the River Annan, but their popularity dates from the third decade of the nineteenth century. By the middle of the century these contrivances were quite numerous around the coasts.

'A sail along almost any portion of the coast of Scotland–say that long stretch from Buchan-ness to Fortrose,' said Russel in 1864, 'will show that the shore is draped with salmon-nets, with very little regard to the neighbourhood or distance of a river. To take a single illustration, we see in our mind's eye (but of course we speak of an actual case) a line of coast running out into a bold promontory, then trending inwards to form a bay five miles indented. In the inmost corner of that bay stands a productive stake-net fishery, although there is at the place no run of fresh water which will afford passage to a minnow, and no salmon river debouches within sixty miles.'[11] An example of the efficiency of such gear was found in the Firth of Tay where fixed nets were erected in 1799 and after much litigation declared illegal under the old Scottish statutes in 1812. While they were in existence, catches at two stations immediately above the highest of the stationary nets fell off sharply from an average of 10,875 salmon and 2,200 grilse yearly in 1788–97 to 6,700 and 2,430 respectively in 1801–10; after the nets vanished the fishery recovered.

Wherever fixed engines blocked the migration of fish the river catches usually diminished and in some cases the total yields of the district fell off because they prevented an adequate escapement of spawners. On the north-west coast of Sutherland bag nets were introduced in the 1830s; in 1839 they caught over 16,000 fish but in 1850, although their number had doubled, the harvest had fallen to 1,300, and soon thereafter they were abandoned by the proprietor, the Duke of Sutherland. Similar trends were observed in the fisheries of the Firths of Moray and Beauly. One could only conclude that stake nets and bag nets overfished the stocks and that they had to be reduced in numbers or entirely eliminated if the rivers were not to become barren.

The English Commissioners of Enquiry declared in 1860 that 'we are prepared, after a full consideration of the case, to recommend the total suppression by law of all fixed engines', a verdict endorsed by the Parliamentary Commission of the same year. Stationary nets were therefore prohibited in England and Wales. In Scotland, they remained the chief form of commercial salmon fishing outside the rivers.

Despite Scottish legislation of 1862 and 1868 designed to conserve the fishery, Archibald Young, Commissioner of Scottish Salmon Fisheries, reported in 1877 that overnetting was still rampant: '[Under existing laws] stake nets and bag nets may be placed far too near the mouths of rivers. . . . No definition of what constitutes a fixed engine [is given] in the Acts of 1862 and 1868. . . . The upper proprietors complain that they–in whose waters the salmon are bred–have too little power; and that they have no interest to preserve the fish and prevent poaching, as only a miserable remnant of salmon is permitted to reach their waters during the fishing season and that, until the nets are off, the lower proprietors have a practical monopoly of the fishing.'[12] Twenty-five years after Young made his report, Augustus Grimble complained that there were still too many nets, operating too close together: 'The hundreds of miles of coast from Fifeness in the south to Peterhead in the north is just one mass of nets, which are rapidly depopulating the Tay, the two Esks, Dee, Don, Ythan and Ugie.' The rivers themselves were overfished in many instances. Thus, speaking of his beloved Tweed about this time, Sir Herbert Maxwell said, 'It was a marvel with the improved machinery for netting, the pains taken to remove every stone that might hamper the free sweep of the net, the facilities of transport, and the constancy of the market for salmon, that any head of fish escapes to the upper waters at all. In the Tweed, particularly, hardly any do escape until the autumn.'[13] This great salmon river was but a pale shadow of its former self, and other rivers in Scotland were in an equally parlous plight.

Table 17 shows that recorded Tweed catches dropped precipitously during the nineteenth century: from an average of about 110,000 salmon and grilse in 1811–1815 and 125,000 in 1816–1820 to a mere 16,000 in 1895–1899.

Next to the Tweed, the Spey and the Tay were probably the most prolific Scottish rivers in the early nineteenth century. The Duke of Richmond's waters on the Spey produced an average of 57,000 salmon and grilse annually in the 1850s, while the Tay's production

Table 17

Salmon and grilse catches in River Tweed, 1811–1899
(*numbers of fish*)

Year	*Salmon* (*annual average*)	*Grilse* (*annual average*)	*Total* (*annual average*)
1811–15	40,297	68,057	109,354
1816–20	37,938	87,089	125,027
1821–25	22,930	57,647	80,577
1826–30	9,804	53,990	63,794
1831–35	14,416	65,112	79,528
1836–40	14,149	52,283	66,432
1841–45	18,846	81,047	99,893
1846–50	11,479	56,190	67,669
1851–55	9,085	23,905	32,990
1856–59	7,489	18,756	26,245
1860–64	6,131	15,118	21,241
1865–69	6,214	5,681	11,895
1870–74	8,266	10,603	18,869
1875–79	5,733	7,341	13,074
1880–84	7,262	8,427	15,689
1885–89	7,267	9,359	16,636
1890–94	6,440	11,432	17,872
1895–99	7,366	8,458	15,824

Sources: Grimble, *Salmon Rivers of Scotland*; Alex. Russel, *The Salmon*, and W. L. Calderwood, *Salmon Rivers and Lochs of Scotland.*

fluctuated between 60,000 and over 70,000 fish in the period 1830 to 1846, reaching a peak of over 100,000 in 1842. The Duke of Sutherland's rivers flowing into the Moray Firth and Pentland Firth brought aggregate annual catches of almost 60,000 salmon and grilse between 1864 and 1876. The North Esk yielded 25,000 to 30,000 salmon and grilse annually; the Dee about 12,000; the Don over 10,000; the Beauly around 5,000; and the Findhorn 4,000 in the 1860s.

Poaching!

Poaching of fish and game was probably more prevalent in Scotland than in any other part of Great Britain. The snatching of salmon was regarded as an exciting rural sport, like baiting badgers and hunting hares, and was pursued by farmers, cottagers, servants and sometimes by the lairds. Walter Scott cast a halo of romance over the spectacle in several novels, notably in *Guy Mannering*, where he described a wintry nocturnal performance by torchlight such as he and his guests, warmly clothed and well supplied with 'Edinburgh ale', had witnessed:

> On the present occasion the principal party were embarked in a crazy boat upon a part of the river which was enlarged and deepened by the restraint of a mill-wear, while others, like the ancient Bacchanals in their gambols, ran along the banks, brandishing their torches and spears, and pursuing the salmon, some of which endeavoured to escape up the stream, while others, shrouding themselves under roots of trees, fragments of stones, and large rocks, attempted to conceal themselves from the . . . fishermen.

The game was 'inexpressibly animating', the shouting on the banks, the vigorous exertions of the men in the boat, 'now holding high their weapons, now stooping to strike, now standing upright, bronzed by the same red glare into a colour which might have befitted the regions of Pandemonium'. It was dangerous sport, too, for broken ice filled the stream, fish madly scurried to and fro, spears flew. But soon the boat was filled with bleeding salmon, flapping about futilely.

When the spectacle ended, more from exhaustion of the spectators than the participants, 'the sportsmen returned loaded with fish, upwards of one hundred salmon having been killed. . . . The best were selected for the use of the principal farmers, the others divided among their shepherds, cottars, dependants, and others of inferior rank who attended. These fish, dried in the turf smoke of their cabins or shealings, formed a savoury addition to the mess of potatoes, mixed with onions, which was the principal part of their winter food. In the meanwhile a liberal distribution of ale and whisky was made among them, besides what was called a kettle of fish–two or three salmon, namely, plunged into a cauldron and boiled for their supper. . . . All was hearty cheer and huzza, and jest and clamorous laughter, and bragging alternately, and raillery between whiles.'

After supper some of the men retired to the public house, 'where the punch bowl was often replenished. . . . The fiddler and piper next made their appearance, and the best part of the night was gallantly consumed in dancing to their music.'

The eulogists of fish poaching *par excellence* were William Scrope and Thomas Tod Stoddard, who in his *Art of Angling* (second edition, 1836) gives a full description of this boisterous sport. 'Our waters', he says, 'differ very essentially from those of England; we have clear and rapid rivers–torrents black with mosses, or pellucid as diamonds–lakes large, and gleaming tarns deep, still and terrible, and of these, some are stored with prime, subtle trout, and others are frequented by the active salmon.' Most enticing of all is the Tweed: 'Its banks . . . are in keeping with its other advantages–not naked and barren, neither spongy and overgrown with rushes, nor yet crowded with close and impervious wood, but mostly dry and inviting, fringed in many parts with oak, ash, elm and beech, and in others hung over with pleasant alder.'[14] Leistering is Stoddard's favourite method: by it 'vast numbers of salmon loaded with spawn are annually slaughtered, at a time when they can be turned to very little profit, but we are by no means prepared, seemingly, to condemn a practice permitted by immemorial usage, and which obtains the character of a manly and vigorous sport. . . . We would rather see it encouraged, within certain limits, than tyrannically suppressed, which we know, in the south of Scotland, it can never be, as long as exists the old spirit of the Border.'[15]

Stoddard was a fairly talented poet and among his better effusions is 'The Leisterer's Song', which he recited with dramatic fervour to many people who, like himself, warmed by whisky toddy, congregated in some village inn after a cold night's vigorous poaching:

Glances the shining spear
 From harmless hands unheeded!
On, in its swift career,
 The dream-like fish hath speeded.

It is the leisterer's cry!
 The salmon, ho! oho!
Along its wake the torches break,
 And waver to and fro.

Wildly the eager band
 Closes its fatal numbers;
Across its glistening sand
 The wizard water slumbers.
It is the leisterer's cry!
 The salmon, ho! oho!
And, lightning like, the white prongs strike
 The jaded fish below.

Rises the cheering shout,
 Over the rapid slaughter;
The gleaming torches flout
 The old, oak-shadow'd water.
It is the leisterer's cry!
 The salmon, ho! oho!
Calmly it lies, and gasps and dies,
 Upon the moss bank low!

More salmon, bragged Stoddard in his second book, *The Angler's Companion* (second edition, 1853), were killed by means of the leister than the rod on some rivers. 'At Kirkbank, for instance, as many fish are sometimes killed in this way in a single night, as would suffice to exercise the ingenuity and encourage the perseverance of twenty honest anglers throughout the season.' Alas, the Tweed Acts prohibited this kind of fishing; the very possession of a leister rendered a person liable to prosecution, and the booming days of yore, when '300 breeding fish writhed and bled on the prongs of a single leister, and at least six thousand, which had escaped the toils of the Berwick fishermen, and formed the hope and stay of future seasons of abundance, were cut off by means of the same deadly instrument', were coming to an end.

In addition to the flamboyant depredations of country folk, the rivers were quietly looted by small gangs of pirates who made their living from the sale of illegal fish. There was in fact a well-organized bootleg traffic, facilitated by the advent of railroads. Local poachers worked with middlemen who collected the fish and game and shipped them, in disguise, to black marketeers in Liverpool, Manchester and London. It was estimated that at least 100 tons of Scottish salmon were dispatched yearly out of season to England and France, and for every two fish legally caught on the Tweed another was stolen.

No man on Tweedside considered poaching a crime and many families obtained their winter's supply with their own hands. Even netsmen who fished legally during the open period on the Tay or Tweed were known to keep their hands in, as the saying went, during the close season. However, those who were caught received short shrift, since local justices like Sir Walter Scott, sheriff of his county, might wink at a person who poached for the pot but not at one who poached for money.

Yet, there were characters who could always furnish salmon out of season. Such was 'Fish Tam' who lived in a gypsy colony near Kelso and made frequent trips through the countryside, sometimes as far as Edinburgh, disposing of salmon kippered according to a secret gypsy formula, so he claimed. His outlets were chiefly inns frequented by carriers and stage-coach drivers. Fish Tam came of a long line of poachers and knew all the artifices of the trade. When he died he left £700 and two small houses (a sizeable estate) to his only child, a half-wit daughter. It is certain that in his day he killed thousands of fine Tweed salmon.

'Salmon Job' was ostensibly a fish cadger travelling between Perth and Edinburgh. His horse-drawn cart containing barrels of salted herrings and bundles of cured cod was a familiar sight on the muddy roads. It was well known that he could supply salmon all the year round, usually below the market price. He did not deal, like other poachers, in 'black fish'–that is, baggots or kelts–but sold clean salmon. Job, who had many assistants, was never caught and continued to peddle his illegal wares to the very day of his death: he was accidentally drowned one night working the River Forth and his body was fished up above Stirling. Originally a lowly-paid weaver at Kinross, he bequeathed £1,700 to his granddaughter.

The wild, uninhabited stretches of the sparsely-settled land made poaching relatively easy. Besides, as Sir Walter Scott said, 'All men, and women as well, of the peasant class born within sight of the silvery stream think they have as much right to the fish as the lairds have.'

Protection improved on many rivers, yet the problem was far from solved. Grimble, at the end of the nineteenth century, noted that the Aberdeenshire Dee was guarded by a staff of 22 bailiffs and the united district boards of Dee and Don maintained a launch to watch the coast. As a result, poaching had almost entirely ceased at the mouths of the rivers, but the Dee itself was still plagued by this evil, 'for the annual prosecutions are numerous, and very rarely unsuccessful'.[16] The North Esk was guarded by a powerful corps of well-trained watchers who had stamped out the practice, by farm workers and others, of 'sniggering'–hooking the shoals of salmon that were immobilized at times of low water in the pools and below Craigo dam. In contrast, a great deal of fish stealing occurred on the Annan and its tributaries where there were only a few regular bailiffs, assisted, when they had time, by 30 gamekeepers. It was not unusual for gangs to kill 70 spawners with leisters (even though this instrument had been outlawed) in one night, salt them on the spot, pack them in barrels and bury them in the moss until they could be safely transported.

The impact of industrialization

In the year 1759 two Englishmen, John Roebuck and Samuel Garbett, were joined by a Scot, William Cadell, in a partnership that undertook to build an iron works near Falkirk, about 2½ miles from the Firth of Forth. In the same year an Act of Parliament empowered the Glasgow town council 'to cleanse, enlarge and improve the channel of the river Clyde'. These events may be said to have started Scotland's industrial revolution which, as in England, was destined to alter greatly, and adversely, the habitats of anadromous fish.

The first phase of Scotland's industrial development centred mainly around textiles, an industry located in western Scotland, in Renfrewshire and Lanarkshire. Cotton mills arose at Neilston, East Kilbride, Glasgow, and at Deanston and Stanley in Perthshire in the last two decades of the eighteenth century. Because of the need for water power they were usually built on or near limpid waterways, rich in salmon, trout and other fish, such as the Clyde, Leven, etc. Later, mills appeared on the east coast around Dundee on the Firth of Tay, while another cluster sprang up in north Ayrshire.

The rise of the cotton industry inspired the growth of subsidiary processes such as bleaching, dyeing, printing and embroidering the cloth. Jute and woollen textile manufacturing also became prominent. Nearly all of these industries had some adverse effects on the fisheries. Thus, bleaching was concentrated in the Vale of Leven in Dumbartonshire and the Cart Valley in Renfrewshire, making full use of the lime-free waters of the rivers and lochs (such as Loch

Lomond). Jute manufacture arose in and around Dundee while woollen manufacture spread in the Tweed valley, especially at Galashiels on the main river and Hawick on its pleasant tributary, the Teviot. Carpet-making was centred at Kilmarnock.

The beautiful Scottish countryside was blighted by the spread of mines and mills and ugly towns which bourgeoned around them. Steel and machinery manufacture were established in the central lowland belt stretching from central Ayrshire to Midlothian and mid-Fife, with outposts as far north as Dundee and Aberdeen. Here were good harbours, estuaries and canals. Rich coal and iron deposits added their fatal attractions, so that in this area, especially in north Lanarkshire, heavy industries proliferated. Around Glasgow, where the River Clyde was deepened and a channel cut to the sea, smelting works, furnaces, steel mills (in the late 1870s), and shipyards cluttered the landscape; later came locomotive and automotive plants. New industrial towns sprang up downstream on the lower Clyde, once a prolific salmon river, to form Scotland's greatest industrial complex.

Old towns expanded and new ones arose to house the armies of workers who left their quiet rural homes to work in factories, mines and mills. Glasgow lost its medieval air as its population swelled from 13,000 in the mid-eighteenth century to 395,000 in 1861, when it was Scotland's largest city. Pollution ruined the Clyde. Fishermen's huts on the banks of the river disappeared.

Glasgow was for the most part an ineffable slum. Families lived in one- or two-roomed houses lined back to back on dingy streets marked by columns of smoking black chimneys. These crowded tenements, some of them facing sunless and malodorous courts and lanes, had no drains or proper water supplies. Refuse piled up in the streets to be flushed down a ditch or creek. In time a piped water supply was provided to supplement local wells, and municipal sewer systems were built, but they merely carried the sewage straight into the nearest river or loch. Factories were accustomed to using the adjoining streams to get rid of their noxious wastes, totally heedless of their effects on fish life.

---

13. Tummel-Garry Scheme, Scotland. An observer watching an adult salmon and some parr below, in the observation chamber at Pitlochry fish pass.

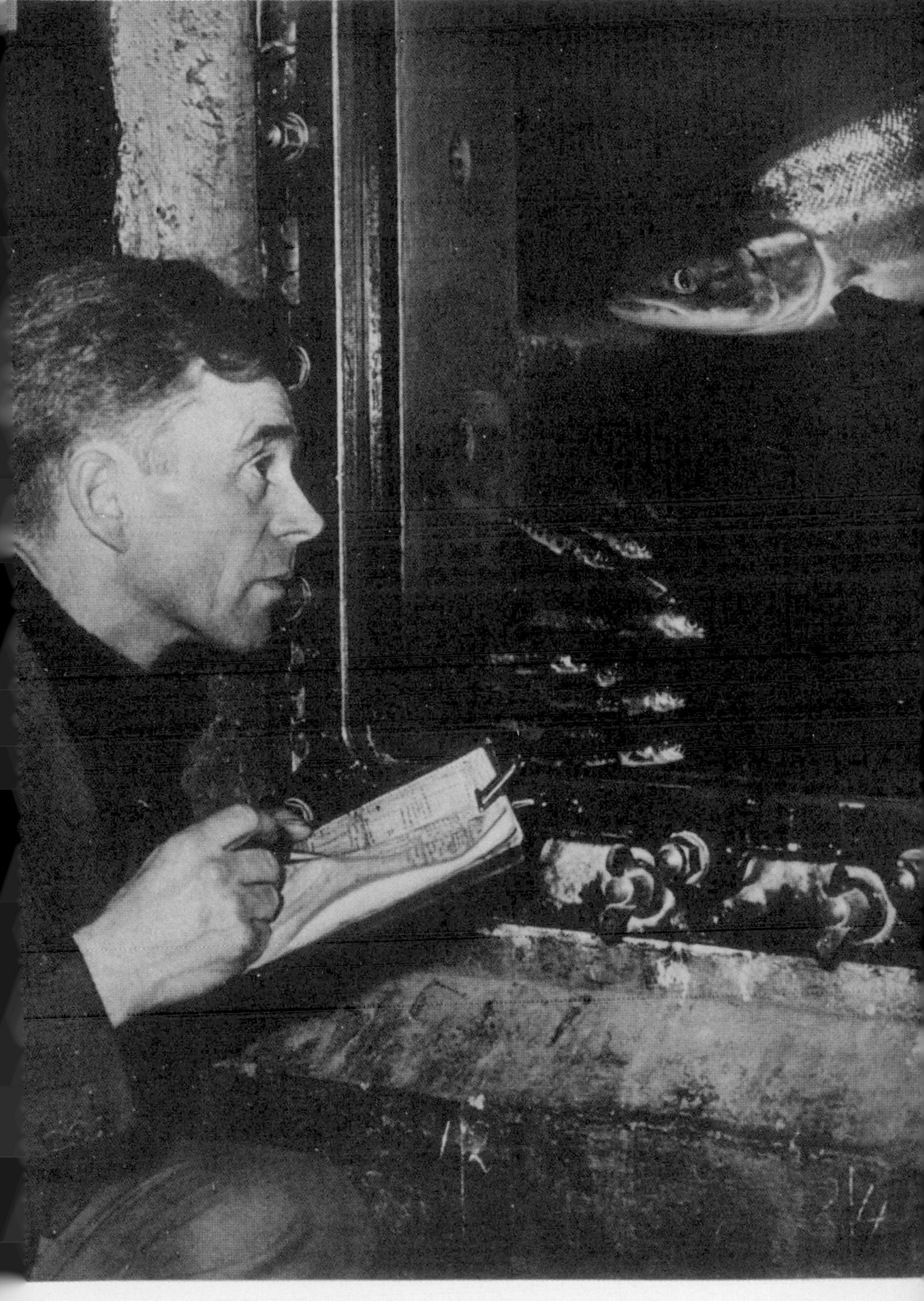

These industrial pollutions were of numerous kinds but they fell into two broad categories: (1) those which consist of organic matter, resembling sewage, though generally much stronger, that putrefy quite readily and must be promptly treated; and (2) those which contain poisonous matter like acids, cyanides, or solids in suspense that eventually settle on the bottom of a river and smother insect life, or they contain a large amount of very fine matter in solution that interferes with the light and affects the respiratory organs of fish and some insects. The first kind of pollution is associated with food processing, textile mills, whisky, beer, and other liquor-making establishments, the second with coal-mining and the by-products of the coking industry, with steel pickling, and wastes from copper and other metallurgical operations.[17]

When dust, stone and very fine particles of coal wash down a stream from a coal-washing plant the gravel is choked so that insect life is killed off and as a result the water becomes dead and no fish can survive. Waste water from coke ovens and gasworks is even more injurious.

The dumping of organic and inorganic wastes into clean watercourses had the same baneful effects in Scotland as in England and Wales. In 1877 Archibald Young reported that 'although a majority of Highland streams are uncontaminated by pollutions, the lowland rivers, and several in Perthshire, Forfarshire, and Aberdeenshire are much polluted'. The Tweed and its tributaries were seriously affected. There were 93 mills and factories in the four counties through which they flowed and most of them discharged refuse of a more or less injurious nature into the waters. In only eleven instances, or one in nine, were tanks or other means of purification found in these establishments. 'The sources of pollution', said Young, 'are yearly growing in number and magnitude.' From 1879 to 1892, 95,000 salmon, grilse and sea-trout, killed by disease, were removed from the Tweed.

14a. Tummel Valley Scheme, Scotland—boom at Pitlochry dam. The boom prevents debris piling up against the dam and intakes. The photograph shows Lock Faskally which drowned an idyllic and rich stretch of salmon water.

14b. Pitlochry dam and power station. Smolts pass through the turbines here, with a certain amount of mortality.

In the Forth district the Rivers Devon, Almond, Avon, Carron, Leven and Esk were salmonless, said Young, 'owing to pollutions acting in combination with artificial obstructions'. In the Tay district the Almond, Ericht and Dight 'are entirely ruined because of the same causes, while the South Esk below Brechin is very much injured'. In Ayrshire the Irvine 'has been utterly destroyed as a salmon river by town sewage and other impurities, and the Ayr, Doon and Garnock have also suffered terribly from pollution of various kinds'. The Leven and Clyde teemed with foul effluents, while fisheries in the Nith, at and below Dumfries, were greatly affected by the same causes.[18]

Twenty-five years later Grimble reported that some of the streams surveyed by Young had scarcely improved. The Nith, for instance, was in worse shape. A tacksman told the Nith District Board in 1891 that

> When the river is low I consider the pollutions the sole cause of deterioration. Scarcely a fish will run up, and I have seen them at the ford at the New Quay making back to the sea on Monday mornings after meeting the refuse from the mills. The dyes are plainly seen in the waters–black, violet, drab–and at Castle Dykes I have seen several colours at one time. During the six weeks of drought I have seen the water so black from bank to bank that a piece of white paper could not be seen a foot deep; and what with the sewage and mill effluents, the smell is so bad that I could compare the river to nothing but a stinking canal.[19]

Pollution also heavily damaged the Spey, second largest Scottish river. From its cradle in Loch Spey the river courses for some forty miles through the Highlands of Inverness-shire, gathering volume from many small, pellucid tributaries until it expands into Loch Insh, about two miles wide, and then dashes serenely for another sixty miles to reach the North Sea at Garmouth. In its Highland stretch the Spey valley was a sportsman's paradise. Salmon and trout abounded in the river, stags on the hills, grouse on the moors, roe deer and pheasants in the covers, partridges in the fields, and duck and snipe in plenty. But downstream the picture was depressing, for the river was fouled with discharges of 'burnt ale' from numerous whisky distilleries. This material was far more deadly than raw sewage; it killed fry, parr, and smolts and sickened adult salmon. Grimble said that when angling below Aberlour Burn, where there was a large distillery, he saw the clear water turn muddy yellow and masses of froth, 'varying in size from a saucer to the top of a small tea-table', float on the surface. Instantly the fish vanished to a half-mile below the burn. Some of the Spey proprietors, led by the Countess of Seafield, took the distillers to court and after a lengthy legal battle forced them to find a means of keeping the burnt ale out of the river.

Legislative action

As in England, the decay of the salmon stocks was alarming enough by the middle of the nineteenth century to prompt owners to call for Parliamentary action. First came the Tweed Acts of 1857 and 1859. They reduced the open season for nets and extended it for rods; lengthened the weekly close period; outlawed the use of the spear and leister; banned the stell net (a kind of fixed net) from the lower or tidal portion of the rivers and the cairn net from the upper rivers. This legislation also prohibited the dumping of poisonous substances into the streams; restricted mesh sizes of nets to 1¾ inches from knot to knot; established distances and times for working ordinary nets in rivers; and attempted to modify or remove obstructions to fish migration caused by dikes or dams. The Tweed was henceforth to be governed by Commissioners, a body consisting of all those owning salmon fishings having an annual value of £30 or a prescribed length of river-bank.

In 1858 a special Act, modelled on the Tweed Bill, was passed to deal with the Tay.

In 1862 and 1868 came fishery laws for all Scottish rivers north of the Tweed except the Tay, the first comprehensive revision in many centuries.

These Acts resulted in the appointment of Commissioners who determined the limits of each river district, the point in each estuary above which fixed nets might not be used, together with a point farther upstream dividing the proprietors into upper and lower groups. The Acts also created a system of district boards, selected in equal numbers from the rolls of upper and lower proprietors, which were responsible for the general policing and oversight of the fisheries. The annual close time was extended to 168 days a year and the weekly close time fixed at 36 hours. This closure was extended to 42 hours and penalties for poaching were greatly increased by an Act of 1951. Otherwise the fishery code established a century ago is still substantially in force in Scotland.

Since formation of a district board was not made compulsory and the initiative rests with the owners, there are only 45 boards out of the 107 salmon fishery districts in Scotland. These, however, cover all the major salmon streams.[20]

It was widely recognized that the nineteenth-century Scottish Salmon Acts were weaker than the English. For instance, the Commissioners had no power to make annual or biennial inspections of the fishery and issue reports, as they did in England. In fact, the district boards had very little power. They could not move against polluters, said Archibald Young in 1877, remove obstructions to fish migration, or prevent overfishing. The initiative for conservation was largely left with the individual owners. In some instances, as for example on the Spey and Nith, they worked together to limit exploitation of fish runs, restocked barren waters with salmon ova and fry, and made other improvements.

As regards the Tweed Acts, Commissioners Spencer Walpole and Archibald Young, reporting to the Secretary of State for Scotland in 1875, concluded that they 'have failed . . . for the following reasons: (1) The increasing pollution of the river, and (2) the wholesale poaching which is practised on it. Sections 65 and 66 of the Act of 1857 deal with the first of these subjects, and forbid the pollution of the Tweed by noxious substances or rubbish; but, unfortunately . . . they have proved utterly inadequate to prevent this great and yearly increasing evil, and at the moment the sewage of all the towns on their banks, and the dye-stuffs and refuse from all the mills and manufactories, are poured . . . into the Tweed and its tributaries.'

Tough anti-poaching measures did not come for three-quarters of a century: the Salmon and Freshwater Fisheries (Protection) Act of 1951 is probably the most severe statute of its kind enacted in any land except Spain.

Simple poaching–fishing for salmon with rod and line without the owner's written permission–is now punishable by a substantial fine and forfeiture of the rod and fish. As the poaching becomes more severe by the use of illegal devices (chemicals and the like) or the number of people involved, fines rise steeply to £500 or two years' imprisonment, or both, together with confiscation of the catch, gear, and even the bus or vehicle used by the poachers. The prospective punishments can now be made sufficiently expensive to give the wealthiest poacher food for thought. Restrictions were also placed on the shipment of salmon to close any loopholes that might exist for black marketing.

Scotland was provided with a Rivers (Prevention of Pollution) Act in 1961, hailed as a belated step forward in the fight for clean waters. This measure was strengthened in 1965. It is now an offence to discharge any factory or mill wastes into rivers, streams and watercourses without the consent of the River Purification Authority. Those who applied for consent before a specified date would be protected from prosecution. The Act also makes it illegal to bring into use any new or altered outlets for, or to begin to make new discharges of, effluents or sewage in certain tidal waters without the approval of the authorities. In a schedule appended to the law, various estuaries around Scotland where pollution has been detrimental to fish runs, are included among 35 controlled waters; other tidal waters can be added to the forbidden zones by the Secretary of State to ensure that existing conditions will not deteriorate. Anyone found guilty of contravening the Act is subject to fines rising from £100 ($280) per day the first time to a limit of £1,000 ($2,800) per day, or six months in prison or both, for repeated offences.

Dams vs. fish

It was inevitable that some of the lochs and rivers of Scotland should be harnessed to generate the power an expanding economy needs. The earliest hydro-electric schemes were developments by the British Aluminium Company at the Falls of Foyers on the east side of Loch Ness in 1895, at Kinlochleven in 1906, and at Lochaber in 1921. These were followed by the harnessing of the falls of the Clyde in 1924 and the falls at Conon in Ross-shire in 1926, and the Grampian Electricity Company projects in 1930 and 1933. In American terms, these were all small developments, as was the Galloway scheme of the Galloway Water Power Company with a total capacity of 107,500 kilowatts in five generating stations, also opened in the 1930s. Some fish runs were affected but not on the scale of developments started after World War II. Figure 17 shows hydro-electric schemes completed in the British Isles to about 1960.

The British electric power industry was nationalized shortly after the end of World War II, including generation and distribution. The need for energy to supply new and growing industries and rising consumer demand was urgent. The British people were enjoying higher standards of living that required more household appliances and more electricity. Every year appliance sales increased and the use of power by industry accelerated, so that power requirements in the 1950s were doubling at the rate of every seven or eight years.

In the swift waters of the Highlands, tumbling down waterfalls and glens, sweeping with powerful current, resided a vast amount of energy which could be harnessed at relatively low cost, lower than generation from thermal sources. Large schemes for tapping these waters came under way after passage of the Hydro-Electric Development (Scotland) Act of 1943 which created an operating agency, the North of Scotland Hydro-Electric Board. A counterpart for southern Scotland was established, the South of Scotland Electricity Board. The bulk of the postwar hydro-electric development has been in the north, but the south of Scotland, with its concentrated population, consumes about five times the amount of power used in the north. The existence of coalfields in the central belt has led to the development of large thermal stations in that part of Scotland.

Highland electricity, transmitted long distances over the Highland grid, has been brought to both urban and rural districts, to isolated farms and crofts and cottages of farm and forestry workers who formerly lived in the pre-electrical age, as their nineteenth-century ancestors did. It has lessened drudgery and brightened lives, permitted cooking and heating of homes with electricity, the operation of power machines and the enjoyment of such amenities as radio and television. In south-west Scotland most dairy farms now have electrical equipment for milking cows and processing the milk. On some northern farms successful experiments have been conducted in drying hay by power while many rural industries are now based on electricity. The coming of power has made possible the establishment of small industries in the Highlands and provision of new jobs and thus has helped to stem the flow of population out of this depressed area. The postwar tourist boom too has been aided by the availability of electric power in remote areas.

In 1965 there was a total of 1,047,000 kilowatts of capacity installed in the north of Scotland–the equivalent of one major dam on the Columbia River–mostly in small plants. An additional 400,000 kilowatts of capacity were under construction and other projects were under consideration.

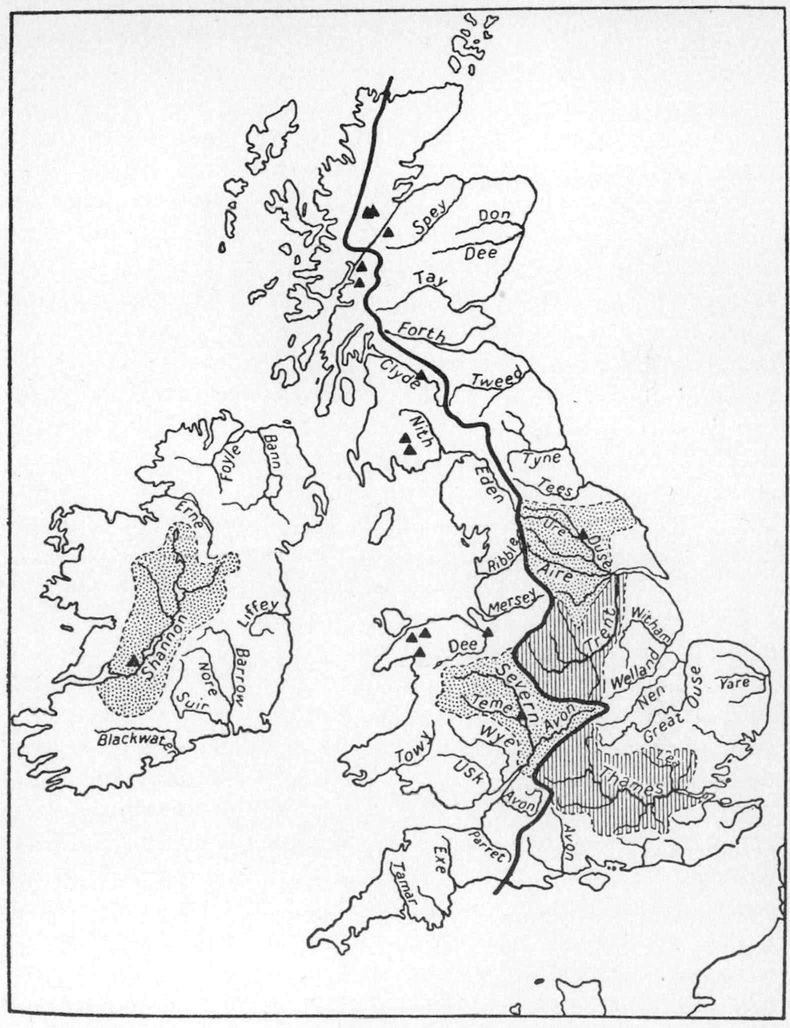

Figure 17

Rivers of British Isles showing hydro-electric schemes (1960).

Many of the northern Scottish river developments have affected the salmon fisheries. Of the 35 fishery districts which in 1963 reported a catch of at least 3,000 salmon, grilse and sea-trout, nine are affected by hydro-electric schemes, including the Conon, Ness and Tay. The dams have created barriers to fish migration while the new reservoirs have eliminated salmon spawning and feeding grounds.

Parliament has specified that all schemes undertaken by the Electricity Boards 'shall have regard to the desirability of avoiding as far as possible injury to fisheries and the stock of fish in any waters'. This rather loose language has been interpreted to mean that every development must satisfy all the interests affected.

'The only way to make a success, from all points of view, of a hydro-electric scheme', says Menzies, fishery consultant to the North of Scotland Hydro-Electric Board, 'is for all interests to consult together at the earliest stage possible. . . . Sometimes there are, of course, differences of opinion or differences of view which cannot be reconciled.

'The normal procedure is for a scheme first of all to be selected from mere map inspection. The engineers then make preliminary inspections and investigations to discover the possibilities, especially of sites for dams and power stations. As soon as this work has proceeded far enough, the fishery interests concerned are told of the proposals and their reactions are considered.

'The preliminary proposals indicate the nature of the works intended, and the arrangements of waterflows to safeguard fish. Discussion on this basis continues and the whole matter is referred to the Statutory Fisheries Committee who have to advise both the Hydro Board and the Government.

'Finally, all the arrangements for fish passes, water flows, hatcheries, and so on, in fact, all the measures for the protection of the fish may be agreed upon by all the interested parties.' A project does not get the green light until arrangements are acceptable to both the power and fishery people. If there is a seemingly irreconcilable conflict, the Secretary of State for Scotland refers the matter to a Commissioner, 'who hears expert evidence and legal arguments from both sides and reports with recommendations to the Secretary of State'.[21] These recommendations form the basis for an agreement so that the plan adopted will be best for the nation as a whole. The proposed hydro-electric development then goes to Parliament for approval.

Among the measures taken to safeguard the stocks of anadromous fish are passes to permit the salmon to surmount the dams, traps to enable adult migrants to be taken and stripped of their eggs and milt, hatcheries in which the fertilized eggs are incubated, and 'facilities such as the easing of obstacles to enable salmon to reach previously unused spawning grounds'. Fish passes have only been provided at those dams where spawning grounds remain in the river system above them. In other words, where spawning areas have been flooded out above an impoundment no fish ladder or lift is provided. Instead the upstream migrants are stopped at a barrier. After their eggs are incubated the fry are planted in suitable waters where they can develop naturally. Hatcheries have been built at Contin, Invergarry, Pitlochry and Inverawe. Only a relatively small number of fry are kept for feeding up to the yearling parr and smolt stages.

To offset the loss of spawning gravels, the North of Scotland Hydro-Electric Board has opened up some waterfalls which were impassable to salmon so as to provide access to new stretches of rivers like the Lochay and the Braan.

The Tummel-Garry scheme in the Tay watershed (Figure 18) offers a good example of how fish problems are handled. Water is collected from a catchment area of the Highlands in central Perthshire. A 12-mile tunnel conducts the water from many streams to a new reservoir built in the upper part of Glen Errochty, while another six miles long carries it from there to the Errochty station (75,000 kilowatt capacity) at the western end of Loch Tummel. At the eastern end of this loch a dam was constructed which enlarges the loch and raises its level by 15 feet, and thus converts it into a reservoir. Thence a tunnel aqueduct carries water to the Clunie plant (61,200 kilowatts) on Loch Faskally which is really a reservoir created in the valley by a dam at Pitlochry. Here there is a small power plant (15,000 kilowatts). Altogether the Tummel group contains eight generating stations with total installed capacity of 245,000 kilowatts.

Salmon anglers understandably bemoaned the flooding of the River Tummel, where good runs of fish used to come up as far as the Falls of Tummel. Only during high water could fish ascend this cataract. There was talk in Grimble's day of laddering the falls, but it came to naught. Sometimes baskets were hung on each side to catch the fish that fell back in their leaps. Faskally water, which comprised both banks of the Tummel for several miles below Clunie Bridge, offered, said Grimble, 'as fine a bit of angling as is to be found in Scotland'.[22] It no longer exists.

At Clunie dam there is a ladder consisting of 35 pools connected

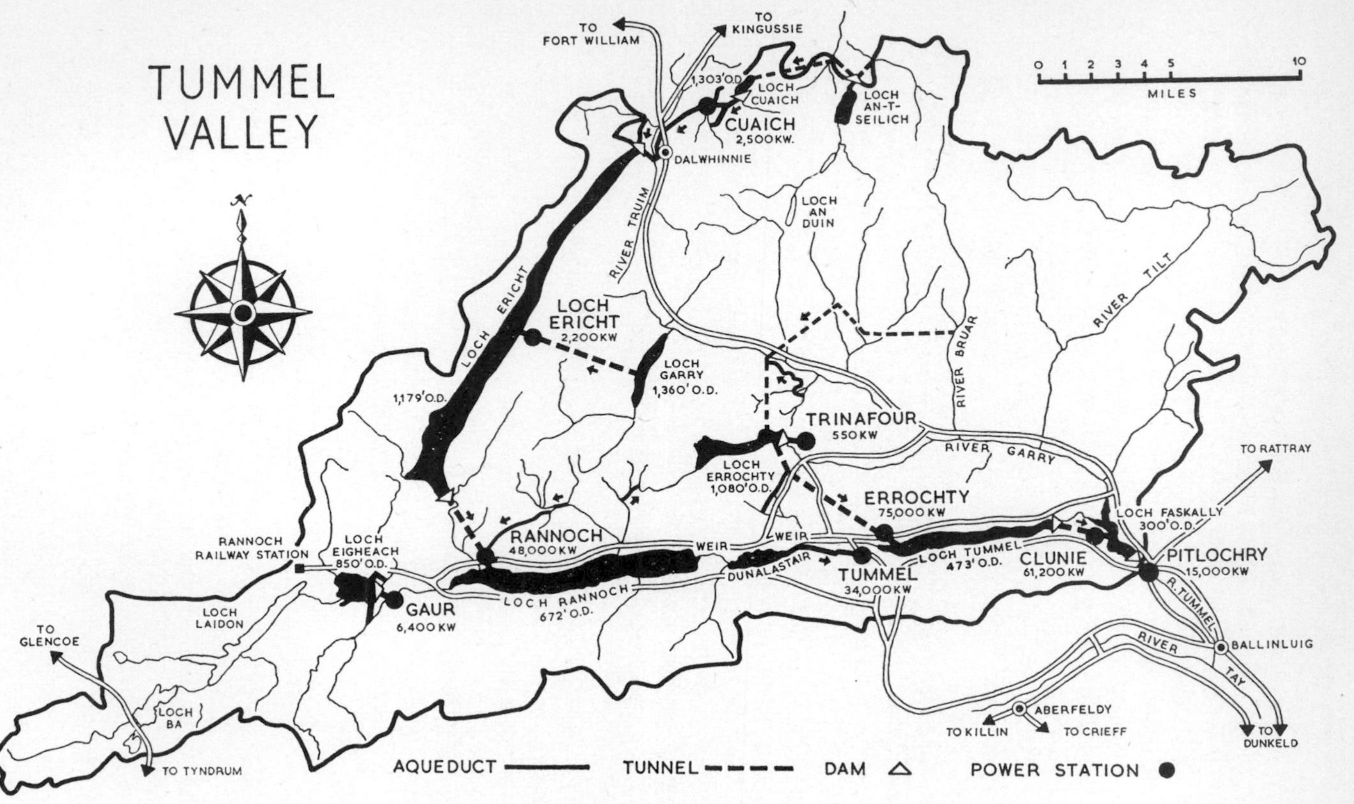

Figure 18

Tummel Valley hydro-electric scheme.

by submerged pipes which enables the salmon to negotiate the concrete barrier, reach the reservoir and resume their spawning journey. One can see the silvery fish patiently climb the ladder in ones and twos and sometimes more. As they pass they are photographed automatically and counted by an electric recorder which distinguishes grilse, salmon and kelts. Smolts are diverted from the mouth of the tunnel to the fish pass by small meshed screens.

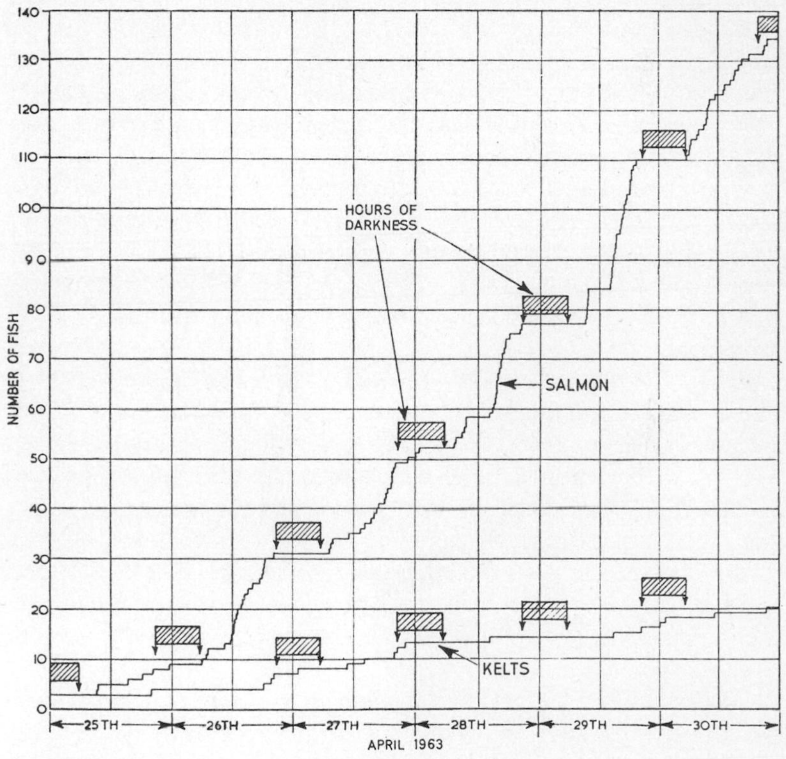

Figure 19

Fish movements recorded through Pitlochry Pass (recorder operated from a fish counter).

At Pitlochry dam the smolts can pass through the turbines, though some of them, of course, pass down the ladder. Here, too, the fish are counted and their movements studied (Figure 19).

Research has uncovered much knowledge about the migratory habits of the salmon in Scotland. Counting of kelts at Pitlochry dam reveals that the majority descend in two waves, the first during November and December until the water temperature falls below 40 degrees F., and the second when the water temperature rises to 40–45 degrees F. in the spring. It has also been learned that fish will not move up the ladders at all times of the year with equal readiness. Temperature seems to be the main factor in the spring, as fish will not ascend until the water reaches 41–42 degrees F. Sometimes they will move freely and at other times few will appear at the ladders for weeks. If there is a series of dams in a river they may hurdle one obstruction and then linger and delay the attempt to pass another.

Projects built after the Tummel scheme was completed in 1952 are equipped with fish locks developed by the Scottish engineer Joseph Borland and first successfully used at Leixlip on the River Liffey in Ireland (Figure 20). There are now 11 pool-type and 17 Borland passes in the north of Scotland system and four pool-type passes operated by the South of Scotland Hydro-Electricity Board,

The Borland lock is a simple device, consisting essentially of two chambers, one of which is completely enclosed at the river level immediately downstream of the dam and the other is enclosed at the level of the impoundment above. The pools are joined by a sloping or vertical shaft. Water flows out through a sluice to attract fish into the lower pool. From time to time the lower sluice is closed so that water rises in the shaft until it reaches the level of the upper pool. The fish rise with the water and when the lock is opened they swim out into the reservoir and head upstream. After a sufficient interval the bottom sluice is opened and the cycle begins again. Electronic devices count and may photograph the fish going through the lock.

The most pressing problem in passing fish over dams is to safeguard the finger-size smolts and the kelts. Since most of the water must go through the turbines, downstream migrants will flow with the stream unless they are deflected. In stations equipped with Kaplan-type turbines with heads of about 100 feet or less, smolts are usually allowed to go through the revolving blades. Kelts are too large to take this route and have to be deterred by means of grids or screens. However, the passage of downstream migrants is not always as easy as this. Smolts which find themselves in a long and deep body of artificially-impounded water may not behave normally.

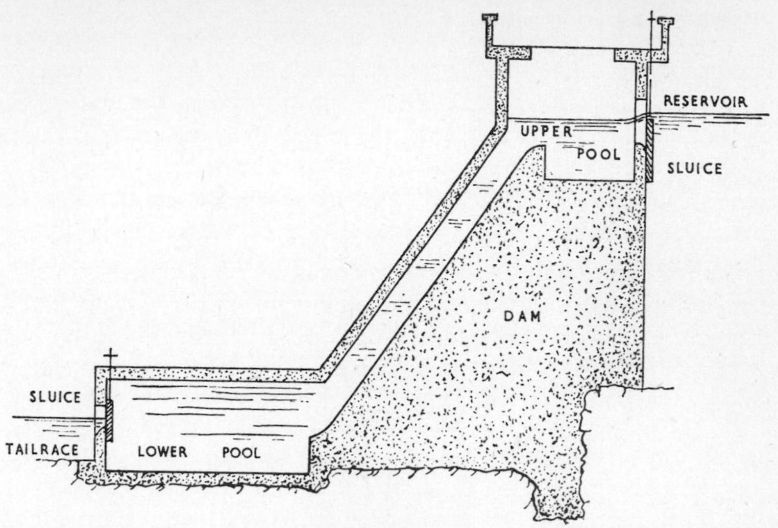

Figure 20

Borland type fish lift.

K. A. Pyefinch, director of the Freshwater Fisheries Laboratory at Pitlochry, says that 'there is no evidence that smolt deaths are caused by pressure changes during passage through the turbines; nor are Scottish dams high enough to cause heavy mortality to young fish going over spillways'.[23]

That there is nevertheless a certain loss of kelts and smolts at dams is obvious but no valid statistical data are available to measure it. At the Galloway project in south Scotland there was a progressive falling off in the salmon runs at least until 1956 and 1957, 'possibly attributable to predation by pike in the lochs, but the most striking fact is that this highly artificial system has continued to carry a fair stock of salmon for over twenty years which it would not have done if an appreciable proportion of the smolts were being killed or injured in the turbines through which they are allowed to pass at all three generating stations'.[24]

What has been the impact of the Scottish hydro-electric projects on the salmon runs? Table 18 suggests that at most of the installations the runs are being maintained but at others, such as Lairg, there has been a sharp decline, while in some cases–for example,

Pitlochry and Meig–there has been a decline followed by some recovery.

Many anglers have watched the usurpation of beauteous Highland streams, where they were accustomed to enjoy glorious sport, with apprehension and sometimes with bitterness. Everywhere that salmon resides the *aficionados* of the hook and line cast malevolent eyes at engineers, builders and all those who seek to dam, obstruct or impair the sparkling waters where salmon and trout and other fish are wont to breed and dwell. The lamentations and diatribes hurled against hydro-electric schemes in Scotland are similar to those heard in Spain, France, Finland, and perhaps most vocally in Canada and the United States. Must the power planners spoil rivers teeming with fish? Cannot other methods of generating electricity be found, especially atomic energy, so that no more rivers will be sacrificed to this Moloch? I have heard fishermen and biologists even voice the question whether we need electricity at all if it means destruction of fisheries and favourite rivers. On the other hand, a few proponents of hydro-electric schemes speak as if they wished the salmon would utterly vanish and thus remove all opposition to their plans.

Reconciliation of die-hard lovers of the fishery to harnessing their favourite rivers seems to be impossible; some of them eventually, fatalistically, accept the fact that progress, so to speak, cannot be stemmed. Others never yield. Typical of the former is the viewpoint expressed in the London *Times* of March 23, 1963, by a Scottish angler:

'In general,' he says, 'Highland opinion, traditionally empirical, is becoming less pessimistic in regard to the survival of salmon in power-harnessed rivers. They recognize the increasing experience of the Board's personnel, and the degree of success which they now achieve.'

An opposite view is taken by Arthur Oglesby (*Trout and Salmon*, February 1965), who claims that rivers like the Tay, Tummel and Garry have paid a very high price for 'the doubtful benefits of increased electricity'. Looking at the Awe, where magnificent pools were drowned by rearrangement of the river, but where the stock and catches have been well maintained, he quotes an old gillie who had fished these waters for over forty years: 'It's not the river I knew.'

Table 18

Numbers of salmon (including grilse) passing through fish passes at hydro-electric dams in Scotland, 1951–1965

Year	Mucomir Barragg	Pitlochry	Clunie	Lairg Dam	Lairg Diversion	Tor Achilty	Meig	Luichart	Dundreggan	Invergarry	Kilmorack	Aigas
1951		5,630										
1952		5,790										
1953		5,368	268									
1954		5,357	424									
1955		4,182	142			3,019						
1956		3,555	118			2,283				596		
1957		4,339	95	638		3,217	613			515		
1958		3,513	77	404	550	1,557	256	73	235	559		
1959		3,074	124	304	402	2,027	246	269	316	783		
1960		3,930	113	602	562	1,793	220	289	368	954		
1961		3,741	122	409	437	743	149	93	322	750		
1962		3,998	158	170	317	1,277	231	96	331	770		
1963	951	4,353	167	168	249	1,644	375	254	456	753	9,832	7,436
1964	621	4,522	228	89	97	2,338	479	384	370	409	11,200	10,896
1965	959	4,558	168	199	239	2,883	829	526	347	378	8,900	8,641

Source: North of Scotland Hydro-Electric Board, *Reports and Accounts*, January 1, 1964 to March 31, 1966.

Seals and salmon

The animals who prey on the salmon in its various stages are legion, ranging from seals, porpoises and numerous fish to a variety of water birds. Relatively little can be done to control these predators with the possible exception of the grey seals that have become a serious menace off the coast of north England and Scotland.

The grey is a winsome, sad-eyed creature, the rarest among the world's species of seals, numbering perhaps only 50,000. There are three main groups, inhabiting the west Atlantic, east Atlantic, and Baltic Sea. Substantial colonies dwell in the Orkney and Shetland islands, the Hebrides, and other places off the north-west coast of Scotland, while lesser groups are found in the Farne islands, off the Pembrokeshire coast, and around Ireland.

Larger than the common seal, the grey is a sleek animal, weighing 550 to 650 pounds. He breeds on exposed rocky coasts and likes to prowl the estuaries of rivers, feeding on whatever fish come his way, especially salmon and cod. He brazenly enters the river and catches fish off the breakwater, as at Berwick-on-Tweed. He haunts the nets on the coast, quickly nabs a fish and moves out before a keen-eyed watcher can spot him and take aim with his rifle. In fact, it is difficult to shoot a swimming seal, especially in fading light. Rae and Shearer in their exhaustive study, 'Seal Damage to Salmon Fisheries', report that in the years 1956 to 1961 only 55 of these animals were killed at the Sandstell fishing station near the mouth of the Tweed and 117 in the Tweed area as a whole.[25]

The extent of seal depredations off the Northumberland and Scottish coasts has long been a subject of controversy. Fishermen claimed that the colonies in the islands of Farne, Orkney and Shetland are multiplying too rapidly. They pointed to the large numbers of fish bearing claw marks in their catches, to torn nets, and to mutilated dead salmon frequently washed ashore.[26] They urged that the animals be removed from the protection they have enjoyed since 1914.

On the basis of scientific studies of the problem, notably by the

---

15a. Fisherman on footrope of fly or stake net near Montrose, Scotland.
15b. Scottish bag net on net green showing 'small door' or final entrance to trap.

Nature Conservancy, the British Government in 1963 agreed to permit the killing of calves and adult female seals as part of a five-year plan to curtail the breeding potential. Permits were granted fishermen to destroy the animals in their netting areas and hunters to shoot them during the breeding season (when they are legally protected) in the Orkneys and Shetlands as part of the culling programme. The slaughter, however, touched off public resentment.

It is difficult to assess the validity of the seal-culling programme. Fraser Darling, the ecologist who advised the Tweed Commissioners as long ago as 1940 to hunt down the seals frequenting the river–advice they did not take–argues that the killing of breeders is justified. 'A limited amount of disturbance of the grey seals will do no harm to them as a stock,' he says, 'because they will spread their breeding over more of the possible sites, rather than overcrowding on a few. Surely it is no lack of respect for life, but high courage to face the necessity of killing in order to conserve when the situation is so contrived that the creatures cannot be allowed their total range?'[27]

The drift-net fishery

Drift-netting is an ancient type of fishing for many kinds of fish. In Scotland it has been used mainly to catch herring, rarely for taking salmon. There was some drifting in the Tweed and other areas in the nineteenth century but it seems to have ended by a decision of the House of Lords declaring it illegal in 1900.

Almost without warning, the commercial salmon industry of Scotland was confronted in 1960 with the competition of drift-netters in the open sea. The year 1960, incidentally, also marked the start of drifting for salmon at sea off north Norway.

The beginning was modest enough. Six or eight boats about 45 feet long, with crews of four to six men, based at the Northumberland port of Seahouses, spent the months from January to April fishing for salmon outside the three-mile territorial limit. They used nets about 10 feet deep suspended from a corked head rope and

16. Cathaleen's Fall Station, River Erne, Ireland. Pool-type pass can be seen on left bank. Salmon successfully negotiate the pass.

weighted very lightly at the bottom or not at all. The size of net varied, but it was customary for boats of 40 to 50 feet to use twenty sections of net, each about 100 yards long. 'These sections were divided into two fleets, each consisting of about 1,000 yards of netting. When rigged and shot, each section would extend to about 800 yards in the water, so that each boat would be working in effect approximately one mile of drift net.'[28] At first the boats fished only at night, but later it was discovered that good catches could be made under suitable conditions in daylight.

When news leaked out that the Seahouses fishermen were having good luck, they were joined by boats from the Scotch ports of Eyemouth and Burnmouth. By the end of May, when the 1960 season ended, about 9,000 salmon had been landed by the drifters.

In 1961 the number of boats multiplied and the area of operations was extended. Larger craft came into the picture. As the season opened in January, the Seahouses fleet was competing with a dozen craft from Berwickshire ports. When their season ended in May, 13,000 to 15,000 salmon had been landed in the Tweed area, an increase of 50 per cent over the previous year. Towards the end of May drifting started off the east coast of Scotland around Montrose and by early July forty boats, mostly seiners and line fishing craft, from Arbroath and neighbouring ports, were pursuing the salmon. Operating outside territorial waters, they were under no restraint and could work every day of the week. Other drifters, some only 30 to 40 feet long, worked with fair success around Buckie, while a few plied the waters from east-coast ports such as Stonehaven, Aberdeen, Fraserburgh, Macduff and Helmsdale. It is estimated that about 42,000 salmon and grilse were caught by drifters in 1961, all on the east coast.

In 1962 the pace was greatly stepped up, for it seemed that a crew could make more money drifting for salmon, which fetched six to eight shillings per pound, than for herring or white fish, then in short supply in Scottish waters. At the peak of the season about 160 boats were engaged in salmon fishing, including herring drifters, creel fishing boats, line fishing boats and seiners. About sixty vessels worked the Tweed area alone. It was a good year, for before the season closed and the last boats had hauled in their nets and steamed home, some 115,000 fish were caught, equal to about 30 per cent of the total taken by nets on the Scottish coast and in the rivers.

Responding to the alarm of the salmon industry, the British Government on September 15, 1962, issued an order under the Sea Fishery Industry Acts of 1959 and 1962 forbidding drift-net fishing for salmon at sea and prohibiting the landing of fish caught in this manner in any port in the United Kingdom. The salmon 'mine' in the sea has not been worked since.

The Committee headed by Lord Hunter appointed by the Secretary of State for Scotland, to make a thorough study of salmon fishing in Scotland, took up this crucial problem. Its first report was issued in 1963 and final report in 1965.

What impact did drift-netting have on the resource and why was it stopped? The primary reason for terminating this lucrative fishery was the fear that it would lead to overfishing and thus reduce the numbers of salmon heading for the rivers and ultimately the escapement needed to perpetuate the crop. Catching salmon in large numbers at sea, whether in Greenland waters, off the coast of Norway, or in the Baltic, places a heavy and perhaps intolerable burden on the migrant stocks. The ban on drift-netting is regarded as a wise conservation measure. In contrast, Norway permits drift-netting to continue although it has created sanctuary areas where it is forbidden in order to protect the runs in northern rivers. In Ireland recent legislation enables the Minister of Lands to prohibit, restrict or otherwise control salmon fishing at sea as well as the landing of salmon caught at sea, and also makes illegal the mere possession of fish caught in defiance of this order.

The salmon industry

Scotland now produces usually as much salmon as any country in Europe (or Canada). About one-sixth of the harvest is taken by rod and line and the rest by nets. The major portion of the catch comes from the east coast since the most productive salmon rivers, such as the Tweed, Tay, North Esk, Dee and Spey, flow into the North Sea.

Netting is by means of fixed engines or traps along the coast and by net and coble in the lower stretches of the rivers. In the middle and upper stretches only rod and line fishing occurs. The most intensive net fishing is on the long stretch of coast facing the North Sea from Montrose to the Moray Firth. Here, as the shoals of fish come in from Greenland and elsewhere, their paths are barred by many hundreds of stationary traps called bag and fly nets.

The bag nets are anchored along the rocky coasts, sometimes 70 to 80 yards apart, each constituting a formidable wall of netting with a leader 80 to 100 yards long to guide the fish into the head or trap. Men come out at various times, according to the tides, in large wooden boats called cobles, usually equipped with an outboard motor, to inspect the nets and collect the fish. Fly nets are set between tidal high and low water on sandy shores, so that a man can clamber out along the ropes to the head before low water. Sometimes the net is destroyed in the white mist amid the furious waves breaking on the shore. The net may contain only a few or no salmon or as many as a hundred may be lifted in a tide.

When taken ashore to the netting station, the fish are boxed and iced and sent on their long journey to Billingsgate or other markets. Some of the inlets are so small and steep-walled that the boxes, as well as the nets for drying and cleaning, must be hoisted up from the beach to the top of the cliff.

The nets work night and day except for the 42-hour weekend close time, when the bag net leaders are brought to shore to dry, be checked and mended, if necessary. The heads of the fly nets are tied up on the poles, so that they are ineffective.

On the west coast, the bag nets are 50 to 100 yards from the shore on points of land such as Rhu Stoer, Rhu Coigach, Cailleach Point, Greenstone Point and Ardnamurchan, along the track of the fish migrating towards the sea lochs and river mouths.

The sea fishings on the West Highland coast are held by the lairds or by the Crown Estates Commissioners, and leased to individuals or companies who hire local labour.

In the rivers commercial fishing is permitted only with net and coble. The net is loaded on to the boat and attached to it is a rope carried by a fisherman on the shore. The coble moves slowly across the river, shooting the net as it goes. Its course is roughly a semicircle finishing at the landing ground where the crew in the boat are joined by the fisherman who carries the rope. The ends are then hauled in and the enclosed fish, flapping wildly, are removed. In this kind of fishing the net must be kept moving continuously. Where the tides are high and water turbulent the fishermen may be assisted by a power winch pulling the rope. The net must not be allowed to remain stationary or drift with the tide. Since the fish taken in the sweep are guided by the net, but are not enmeshed in it, the gear can be used for catching fish of different size, including small grilse and sea-trout. The season usually begins in February and lasts till the end of August.

The fishermen are employed by the fishing companies. Many of them come from distant places and live in 'bothies' near the fisheries. Their life is hard while the fish are running. They have no regular hours, work in foul weather or fair, and must always keep their equipment in good repair. They may not see their families for weeks at a time, and then only for a day or two. But the tang of the sea is in their nostrils and the love of fishing in their blood. They are paid relatively well. When the season ends and boats and nets are taken to the storehouse, many return to their homes to work as labourers or while away the winter in idleness. A few are kept by the companies, repairing nets.

Anglers' Eden

King Edward VII and his son George V gave royal cachet to salmon fishing in Scotland and brought a number of aristocrats in their train to the River Dee. The royal family owned eight miles of one bank of this stream and leased about nine miles. The Queen Mother fishes for salmon fairly frequently and Queen Elizabeth and the Duke of Edinburgh also fish when they are in Scotland.

As in other countries, the sport has been democratized in recent years. A person may fish for a few pounds a season on waters controlled by an association or club, or hire a beat at much greater expense from an hotel or private owner. The fisherman on association waters, usually hard fished, must be content with a dozen salmon a year or less, while the angler on a more exclusive preserve may take dozens in a week at the peak of the season. There are no bag limits.

The growing demand for salmon fishing, however, is making it difficult for clubs to obtain leases at reasonable rates, and thus the sport is moving out of the reach of the common man. Record prices have been paid in recent years for prime sections of rivers: £40,000 ($112,000) for a stretch of the Ness and Dee, and £420,000 ($1,176,000) for the famous Balnagoun estates in Ross-shire with fishings on the minor rivers Carron, Cassley and Oykell.

Salmon anglers nowadays constitute a cross-section of the people.

There are working folk as well as peers of the realm, bankers, industrialists, bishops and retired colonels. They belong to clubs like the Sports and Social Club of the National Cash Register Company which has factories in Dundee and leases a stretch of the Tay for the benefit of its employees. Some of the workers come out every night and weekend during the season. There is a limit of six fish a day.

In the city of Perth, where the local authority owns the fishing in the Tay, one may fish for a shilling a day. Above Perth there is a stretch of the river, purchased by a group of London businessmen from Lord Mansfield, where angling costs £15 daily, including the use of two boatmen. It is very difficult for an outsider to hire a beat on the Tay during the spring and autumn, while in the summer, when the run is slack, one can find a beat but may not land a fish. This situation prevails on many prime rivers although the Hunter Committee Report of 1965 says there are waters which are underfished, presumably for lack of anglers, and the gillies are instructed to catch salmon for sale when the proprietor himself is not fishing.

Another opportunity of fishing on a shoe-string is offered in the Highlands by the Strathspey Angling Improvement Association at Grantown-on-Spey. The organization was formed in 1914 after the Countess of Seafield and other proprietors, having forced the whisky distillers to keep their burnt ale out of the river, agreed to lease a stretch of the Spey at a token rental of ten shillings per annum. The Seafield estates have permitted this arrangement to continue.

The Spey is a fast river, flowing through rocky and gravelly pools amidst pine trees, with the snow-capped Cairngorms in the distance. Grantown has a wide choice of hotels where the fishermen congregate. Every morning the well-to-do anglers take off in their Bentleys and Rovers for the famous beats at Tulcan, Cromdale and Knockando while the others, carrying their own gear, walk or cycle the short distance to the public waters.[29]

Scotland is famous for salmon angling exploits. An all-time record was set on the little River Grimersta in the Island of Lewis by a Mr. Naylor in 1888. The creation of an artificial spate sent shoals of fish upstream. Naylor caught 214 salmon weighing 1,307 pounds and 304 sea-trout in 19 days. In one day he fished for nine hours and quit with an hour and a half of daylight remaining, saying he was tired of the slaughter. Several times he landed two salmon at once. It was on the Grimersta that in 79 days beginning July 15, 1873, five rods took with the fly 913 salmon weighing 6,300 pounds and 1,073 sea-trout.

The record for massive catches belongs to Alfred Denison, who fished the Tweed and Ness for twenty-seven years, from 1860 to 1887, when he killed with his own rod a total of 4,600 salmon and grilse, an average of 170 each year. A bachelor, he devoted nearly all his time in later life to the sport and in fact fished almost to the day of his death. 'It was remarked of him that he never threw a better or straighter line than on the Saturday (before his death); but the over-exertion and a chill proved too much for him.'[30]

The largest salmon ever taken by rod in Scotland weighed 70 pounds and was killed by the Earl of Home, ancestor of the former Prime Minister, on the Tweed about 1730. Next are a 67-pounder caught on the Nith in 1812 by the notorious poacher, Jock Wallace, and a 64-pounder hooked by Miss G. W. Ballantine on the Tay in 1922. Fish from the Tweed, Tay and Awe are most numerous in the list of record-size (50 pounds and over) rod-caught British salmon; specimens from the Dee, Spey, Don and Deveron also appear.

The Scottish resource today

The condition of the Scottish salmon runs and their future is of concern to many people, not only river owners, commercial and sports fishermen, but the tourist industry, manufacturers of boats, gear and the like, and the public generally. The value of salmon taken in the commercial fishery is about £1,200,000 ($3,360,000) annually.

The major forces working against the resource are much the same as in other industrialized countries: (1) destruction of habitat, chiefly through pollution; (2) probably overfishing; and (3) radical alteration of river systems as a result of hydro-electric developments and other impoundments. An underlying problem is Scotland's failure to develop an adequate system of administration comparable to the river authorities, formerly river boards, of England and Wales, equipped with power to protect and conserve the inland fisheries.

Pollution has had a serious impact on some of Scotland's rivers. H. D. Turing's survey of Scottish rivers for the British Field Sports Society in 1946 revealed the deterioration of some of the best streams owing to 'indifference . . . procrastination or reluctance . . . [and]

neglect'. He found that the Dee, which contained valuable salmon fishings that brought yearly rentals of £33,000, was relatively clean for the most part, thanks to the power of the city of Aberdeen by its water acts to prevent pollution. However, there were bad spots, as below the paper mill at Culter: a hundred yards above the mill the burn hummed with life, with 'nymphs of the March Brown and olive types, caddis, shrimp, and some snails. . . . The bottom had a healthy growth of water moss and algae on every stone.' Below the mill the picture was quite different. 'The bottom was covered with dirty brown scum, no weeds were apparent, except a few rushes, and no life, except a few tubifex worms, seemed to exist.' This dead water, sometimes bearing soapy foam on the surface, generally at the end of a day's operation, could be traced far below the point where the burn entered the Dee on the left bank.

The River Don appeared to be fairly pure or badly polluted, depending on the height of the water. 'It is likely that the salmon runs up the Don are much less than they should be . . . due largely to pollutions which occur mostly in the lower reaches and affect the salmon smolts on their way to the sea, though man-made obstructions and abstraction of water at mills also play their part.'[31]

What of the Forth, once one of the richest waters in Scotland? 'Its decay . . . has been evident for forty years, and it is now in imminent danger of extinction . . . due almost entirely to the foully polluted state of its estuary, which is increased by the pollution of many of the streams entering it.' Sewage from the city of Stirling and noxious discharges from factories along the river-bank flowed into the long, winding estuary, so that upstream-bent fish could enter only at the risk of asphyxiation while smolts had to descend through water low in oxygen content. The Forth, concluded Turing, 'is quite obviously approaching extinction as a salmon river'.[32] In 1965 the Hunter Committee commented, 'We hope that this unfortunate example of how a salmon river can decline will not be forgotten.'

Ayrshire rivers such as the Ayr, Stinchar, Doon and Irvine used to support a thriving netting industry at their mouths and provide a reasonable amount of sport. The net catches had fallen sadly, reported Turing, 'although all hold a small stock of salmon capable of being nursed back to remunerative proportions when, and if, the state of the waters allows, and the baneful effects of an earlier age, when manufacturers and local communities treated the rivers as open sewers, will be overcome'. Constructive action was already started by the Ayrshire County Council which ran a sewer the length of the Irvine Valley, taking in the sewage of Kilmarnock and smaller communities along the river and passing it directly to the sea. 'The river [Irvine] is recovering rapidly and is now fairly clear and pure . . . with a small run of salmon . . . and there is good hope that in a comparatively few years, when the old deposits on the river bed have finally oxydized away, [it] will recover completely.'[33]

Alas for the much-abused Tweed! 'The present-day harvest is only a shadow of its stock 200 years ago. Much of the trouble comes from woollen mills in the watershed, washing their soapy effluents into the streams, like the blanket mill at Cumledge; also untreated, or partly treated sewage from towns.' Typical of the ruined Tweed watershed was the little River Jed, which received the wastes disgorged by several woollen mills, a tannery and silk mill, plus domestic sewage from the town of Jedburgh.

The Clyde was fortunate in coming almost entirely under the control of the Lanarkshire County Council, whose officials 'have been commendably active in fighting pollution and are rapidly restoring this attractive river to something like its original state of purity.' All small towns and larger villages in the county proper had installed or were planning to install sewage-treatment plants. However, coal-mine washeries were still a source of sporadic contamination although most of them were now equipped with at least settlement tanks. Industrial effluents continued to be washed straight into the rivers; for example, the South Calder 'has the reddish brown appearance of a gas works effluent and all life is extinct, both animal and vegetable'.

In Glasgow the scene was deplorable. Here the Clyde was a foul-looking river where fish could not live. Much of the salmon stock had been killed off by industrial and domestic pollutions in the nineteenth century, and in any case, they could not hurdle the falls of Lanark to get to the upper reaches, although they used to spawn below this point when the river was crystalline.

Salmon still ran up the Leven, which issued from Dumbarton Valley a few miles below Renfrew, a town that once owned fisheries of considerable value. These had vanished, yet this tidal water, like the tributaries Kelvin and Cart, could be rather easily purified with modern methods, according to Turing.

On the productive border stream, the Nith, the catch had dropped sharply in the twentieth century primarily because the twin towns of Dumfries and Maxwelltown, harbouring grain and feed mills, textile plants, a rubber plant, and other works, discharged their poisonous wastes practically untreated into the waters. Sewage sludge emanating from the towns (total population 25,000) built up in the channel to a depth of two or three feet through which no fish could penetrate once it had been churned up by tidal action. Pollution was not the only cause of ruin: overnetting below the weir, where such fish that managed to negotiate the foul water collected in a pool, was a contributing factor. There were also obstructions upstream. And so it went.

In recent years, a few of the Scottish rivers such as the Nith were given a new lease on life thanks partly to anti-pollution legislation. First, nationalization of the coal industry brought a more conservation-conscious management, and the upper waters, cleansed of coal murk that was fatal to every aquatic organism, is now a reasonably healthy stream. Between New Cumnock and Dumfries two obsolete sewage plants are being replaced and a third is being extended. On the tidal river, a purification plant came into operation in 1958, so that comparatively clean water is now available to ascending fish and smolts are provided with a safe exodus to the sea. The Solway River Purification Board, constituted in 1953 under the 1951 River Purification Act, hopes to clean up all the rivers in its jurisdiction, including tidal waters and estuaries, in terms of an Order issued by the Secretary of State in 1962.[34] Netting has ceased in burgh waters and a programme of restocking with salmon eggs brought to the eyed stage has begun. The salmon have responded to these improvements and catches have risen steadily from the low point of less than 200 in the mid-1940s to over 2,765 by rod and line in 1964. The future of the Nith looks bright from the fisherman's point of view.

Some of the contaminated rivers examined by Turing had not improved by 1965, when the Hunter Committee studied them. The Clyde and Forth and their tributaries presented the worst examples but the Don, Spey and others were also subject to heavy pollution in places. There were threats of greater defilements arising from advancing industrialization and increasing use of chemicals in agriculture and food processing. Moreover, said the Committee, 'new agricultural developments, such as intensive rearing [of chickens] in broiler houses, give rise to effluents which may not be poisonous in themselves but can cause harm to fish life'. The Committee hoped that the 1951 and 1965 River Purification Acts for Scotland 'would bring about an improvement in the condition of polluted rivers, provided that River Purification Boards and Authorities use their powers' in such a way 'as to secure at least that all waters which now sustain fish life will continue to do so, and . . . that in time some waters which have ceased to support a stock of migratory fish may once again do so'.[35]

Much of the stimulus for fishery conservation in Scotland has come from the owners. Some barriers to upstream and downstream migration have been removed; excessive netting in the estuaries has been reduced or controlled in several localities, as in the Nith; cruives or traps were eliminated in the upper waters; depopulated streams were restocked with salmon fry or eyed ova by owners, sometimes under the stimulus of angling clubs.

The expansion of hydro-electric development poses a continuing potential threat to maintenance of the runs in affected river systems. The Hunter Committee in 1965 noted that no new major construction had been approved for six years but that projects totalling 400,000 kilowatts, or 40 per cent of existing capacity, might be added in north Scotland by 1980.

While it is difficult to measure or assess the impact of hydro-electric developments on anadromous fisheries, even where, as in Scotland and the western United States, costly efforts are made to cushion the damage by providing the best-known means of passing fish over dams and restocking rivers, there is surely some loss. We know very little as yet about the ecological changes resulting from reservoir construction. The most obvious change is that part of a fast-flowing river has been transformed into a slack-water reservoir; less obvious are the environmental modifications below the dam. Water flow and temperature are altered, both daily and seasonally, especially by fluctuations in drawdown; turbidity is lessened, thus affording less protection to the fish; and frequently the chemical composition of the water is affected. All these changes in habitat, added to the need of climbing a series of ladders or being lifted by locks, may be quite detrimental to the salmon.

Partly because of the advent of hydro-electric projects on some of Scotland's best salmon rivers, a stepped-up programme of fishery research was launched some years ago. The Freshwater Fisheries Laboratory at Pitlochry, maintained by the Department of Agriculture and Fisheries for Scotland, has made numerous investigations of the salmon's efforts to survive in both natural and man-made environments–including its migrations across the ocean. Under the direction of K. A. Pyefinch it has published many scientific studies which have added enormously to our knowledge of the life history and migrations of *Salmo salar*. The Laboratory is probably the pre-eminent salmon research institution in Europe.

The North of Scotland Hydro-Electric Board maintains a laboratory at Pitlochry which specializes in the development of devices and know-how designed to facilitate the passage of salmon over dams and through reservoirs. It has pioneered the development of fish ladders, counting devices and other things that have been adopted by other countries.

So far as fish are concerned, conditions within a reservoir depend on many factors: depth, surface area and volume of the water; quality and quantity of inflow; operating schedule of the generating stations (that is, drawdown); etc. No two reservoirs have the same ecological conditions. Yet, about all we know with certainty is that a reservoir's productivity, so far as anadromous fish are concerned, tends to decrease within a number of years after its construction. This has been the experience on the Columbia-Snake Rivers, and it may be assumed to be paralleled elsewhere. However, much more research is needed, especially in Scotland, on the complex problems involved in preserving anadromous fish populations in rivers which carry one or more dams and impoundments.

The Hunter Committee's final report brings into focus essential elements of the problem of maintaining Scotland's still relatively ample salmon stocks. Its major recommendations deal with methods of harvesting the crop. For sound conservation purposes the fishery must be put on a sustained yield basis, yet without knowledge of the size of the runs in a river, this goal is impossible of formulation, much less of accomplishment. The Committee therefore proposes that the commercial catch in every river be taken at only one point by means of a grid or weir. 'Where trapping is impracticable, all net fishing should be concentrated at a single point on each river.' This would make it possible to count the runs and establish a basis for regulating both the catch and escapement, as is now done on the Shannon River in Ireland and the Columbia in the United States. The Committee's recommendation, if adopted, would mean the elimination of coastal netting by fixed engines and by net and coble. All offshore fishing for salmon would continue to be prohibited.[36]

The Committee's other major recommendation would replace the existing district boards, which consist mainly of proprietors, with area boards, but no clear-cut additional powers are spelled out for them.

Finally, the Committee proposes that a system of licensing both anglers and sports fishermen be introduced, a step that seems long overdue. It also recommends that a Scottish Anglers' Trust be established to develop angling both for visitors and residents, a move that would stimulate the tourist industry which is vital to the prosperity of the Highlands.

Whether these proposals will be implemented nobody can say. 'It is no surprise', said *The Field* in commenting on the final Hunter Report, 'that the Committee themselves seem resigned to the idea that nothing much will happen for twenty years or so.'

Since the Hunter Committee's final report was published in 1965

Table 19

Salmon and grilse catches in Scotland, 1954–1964

Year	*Salmon*		*Grilse*		*Total*	
	No.	*Weight*	*No.*	*Weight*	*No.*	*Weight*
1954	256,401	2,653,027	117,916	642,645	374,317	3,295,672
1955	252,109	2,665,496	136,015	678,122	388,124	3,343,618
1956	200,425	2,080,833	117,255	585,195	317,680	2,666,028
1957	217,157	2,103,424	196,974	1,012,995	414,131	3,116,419
1958	224,820	2,315,587	202,705	1,034,867	427,525	3,350,454
1959	270,157	2,744,365	116,109	605,362	386,266	3,349,727
1960	201,793	2,117,420	184,691	1,049,235	386,484	3,166,655
1961	179,917	1,808,469	156,286	828,039	336,203	2,636,508
1962	213,436	2,238,119	280,790	1,597,087	494,226	3,835,206
1963	267,295	2,835,182	166,906	909,077	434,201	3,744,259
*1964**	269,447	2,679,296	268,416	1,537,500	555,683	4,216,796

Sources: *Scottish Salmon and Trout Fisheries*, Second Report by the Committee appointed by the Secretary of State for Scotland, and *Fisheries of Scotland, Report for 1964*, Scottish Department of Agriculture and Fisheries.

*Provisional.

the revelation that salmon issuing from Scottish rivers were caught in the burgeoning Greenland fishery has created considerable apprehension. Menzies, for example, believes that this ocean fishing has already affected the Scottish catches. Although teams of international scientists have been studying the problem in the last few years, it is impossible as yet to assess the impact of huge Greenland catches of feeding stocks on any producing country. We know that the bulk of the tagged fish recovered so far off Greenland emanated from Canada, and the remainder came from the British Isles. All that can be said at the moment is that catches in the distant ocean will in time certainly reduce the number of fish who eventually return to their native lands and thus deplete the resource.

What has been the trend of salmon catches in recent times? Figure 21 and Table 19 indicate a fairly steady level of production, subject to customary fluctuations.

Fixed engines usually take about 55 per cent of the commercial catch, mainly on the coasts of Angus, Kincardine and Aberdeenshire, and net and cobles the rest, chiefly in the Tweed, South Esk, Dee and Spey districts. In 1964 rod fishermen landed 82,000 salmon.

It is difficult to appraise the present status of Scotland's salmon resource. It has not retrogressed in the last few decades. In contrast to England, no statistics are published for individual rivers, as these are regarded as trade secrets. However, according to Colonel R. M. Ryan, Superintendent to the River Tweed Commissioners, salmon catches in the Tweed have been around 40,000 annually in recent years, a considerable improvement since the end of the last century, but grilse catches are only a small fraction of those reported in the early 1800s. The Royal Commissions inquiring into the Tweed in 1876 and 1894 agreed that the major reasons for the obvious deterioration of the river in that century were land drainage, pollution and overfishing (including poaching). Since the passage of the 1951 anti-pollution Act the Tweed and some of its tributaries have been considerably purified; land drainage is not as great a hindrance to salmon as it used to be; and the harvests are reasonably controlled. Colonel Ryan concludes (in a personal communication of April 4, 1967) that 'the produce of the river (as opposed to catches) is greater now than in any period of its known existence. I do not think, except for one or two small tributaries, the Tweed could produce any more adult fish than it does at the moment'.

The Dee, though much less productive than the Tweed, has also

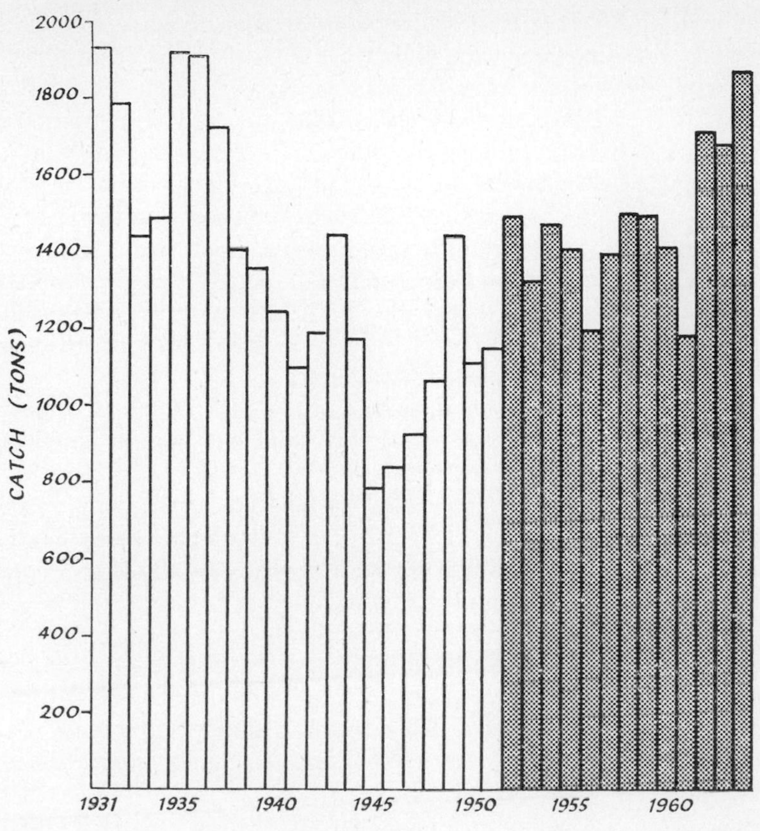

Figure 21

Scottish catches of salmon and grilse, 1931–1964. The blocks in black show actual catch statistics (as required by law in Scotland); figures for previous years are estimates based mostly on shipments of salmon to Billingsgate and elsewhere.

maintained a consistent output in recent years. In contrast, the salmon fisheries of other important rivers, such as the Clyde and Forth, have been virtually ruined. Still other rivers, on which hydro-electric developments have been built, such as the Tay and Tummel, have declined as salmon-breeding habitat.

All the evidence, in short, points to the conclusion that while Scotland remains one of the world's leading producers of Atlantic salmon, its stocks have considerably declined since the eighteenth century, although not in the same magnitude as those of England and Wales.

NOTES

1 W. J. M. Menzies, *The Salmon*, p. 72.
2 W. J. M. Menzies, *The Stock of Salmon*, pp. 58–60.
3 A. Thomazi, *Histoire de la Pêche*, p. 282.
4 Thomas Ashworth, 'Cultivation of a Salmon Fishery', an address delivered to the International Congress to Promote the Cultivation of Fisheries, 1866.
5 Thomazi, *op. cit.*, p. 283.
6 This anecdote, associated with many countries, can hardly be regarded as apocryphal even though no written proof has been found in Britain. Major-General R. N. Stewart, who fished for many years in Iceland, says that at the farms where he stayed, unless you protest, 'you are likely to have salmon for breakfast, lunch and dinner seven days a week. Now the first is delicious, but – to my taste – there is a sharply descending curve in the appetising value of salmon, and about the third day, I wish never to eat another.' (*Rivers of Iceland*, pp. 37–38.)
7 Quoted by Alex. Russel, *The Salmon*, pp. 92–93.
8 Henry Hamilton, *An Economic History of Scotland in the 18th Century*, pp. 360–1.
9 Quoted by Russel, *op. cit.*, p. 94.
10 *Ibid.*, p. 99.
11 *Ibid.*, p. 124.
12 Archibald Young, *Salmon Fisheries*, pp. 233–4.
13 Sir Herbert Maxwell, *Salmon and Sea Trout*, p. 9.
14 Thomas T. Stoddard, *Art of Angling*, p. 5.
15 *Ibid.*, p. 96.
16 Augustus Grimble, *The Salmon Rivers of Scotland*, p. 102.
17 For a concise and incisive account of the causes and effects of pollution, see H. D. Turing, *River Pollution.*
18 Archibald Young, *op. cit.*, pp. 248–9.
19 Augustus Grimble, *op. cit.*, p. 275.
20 *Scottish Salmon and Trout Fisheries*, First Report by the Committee appointed by the Secretary of State for Scotland, July 1963.
21 Personal communication, August 10, 1964.
22 Augustus Grimble, *op. cit.*, p. 288.
23 Personal communication, March 16, 1966.
24 'The Passage of Smolts and Kelts through Fish Passes', H.M.S.O. 1957.
25 B. B. Rae and W. M. Shearer, 'Seal Damage to Salmon Fisheries', p. 21.
26 Rae and Shearer provide considerable data on this subject. They report that in 1962 50 per cent of the salmon in some Scottish catches were seal-damaged, many of them so badly as to be unmarketable. They estimate

that the average annual monetary loss to the salmon fishing industry on the Scottish coast from all kinds of seal damage was £42,000 to £67,000 ($117,000 to $187,000).

27 Fraser Darling, 'Wildlife Conservation: The Ethical and Technical Problems', an occasional paper of the Conservation Foundation. The killing of seals is an established practice in the Columbia River where they prey on salmon.

28 First Report by the Committee appointed by the Secretary of State for Scotland, p. 20.

29 John Lucas, 'Salmon on a Shoe String', *Scottish Field*, August 1965.

30 A. E. Gathorne-Hardy, *The Salmon*, p. 138.

31 H. D. Turing, Pollution Report No. 4, 'Rivers in Scotland', pp. 22–24.

32 *Ibid.*, p. 29.

33 *Ibid.*, pp. 32–38.

34 David W. Laurence, 'The Recovery of a Scottish Salmon River', *Salmon and Trout Magazine*, September 1965.

35 *Fisheries of Scotland, Report for 1964*, p. 71.

36 *Scottish Salmon and Trout Fisheries*, Second Report by the Committee appointed by the Secretary of State for Scotland, August, 1965.

9

Ireland's Salmon Treasure

'The salmon', says Dr. Arthur E. J. Went, 'is the most important fish in the Irish economy and there is evidence that it was also important since the twelfth century and almost certainly from earlier times.'[1] Ireland has been inhabited by man for at least 8,000 years and scattered throughout the earliest historical records are references to salmon and salmon fishing.

Fish was a vital part of the diet of the prehistoric inhabitants, some of whose crannogs or huts built on lakes have been excavated. The Danes, who came into Ireland from the end of the eighth century, were familiar with the salmon for they gave its name to two localities–Leixlip or Salmon Leap on the River Liffey, fifteen miles from Dublin, and the great Lax Weir on the River Shannon just above Limerick.[2] The battle of Clontarf, in which the Irish forces under their King Brian Boru finally defeated the Danes and regained their liberty in 1014, was fought around a salmon weir in the slobland of Dublin Bay. With the arrival of the Normans in 1170 the salmon, so to speak, enter Irish history for these greedy overlords made detailed records of their possessions, as in *Domesday Book*, and as a result we can trace, thanks to Dr. Went's research, the subsequent history of some of Ireland's richest salmon fisheries.

The rivers

Except for the short stretch between Dublin and Dundalk, the Irish coasts present a mountainous appearance. The mountains and hills are clustered in the northern and southern fringes of the island; the centre is a wide, low plain with an undulating terrain. 'In Ireland,' says the French geographer Demangeon, 'the mountains do not form compact masses or continuous chains, but are cut up and subdivided by valleys, depressions, and strips of lowland. In the south the route from the Central Plain to the coast along the Barrow, Suir and Blackwater Rivers shows no appreciable changes of gradient. In the north the whole country from Donegal Bay across the entire breadth of the island to Dundalk Bay is broken up into little, isolated clusters of hills by a close network of river-valleys and lake-filled hollows.'[3] The mountains, which never rise above 3,000 feet, often present blunt, heather-clad summits and steep gradients. Once mantled with thick forests, Ireland is now virtually denuded.

The wildness and ruggedness of parts of the country, especially in the west, where finger-shaped peninsulas reach out to the beckoning Atlantic waters, create scenes of stark beauty. Often the rivers glide between ivy-mantled, moss-grown rocks and through glades of tiny remnants of beech, oak and larch forest. From the air Ireland looks like an emerald isle, bathed in mist, but from the ground the predominant colours often are sepia and grey, with touches of black and dull yellow. The terrain in places, as around Killarney, is a symphony of brooding lakes and rivers winding through seemingly floating mountains. The roads away from the few metropolitan areas are usually empty of traffic except for herds of cows, men leading or riding horses, and women on ponies. Villages are far between and the towns are small, drab and undistinguished. You pass whitewashed roadside cottages, each with its pile of peat stacked in the yard, ruined greystone abbeys and occasionally a round tower built by the monks long ago as a storehouse and place of refuge. You may encounter a band of swarthy gypsies, called 'tinkers', encamped with their bedraggled children around their yellow, barrel-shaped wagons. Prehistoric cairns and ringforts contribute an aura of mystery to the landscape, and you half-expect to see fairies dancing on the green.

An air of poverty hangs over much of rural Ireland, particularly in the remote western sections. Beautiful villages like those which decorate the English Midlands, or the West or South Country, are rare, and distinguished small towns like Bath or Stratford-upon-Avon with their architectural splendours practically unknown.

Ireland's Tourist Board lists over a hundred river and lake systems which contain salmon and the Tourist Board of Ulster lists thirty more in the six counties of Northern Ireland.

As in Norway, salmon run into nearly every suitable stream or streamlet. Many of the rivers are short and drain large lakes, serving merely as channels to the sea. The Cloonee, for example, flowing into Kenmare Bay on the south-west coast, is only two miles long and drains Cloonee and other lakes; the Sligo is also two miles in length and serves as an outlet for Lough Gill into Sligo Harbour, while the Corrib, flowing into the sea at Galway, is 5½ miles long and drains three large limestone lakes, Carra, Mask and Corrib.

In contrast to these truncated streams is the River Shannon, flowing south-westerly, which from its source in the Cuileagh Mountains to Limerick City covers a winding course of 190 miles; the tideway is about 50 miles long and the estuary one to three miles. A deep and slow river, it passes through three large lakes, Lough Allen near its source, Lough Ree and Lough Derg, and receives the waters of many tributaries, some of which are fair-sized rivers and themselves drain a network of lakes. As it spirals across the heart of Ireland, the Shannon floods brilliant-green land and crosses much historic country, including romantic-looking castles and churches burned and plundered by the Norsemen a thousand years ago. On the Shannon, as on other rivers, it is not uncommon to fish beneath the ruins of a medieval castle or abbey whose inhabitants centuries ago angled from the very same spot.

The 90-mile Cork Blackwater, one of the best of Irish salmon rivers, rises in the wild rocky hills of County Kerry close to the County Cork border and flows past flanking hills and numerous wooded stretches, through the towns of Mallow, Fermoy, Lismore and Cappoquin to enter the sea by a narrow 15-mile estuary. Stephen Gwynn calls it 'the most perfect type of these Irish rivers whose general direction is eastward, and are rivers proper, not prolongations of lake systems. . . . From Millstreet to Lismore, a few miles above Cappoquin, it is the kind of river that salmon fishers dream of.'[4]

The Barrow, considerably longer than the Blackwater, is born in the Slieve Bloom mountains of Queen's County, runs north and then east, makes a sudden bend southward and winds up in Waterford Harbour. The Nore also issues from the Bloom mountains, in the north-west confines of Tipperary, and after a short northerly run tips southward, past several towns including Kilkenny, once the capital of the ancient kingdom of Ossory. Above New Ross it joins the Barrow, and shortly afterwards drops into Waterford Harbour, completing a course of 70 miles.

The Suir rises in the hills of northern Tipperary, then heads south past Thurles, Cashel, Clonmel and Carrick-on-Suir to join the Barrow and Nore below Waterford City. Acquiring the flow of thirteen tributaries, it is a broad river for much of its course, and one of the richest in salmon in Ireland.

About as long as the Barrow, the Slaney is a moorland stream issuing from the granitic Wicklow mountains, flows through County Carlow and County Wexford to reach tidewater at Enniscorthy and meets St. George's Channel at Wexford, a town, founded like many others by the Danes, that is redolent of fishing and seafaring. Here the river is spanned by a long and graceful new bridge. The best fishing is upriver between Bunclody and Tullow.

North of the Slaney flows the Liffey, dear to Dublin. It rises in the Wicklow mountains only a dozen miles from the capital and completes a corkscrew course of 82 miles before reaching Dublin Bay. Salmon ascend as far as Barrymore Eustace; above, the Golden Falls constitute an impassable barrier. Dublin is the only European capital where angling for salmon is still possible.

These are a few of the most renowned salmon streams of Ireland.

The runs

Although salmon enter most Irish streams of any size flowing into the sea, there is a wide range of abundance between the watercourse which contains an occasional fish after an autumnal rain and one where they run consistently in large numbers. Grilse (called 'peal' in Ireland) weighing 6 to 7 pounds form a substantial segment of the runs and in some rivers, like the Corrib, may constitute as much as 80 to 90 per cent of the catch.

The great majority of Irish salmon leave the rivers at the age of two. Went reports that 84 per cent of the fish examined during one year from sixteen rivers were derived from two-year-old smolts and the rest were more or less evenly divided among one-year and three-year smolts.

The tagging of many thousands of salmon, both juveniles and adults, in an effort to learn their oceanic movements has yielded results paralleling those reported from Scotland. Almost three-fourths of the recaptured fish travelled less than 50 miles from home waters and another 20 per cent between 50 and 100 miles. A few went farther, as from the west to the east coast of Ireland, a distance of 200 to 300 miles. Others made much longer odysseys: into the Rivers Tay and Aberdeenshire Dee, 800 miles from the tagging station; the Tweed, 615 miles; Conon, 560 miles; and various Scottish rivers closer to Ireland. More sensational journeys were those of Irish salmon which crossed the North Sea and landed on the west coast of Sweden, a distance of 1,235 miles from the point of release, and some that went in the other direction and were netted on the west coast of Greenland, proving that Irish fish share the feeding grounds with salmon of other European and North American countries. One smolt, released in Carrowmore Lake, County Mayo, on September 12, 1963, was captured near Sukkertoppen on October 21, 1964, completing an itinerary of 2,025 nautical miles in over 13 months; another, released in the same lake on September 5, 1963, was taken at Julianehaab on October 6, 1964, 1,700 miles away. Two others made more sensational peregrinations. They were released in the Burrishoole River in Ireland on March 25 and April 20, 1963, respectively, and were netted weighing 9 and 10 pounds near Kangamiut six and seven months later. They had swum at least 2,000 miles at apparent speeds of 10 and 11 miles a day.[5]

There is usually one predominant age group of fish in Irish rivers. Grilse runs normally occur from the beginning of May until September, peaking in June or July. 'Small spring fish' which have spent two winters in the sea appear at the end of the year in some rivers and usually increase in numbers until April, then peter out. 'Small summer fish', with less than three and more than two winters in the sea, arrive about April 20 and are abundant until mid-June, while 'large springers' (three winters at sea) tend to run in the months of December to May but are most numerous in March and April. 'Large summer fish' that have spent between three and four years in the ocean and 'large springers', with four winters in the sea, are rare.

Spring salmon average 8 to 12 pounds while heavier fish, which have spent three or even four years in the sea, weigh from 15 to 30 pounds. The largest salmon ever caught on rod and line were a 57-pounder on the River Suir in 1874 and a 50½-pounder on the Blackwater in 1930.

Among the best 'spring' rivers are the Boyne, Slaney, Nore, Suir and Munster Blackwater. Most of the 'spring' rivers also hold fresh-run fish in summer and autumn, although in a few, like the Boyne and Slaney, these runs are negligible. In the larger rivers the upper reaches do not harbour many salmon until summer or autumn; some of these fish enter the lower waters in spring or early summer and take several months to go upstream.

Waters which contain salmon from June onwards fall into three categories: (a) larger rivers that also provide spring fishing; (b) smaller river systems, usually with plenty of holding pools and lakes in which there is sufficient flow for fish to run more or less at any time; and (c) small spate rivers, with few or no lakes, which depend entirely on floods to bring them up.

Went reports that on the basis of an identification of 2,900 kelts entering Irish rivers, 96·3 per cent had spawned once, 3·5 per cent twice and 0·2 per cent three times. The proportion of kelts reported in the catches is about the same as in Scotland, 5 per cent, but a record of 17 per cent was set in the River Corrib in 1959–61.[6]

Ownership and exploitation of the fisheries

In the Middle Ages most religious establishments in Ireland were located on or near a river or lake, not only because they needed water but also because the waters supplied fish for the community. For example, not far from the neo-Gothic Ashford Castle, now a tourist hotel, was Cong Abbey, an Augustinian establishment which at one time housed 3,000 scholars. Beside the east bank of the serene River Cong, flowing lazily past the ruins of the old abbey, stands the monks' fishing house where there was a trap through which the river flowed. When a fish entered the trap a cord was activated to ring a bell in the monastic kitchen. By this device the monks assured themselves of a plentiful if erratic supply of fresh salmon and other fish. Those caught remained alive until they were removed from the trap.

Some houses obtained permission to keep boats on a river to catch fish, and frequently they were also granted tithes on fisheries in distant waters. Cong Abbey, built in the early twelfth century, had the tithes of the fishing on the River Moy, which is at least forty miles away, and Mellifont Abbey the right to fish in the prolific Boyne for four or five miles above the tideway. The latter house owned sixteen fishing boats as well as four salmon weirs and leased all but the Rosnaree fishery which provided the monks with fish.

According to Went, the bulk of the numerous fishing weirs in Ireland belonged to the monasteries at one time or another before their dissolution by Henry VIII, after which they fell mainly into private hands.

The Abbey of St. Thomas in Dublin received from King John one-tenth of all the salmon brought to his kitchen in Dublin Castle, while the Franciscan friary at Galway obtained from the overlords, the de Burghs, a regular supply of fish from their waters. The priory at Coleraine had the fruits of the fishing on the River Bann for only one day in the year, June 24, but since this fell at the height of the season, it might be worth hundreds of salmon in the Middle Ages.

The Munster Blackwater has always been one of the most prolific rivers in the British Isles. Salmon, sea-trout, eels, sturgeon and other species abounded in its waters. The See of Lismore acquired in the reign of King John the manor of Lismore and its profitable appurtenant fisheries, and clung to it until the end of the sixteenth century. Among those who then obtained the fishings, along with the manor, castle, villages, hamlets, etc., of Lismore, was Queen Elizabeth's favourite, Sir Walter Raleigh. He in turn yielded the property for the princely sum of £1,500 in 1602 to Richard Boyle, who came to Ireland penniless in 1588, was created Earl of Cork in 1620, and before his death had become a magnate on an enormous scale. Boyle had paid Raleigh only £500 when he was relieved of further obligation by the Crown. Raleigh lost favour in the reign of James I, and ultimately his head. The valuable Lismore fisheries remained in the Earl of Cork's family until 1758 when they came by marriage into the hands of the Duke of Devonshire.

It is interesting to note that when the manor of Lismore was leased to Sir Thomas Drury in 1575, some thirteen years before Raleigh gobbled it up, the Bishop of Lismore retained unto himself 'the fourth fish'. This 'fourth fish' was a means whereby the Bishops and their heirs held on to a considerable portion of the yields of the Blackwater fishery, and proved to be a substantial source of revenue. In 1637 it was said to be worth the enormous sum of £80 per annum. The Act of 1869, disestablishing the Church of Ireland, set up the Commissioners of Church Temporalities and the 'fourth fish' was vested in them. In 1881 it was transferred to the Irish Land Commission 'which has collected the rent charge since that date'.[7]

The fisheries of the River Liffey were originally far more valuable than they are today. In 1180 the Archbishop of Dublin 'confirmed to the regular canons of St. Augustine in the Church of the Holy Trinity certain possessions, which included a fishery near the site of the church and the tithes of salmon and all other fish in the water course of the River Liffey'. The Church of the Holy Trinity clung to this possession zealously and from time to time resorted to the courts to enforce its rights.

The Crown took control of the Liffey's fisheries in its lower reaches in 1185. In that year Prince John, as Lord of Ireland, gave the Abbey of St. Mary the right to keep a boat on the water 'to fish with equal privileges as his own boat'. Like the brethren of the Holy Trinity, the monks of St. Mary's valued their prerogatives so highly they were prepared to challenge anyone who interfered with them. Towards the end of John's reign the citizens of Dublin received the royal half of the fishing in the Liffey's tidal waters, and they held on to it as a corporate body for over seven hundred years. When the friars of Kilmainham, who also owned fishing rights on this river, built a pool which prevented the salmon from ascending, the corporation complained to the King, who in 1220 ordered 'the river to be enlarged and the pool so rectified that ships and boats . . . may have free passage up and down the river'.[8]

Quarrels occasionally broke out between the various owners of fishing rights and sometimes violence ensued. In 1261 the Hospitallers of Kilmainham destroyed the fixed salmon net at Dublin bridge owned by the city, and the citizens in retaliation wrecked the Hospital's mill. When word reached King Henry III he ordered the city to pay a fine of ten pounds but stipulated that 'the Mayor and commonalty have to have free fishing in the Avenlif . . . and the passage of salmon great and small is not to be obstructed by nets, standards, weirs, other engines or impediments'. Eventually the city leased the fishery to private citizens but it took steps on every possible occasion to protect its interests.

What was probably the world's first anti-pollution law was passed by the Dublin Corporation in 1466, stipulating that 'no tanner, glover nor any person use limed ware or leather work in the River Liffey on account of the destruction of the salmon. Penalty 3/4*d.* for each offence, one half to be paid to the detector and ½*d.* to the court.'

In 1585 the Corporation reasserted its determination to keep the river clean by ordering the impoundment of pigs found on the strand and forbade anyone 'to put any flax into the ditches near his ground'. Flax water is a destroyer of fish life and special precautions must be taken to keep it out of rivers. The Corporation retained its fishery down to very recent times.

Many of the best fishings on the River Lee were held by the diocese of Cork and by Gill Abbey; also the Dominicans owned a fishing pool and half a salmon weir, and the Augustinians 'a certain salmon fishery'. Some of these properties were eventually acquired by Richard Boyle and became part of his extensive barony.

At Galway there was—and is—one of the most productive salmon fisheries in Europe. Here come in summer hordes of fish fat with the spoils of the sea. They lie shoulder to shoulder in the clear blue waters waiting for a spate to send them up into Lough Corrib. The city of Galway was in existence as long ago as 1124 but we do not know when the first weir was built on the River Corrib. There was certainly an impoundment to harvest the lucrative salmon runs in the thirteenth century. The fishery is first mentioned in historical records in 1283 when, in the Rolls of the Great Pipe, it was among the possessions of Walter de Burgo, first Earl of Ulster, as an appurtenance of the territory of Connaught. It was then valued at £22 per annum.

The fishery was held by several members of the de Burgo family (who later changed their name to Burke) until it passed to Elizabeth, heiress of William de Burgo, who married Lionel, Duke of Clarence, second son of Edward III. (She was the patron of young Geoffrey Chaucer.) Philippa, her daughter, succeeded to the estate and subsequently married Edward de Mortimer, Earl of March. Their son inherited the Galway fishery and he passed it on to Richard, Duke of York, father of Edward IV, on whose death it was owned by Edward IV himself. The fishery remained Crown property until 1602 but various parts were leased from time to time, often to Galway residents.

The fishery was confiscated as a result of the Irish rebellion of 1641. After the Restoration of Charles II Sir George Preston acquired *inter alia* 'all and singular fishings in the sea in and belonging to Connaught', including the Galway fishery. Sir George's daughter inherited the property; she married George Eyre of Eyrecourt, County Galway, and their son in 1710 sold it for £300 to Edward Eyre of Galway in whose family it remained until 1852, when it was purchased by the English fish culturist Thomas Ashworth and his brother Edmond, remaining in their family until the London fish merchants, H. Barber and Son, acquired it for £80,000 ($224,000) in 1954.

Methods of fishing

The gear used in salmon fishing in Ireland from earliest times may be divided into two types: fixed engines in the river or sea, and movable devices (spears, gaffs, snares, rod and line, etc.). The oldest methods of catching salmon on a large scale were weirs built on the seashore and in the rivers. Most prominent was the head weir, a V-shaped structure: the wings were made of stakes and wattles driven into the sand or mud and small branches of trees, twigs, or osiers were entwined between the stakes to form an impenetrable barrier. A conical net attached to two poles fished the gap into which the salmon were lured. A man sat on a platform and held a number of cords to control the net. When a strike was made, he hauled up a line, descended into his boat and took out the fish. Such apparatus was quite common in southern Ireland in the Middle Ages. The weir described by the chronicler of the Battle of Clontarf in Dublin Bay, as well as the head weir in Waterford Harbour, which was in existence from the thirteenth century to the 1860s, was obviously of this type.[9]

The head weir was usually fished only during the ebb tide although in some instances the V was reversed to catch the salmon on the flood. A fish moving upstream would find its path blocked by the obstruction and swim along it until enticed into a trap. Then it would move into a V structure and enter another trap from which it could not escape. Head weirs were at one time or another found on all the rivers flowing into Waterford Harbour, in the estuaries of the Cork Blackwater, Lee, Bandon and Bunratty Rivers, as well as in Dundalk Bay, Oysterhaven and the Tramore and Courtmascherry Rivers.

Riverine weirs were designed wholly or partly to blockade a stream channel, and sometimes they were also used to impound water for power purposes. The rivers of Ireland were studded with such structures until the Act of 1863 severely curtailed their use. Some of the earliest riverine weirs were made of wattles and stakes and had a trap consisting of boxes or cribs of the same material. Heavy floods would sometimes destroy them, and gradually brushwood weirs were converted into stone structures like that at Galway. After 1820 many of the head weirs were replaced by more efficient stake weirs.

The River Nore may be taken as an example. At the beginning of the nineteenth century, according to William Tighe, who wrote a book on County Kilkenny, there were 'several weirs for taking salmon as far as tidewater extended'. Most of them, he said, 'are ebb weirs, open to the descending currents and are fished only during the latter half of the ebb tide; the wings, which are staked and wattled, extend through the part of the river where there is least current, so as not to impede the navigation and are only as high as half the flood water; where they meet in an angle the fisherman has a seat elevated upon four framed poles, where he holds the net. Flood weirs are most injurious, as they catch the fish in their ascent; of these there are a few in the Nore and also in the Suir.'[10]

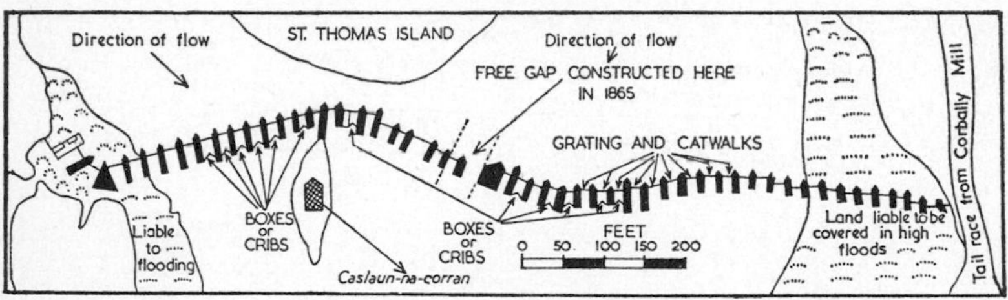

Figure 22

Plan of the Lax weir on the River Shannon. (Based on plan by A. Gray dated July 5, 1864, in manuscript *Stone Weirs* preserved in the Fisheries Division of the Department of Lands, Dublin.)

Legislation was needed to force owners to provide a gap or free passage in these impoundments so that enough fish would escape to perpetuate the stocks, for owners naturally were inclined to take an undue proportion of the runs, and in some instances blockaded a stream. Although the first statute of this kind dates from 1783, not much progress was made in curbing the menace of river weirs until the Fisheries Act for Ireland was passed in 1863. By then their number had been reduced to forty, of which eleven were not in use.

The Special Commissioners of Fisheries, a tribunal created by the Act, were empowered to make inquiries and order the abatement of any weir or fixed engine that did not comply with the law. Many such devices around the Irish coasts were therefore taken down, some because they interfered with navigation. One of the oldest weirs removed was the Duncannon in Waterford Harbour. An appeal by Lord Templemore, its owner, proved futile and the weir was condemned as a menace to shipping, thus ending an existence of six hundred years during which it had been fishing off and on.

One of the earliest and largest of riverine weirs was Lax weir on the Shannon which was in existence in the early tenth century and

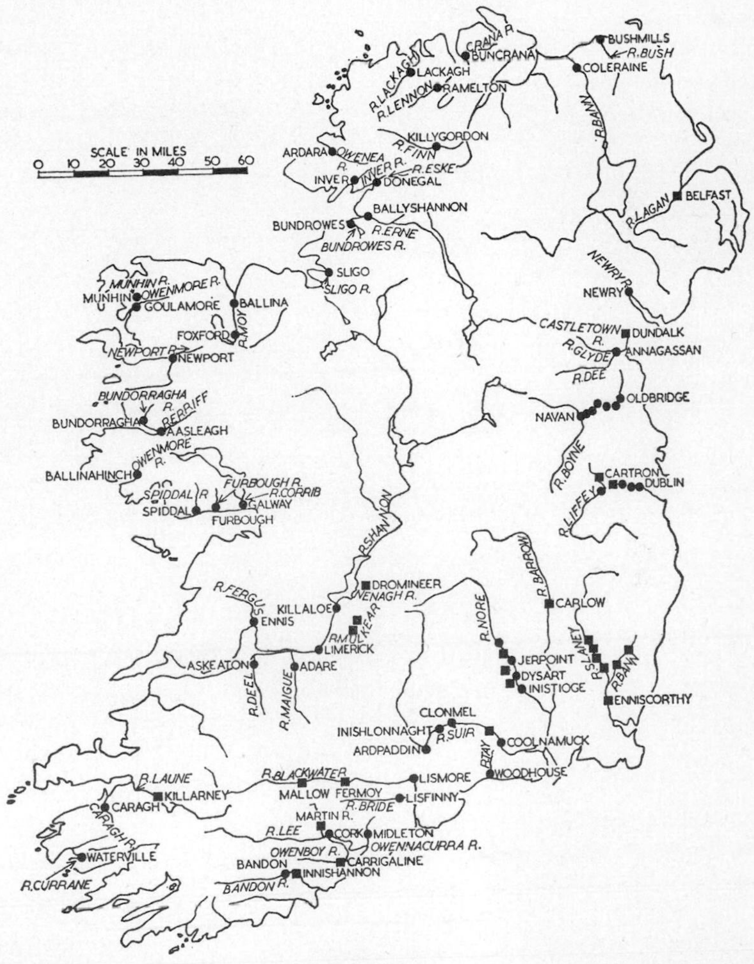

Figure 23

Map of Ireland showing locations of salmon weirs in former times. (Those weirs shown as circles were described as, or known to be, salmon weirs and those weirs shown as squares were described as 'fishing weirs' but they were almost certainly salmon weirs.)

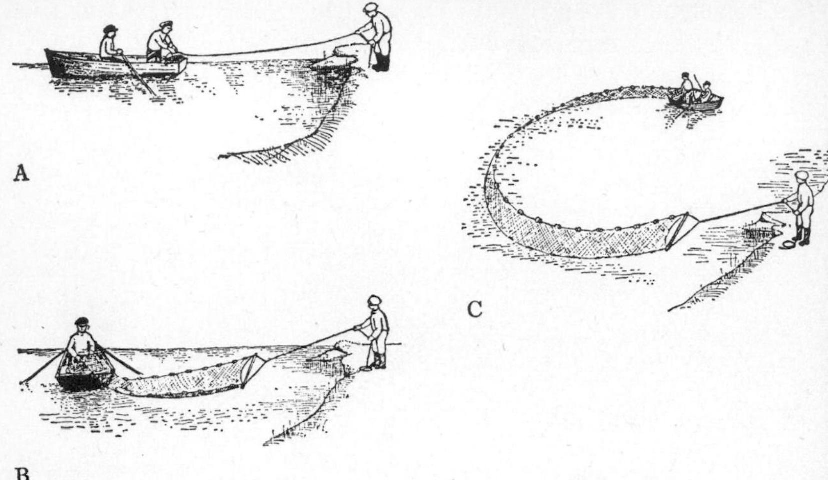

Figure 24

Method of fishing a draft seine or haul net. A. A rope is paid out from the bank; B. Part of the net is paid out; C. More net is paid out; D. The 'circle' of the net is completed and the men in the boat take to the bank; E. The net is hauled in.

fished for over a millennium before it went out of operation in 1934. In 1846 it had 51 stone piers, a small gap, and 12 boxes or cribs. A free gap was constructed in 1865 (Figure 22). Other weirs on the Shannon date from 1062 at Killaloe and the twelfth century at Limerick. There were five weirs on the Boyne in the thirteenth century. The Galway weir was in existence in 1280. In the sixteenth century the Rivers Suir, Liffey, Maigue, Owennacurra, Laune, Lee, Blackwater, Fergus, Boyne, Nore and Newry all had salmon weirs (Figure 23).

One of the most famous, Lismore weir on the Blackwater, built about 1575, consisted in the early eighteenth century of a single part-wood and part-stone structure anchored to a series of islands. Fish had little chance of hurdling this obstruction except on the flood because there was no free gap. Even after the 1863 statute went into effect the owner, the Duke of Devonshire, resisted by legal means efforts to open the impoundment adequately. After a large part was

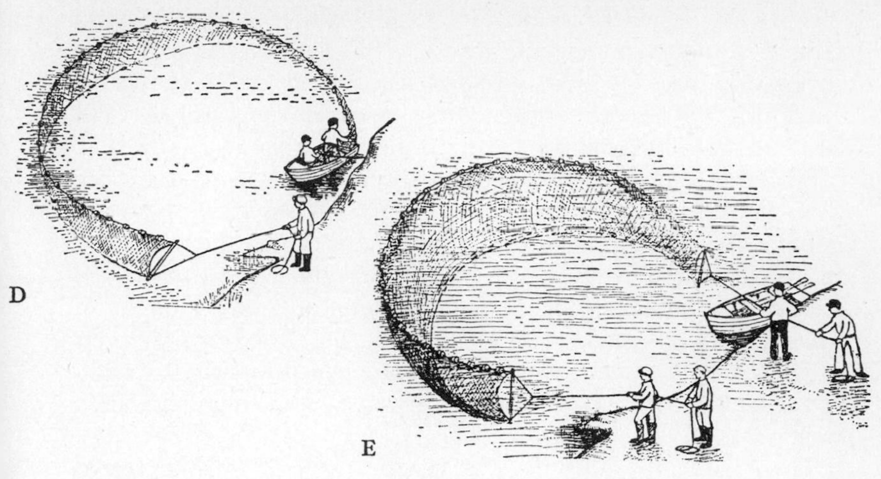

washed away in 1944, the structure went out of operation. It had fished almost continuously for three and three-quarter centuries.

Draft seines or haul nets (Figure 24) were in use in Ireland for catching salmon from at least the second half of the twelfth century. They were fished from boats in suitable bays and estuaries and also in fresh water (where they are now prohibited). Certain religious houses, high Church officials like the Archbishop of Dublin, and other individuals, had the right to use boats for river fishing.

'A very high proportion of the fisheries of Ireland were fished by draft nets down the ages', says Went. 'The method is illustrated in a number of Irish topographical prints. Perhaps the most interesting of all of these is the pictorial map of the city of Cork in . . . [1633], which shows a draft net, almost certainly used for salmon, being fished in the south channel of the River Lee.'[11] A very large proportion of Irish salmon are still taken with this type of gear.

Stake nets or weirs in imitation of the Scottish type appeared in Ireland at the beginning of the nineteenth century and quickly superseded the head weirs because they fished automatically–no watchman was needed–and required relatively little labour. The first one probably appeared on the Munster Blackwater in 1809.

Since stake nets could not be used effectively in the open sea, bag nets, also imported from Scotland, were introduced in the 1830s and multiplied rapidly. Many of them were attached to the outside of stake nets in order to get around the restriction imposed by the Fisheries Act of 1842 which set up conditions governing the use of fixed engines for taking salmon. In 1861 there were 255 bag nets and about 90 stake nets licensed. The number of fly nets, a simplified stake net, reached a peak of 47 in 1855. Head weirs numbered 50 in 1861.

The Act of 1863 amending the fisheries code of Ireland created Special Commissioners. They and their successors, the Inspectors of Irish Fisheries, investigated 'all the fixed engines which the owners proposed to use after 1863', and as a result many of them were declared illegal. Ultimately, as a consequence of this investigation, 56 bag nets, 66 stake nets and one fly net were certified. The severe reduction of such gear, which fished too efficiently, is regarded as a major factor in preventing the serious depletion of Irish salmon stocks, in contrast to other parts of the British Isles where such a ban was not imposed until later.

The number of bag nets dropped to 30 in 1872, later rose to 52, and after 1913 fell to less than 30; now only about 10 are licensed in the Republic. No more than three head weirs were certified from 1865 onwards.[12]

Drift-netting for salmon around the British Isles originated in Ireland in the middle of the last century. The effectiveness of drifters depends upon the fact that the fish on their return from distant feeding grounds travel in shoals, coming in along the coast somewhere between Portrush and Inishowen Head. Like an army on the march, they break up into battalions, each detaching itself upon arriving at the particular river where its youth was spent. As they move inshore the fish are reinforced by new arrivals. Drift-netters intercept the cohorts of salmon, sometimes as far as ten miles offshore, and may make huge hauls. Originally the type of boat used in drifting was the Norway yawl equipped with a sail and rowed by four to six men.

A fairly important device, used at least as far back as 1600 on the Blackwater and Shannon Rivers, is the snap net which is suspended between two light, flat-bottomed boats called 'cots'.

Apart from nets, the traditional method for taking large fish in the river was the spear or leister. A salmon spear made of iron was excavated from a prehistoric crannog at Strokestown and may be seen in the National Museum in Dublin. The leister was declared illegal by an Act of George I in 1716 and the penalty for merely possessing one of these deadly instruments was fixed at 20*s.* to be paid to the informer. In 1842 it was raised to a maximum of £10. Leistering salmon was not a popular rural sport in Ireland, as it was in Scotland. Other means of poaching, however, were well known, especially poisoning. A widely-used poison was the crushed roots of the giant spurge which were put trodden into the waters. Fish in the vicinity soon died and were hauled out by hand or gaffed. In recent times more easily procurable poisons have superseded the spurge.

Pitchforks, garden forks, tridents, etc., were commonly employed for taking fish illegally. The largest spear-head found in Ireland weighed 8 pounds and was 16½ inches across.

Old prints show men spearing salmon from the Great Bridge at Galway in Elizabethan times (Figure 25). Great dexterity was required. The fisherman on the battlement threw down his trident, held by a rope, into the river and neatly impaled the fish.

Fishing with rod and line is known to have been practised in Elizabethan days on the River Bann, on the Galway in the seventeenth century, and on the Liffey as early as 1706. The Salmon Leap on the Liffey was a popular place for anglers. However, this sport interested only a small number of persons. 'People would go down to a river', says Constantia Maxwell, 'to see a haul of salmon or trout taken with nets but fishing was not popular with the gentry (in the eighteenth century).'[13]

Use of the fishery

Fish were vitally important to the monasteries with which Ireland was liberally endowed in the Middle Ages. The monks' wants were simple: 'a little hut hidden in the wilderness . . . a clear pool to wash away sins, a beautiful, enfolding word. . . . Twelve brethren to be

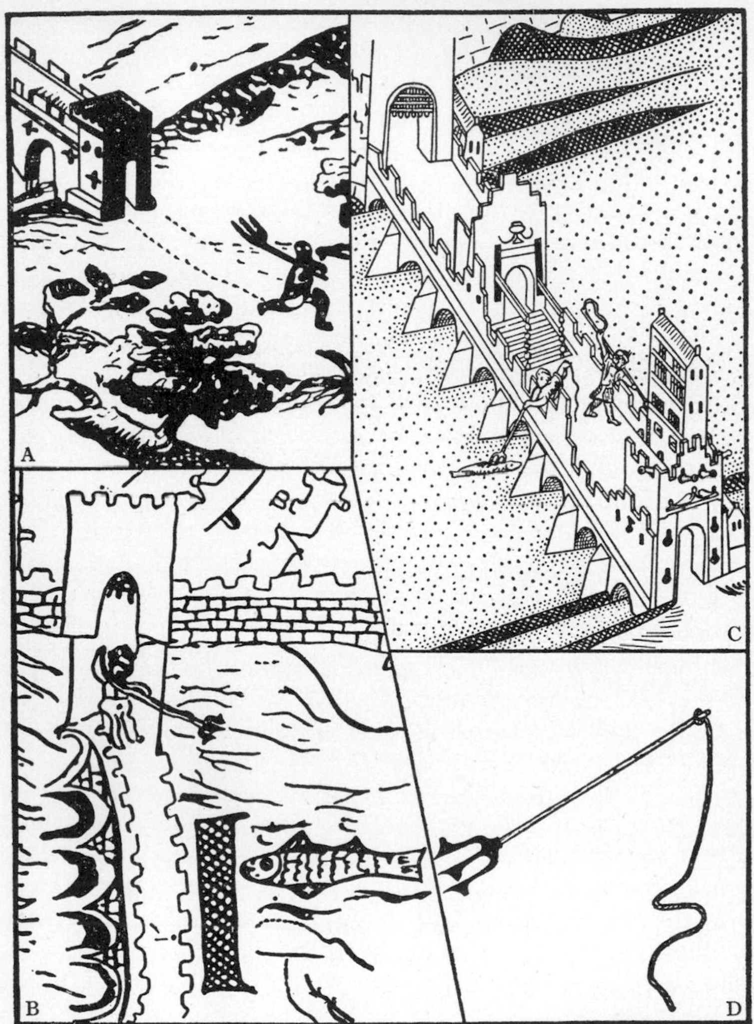

Figure 25

Spearing from the bridge at Galway. A. Man with trident spear (copied from John Speed's map of Galway, 1610). B. Man using trident spear from the Great Bridge (copied from Barnaby Gooche's map (1583) in the *Irish State Papers*, Public Record Office, London). C. Man spearing salmon from the Great Bridge (based on the pictorial map of Galway (1851) in Trinity College, Dublin). D. Casting spear as used at Galway (as reconstructed from various sources).

in the houses . . . salmon to feed them, and trout, and leeks, and the bees' bland honey. Silence and fervour.'[14]

Historical accounts agree that the peasants were not much given to eating fish or dainty meats. Their diet was on a level of that of the 'wild Welsh' or 'wild Scots', or worse. They lived mostly in crude thatched huts, without ovens or chimneys, or furniture. Fynes Moryson, secretary to the Viceroy, who travelled extensively in Ireland in the reign of Elizabeth I, noted that 'they devour great morsels of beef unsalted, and they eat commonly swine's flesh, seldom mutton . . . and therewith swallow whole lumps of filthy butter'. The fare of the lords and their retainers in the sixteenth century was not much better. They seldom ate 'wild fowl or fish, though they have great plenty of both, because they will not take pains in catching them, and so leave them all for the English. They gladly eat raw herbs, as water-cresses and shamrock, and most commonly eat flesh, many times raw; and if it be roasted or sodd, they seldom eat bread with it . . . [and] keep most of their corn for their horses.'[15]

The English Irish, who belonged to the landholding class, retained the English diet which sometimes included fish prepared with savoury sauces, unless they had degenerated, as travellers noted, to the level of the Irish. Luke Gernon, an Englishman who visited Ireland in 1620, where he was entertained in fine houses, does not mention eating fish but reports being served a variety of ill-cooked meats without sauce, especially venison and mutton.

The fisheries belonged to the Irish landlords but the fishing industry was chiefly conducted by foreigners. In the year 1535 three thousand Englishmen 'gathered to the fishing off Carlingford'. Some 600 Spanish ships fished off the southern coast in 1569. 'Besides the sea fishing there was a large export of salmon and eels carried on trading ships from the river fisheries, then of great value and strictly regulated; no swine [were] allowed on the strand of rivers from March to October, and no flax to be steeped there for the linen yarn.'[16]

The wealth of the rivers, as of the land, was mostly shipped out of the country. Salmon exports tallied 905 tons in 1689, and it was said that 'the cargoes of salmon, herrings and pilchards and other fish made up yearly in Ireland and transported into several ports of Spain and Venice and of the ports of the Mediterranean Sea would startle the common people'.[17]

Some of the rivers were crowded with fish, as visitors noted. For instance, an English traveller of the seventeenth century reported that Boyne salmon 'are always fat and never out of season, which is a rarity not to be met with in England that ever I heard'. Provisions were cheap in this fruitful land. After the Restoration of Charles II a large fresh salmon could be bought for only threepence, and even as late as 1802 salmon from the River Nore sold for fourpence a pound in Kilkenny.

The bulk of the fish in prefamine Ireland went to London and Liverpool, although Dublin was receiving considerable quantities. Thomas Cromwell, in his *Excursion through Ireland*, published in 1820, said: 'There is a salmon fishery at Island Bridge [on the Liffey], which . . . during the year 1816 produced 1,762 fish weighing from five to 30 pounds each. The salmon here taken are in greater esteem among the inhabitants of Dublin than those caught in other Irish rivers so universally prolific of the species, but this arises, probably, from their freshness alone, those brought from the Barrow, Suir and Shannon on the roofs of the mail coaches from Ross, Waterford and Cork being considered by many to excel them in quality.'[18]

In the notebooks he kept during his travels in Ireland in 1835 Alexis de Tocqueville frequently comments on the misery of the people and particularly their meagre diets. 'The Irishman', he was told, 'cultivates beautiful crops and takes his harvest to the nearest port, and puts it on an English ship; then he goes home and eats potatoes. He rears cattle, sends them to London and never eats meat.' Before the coming of the railways inland markets for fish were unexploited, so that large numbers of people, especially in the hinterland, never acquired the taste for it. Away from the coast, people rarely bought any kind of fish, although it was plentiful at Galway, Killaloe, Carrickfergus, Arklow, Dungarven, Kinsale, Dingle and other places where there were fishing stations.

The truth was, as Cecil Woodham-Smith says in her study of the famine years, that there was 'scarcely a woman of the peasant class whose culinary art exceeds the boiling of a potato. Bread is scarcely ever seen, and an oven is unknown.'[19] Fishing in the sea was a neglected industry. Men who owned a curragh fished for their own families or for neighbours and were paid in potatoes. Moreover, when the potato crop failed fishermen throughout Ireland pawned or sold their gear to buy meal. Some efforts were made by the

British Government and religious organizations like the Society of Friends to assist the Irish fishermen during the famine of the 1840s but they came to naught.

Condition of the rivers

The Salmon Fisheries Act of 1863, a counterpart of the 1861 legislation for England and Wales, divided Ireland into districts (as Figure 26) with boards of conservators appointed for each. The commissioners had the power to alter close seasons, issue licences for rods, weirs, cruives, fixed nets, bag nets, etc. All fixed nets that were not in legal existence in 1862 were declared illegal. All bag nets placed in rivers and estuaries after July 1863, or within three miles from the mouth of any river, were also declared illegal, but those legally existing within two miles of the mouth of a river, wholly owned by a proprietor, were exempted. Every fishing weir henceforth had to have a free gap. Use of spears, leisters and similar instruments for killing salmon as well as night fishing was forbidden. The weekly closure was set at 6 a.m. Saturday to 6 a.m. Monday.

Archibald Young in his book, *Salmon Fisheries*, published in 1877, listed 56 major salmon rivers in Ireland, of which the best were, in his opinion, the Shannon, Erne, Nore, Suir and Barrow (from which 420 tons of fish were shipped to English markets in 1872), Moy, Ballisodare, Galway, Sligo, Lee, Bush, Bann, Foyle and Cork Blackwater. He estimated the gross annual value of Irish salmon catches at £400,000 ($2,000,000).

The first and so far only comprehensive survey of Ireland's salmon rivers was made by Augustus Grimble and published in his book, *Salmon Rivers of Ireland*, in 1903. He found the Galway in good condition. Each season 6,000 to 8,000 fish passed the weir and King's gap in the city of Galway and went up Lough Corrib during the netting season, and to these must be added an indeterminate number that ran up after the nets were taken off. He does not tell us how many fish were taken at the ancient weir nor by the nets below.

The River Moy, largest and most important in County Mayo, yielded 32,550 salmon yearly from 1882 to 1893 to the Moy Fishery Company. 'In the opinion of many who are in a position to judge, this fresh water netting is carried to an excess, which is doing much harm to the river.'[20] Poachers were numerous and always ready to do battle with the bailiffs.

Ballisodare River in County Mayo had a unique history. It was the first stream in Ireland to be converted from a salmonless state

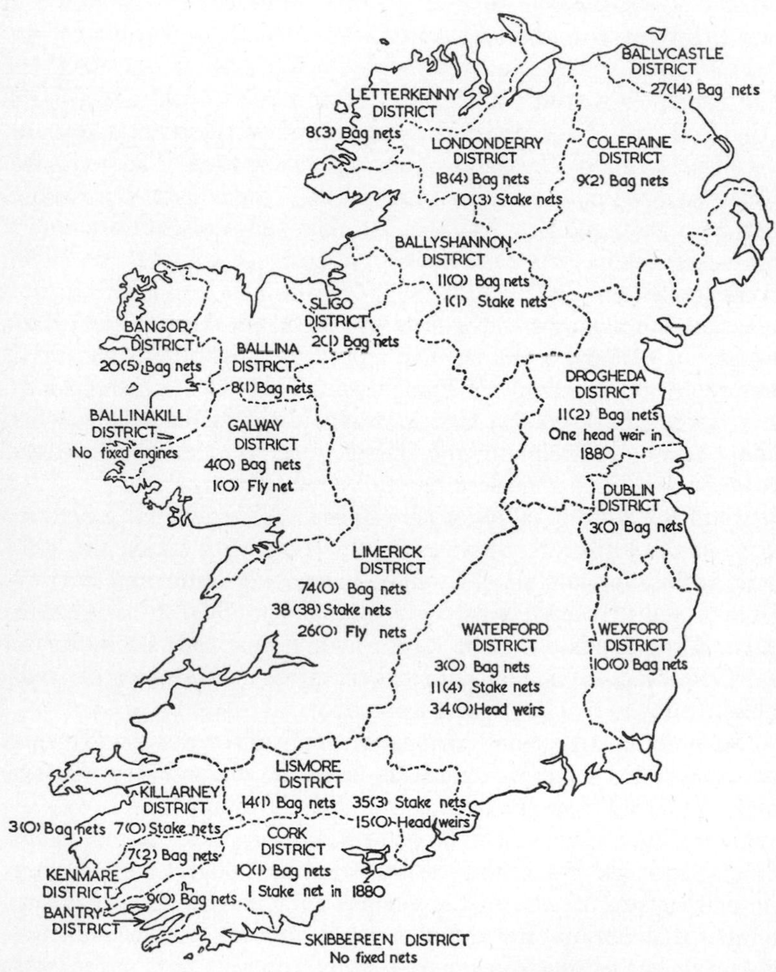

Figure 26

Sketch map of Ireland showing the different Fishery Districts, as set up in 1848, giving the number of licences for fixed engines issued in each district for the year, together with the numbers issued in 1880 (in parentheses).

to a fairly large producer of these valuable fishes. At the head of tideway, where the sparkling river enters Ballisodare Bay, a series of waterfalls aggregating about 20 feet in height used to block the ascent of fish. In 1837 the proprietor of the river conceived the idea of converting the stream into a salmon fishery. He applied and eventually was granted a private Act of Parliament permitting him to do so. In 1853 he completed the erection of a fish pass at the lower falls and in 1855 at the upper falls. He also laddered a tributary, the Owenmore River. At the same time he planted adult salmon and sea-trout and also fertilized eggs in the Ballisodare. In 1854 fish began to move up the river: 179 grilse and 77 sea-trout were netted that year below the upper falls. Catches mounted steadily, and a profitable fishery was created, with 5,000 to 10,000 salmon being taken annually.

At the echoing falls and around the salmon weir the poet William Butler Yeats spent many lazy summer afternoons in his youth. His family owned the flour mill which received power from the falls. I visited the Ballisodare a few years ago. The original old-fashioned fish pass was still functioning. A stream of water flowed down the rocks in a kind of musical torrent. No fish were running for it was late autumn and the salmon had repaired to their spawning grounds upstream amid the bogs. The Middleton and Pollexfen flour mills were still there, humming blissfully, just as they did when Yeats was a boy in the 1870s, unchanged like the salmon ladder. In the churchyard of the nearby town of Sligo, with its monotonous streets of grey stone houses and its leaden sky, lay the remains of Ireland's great poet who by chance was associated with the salmon weir.

Grimble in 1903 reported that the Ballisodare was no longer as profitable a fishery as it had been a quarter of a century earlier. The catches had fallen to about 3,000 salmon annually.

In his tour of County Sligo Grimble was conscious of illegal fishing and heavy poaching on the lakes and their feeder streams. The numerous bailiffs, paid a pittance for their season's work, 50*s*. or £3, were, he said, worse than useless. They were loathe to prosecute offenders, especially relatives, as often happened. If there was an occasional conviction, the fine was negligible. Along the coast of Sligo, according to the Crown Solicitor, there were 'miles of drift and fixed nets illegally worked under the eyes of the Coastguard', while the estuary of the Garavogue 'is ceaselessly netted by small-mesh nets under the pretence of catching small fish and flounders, and these take myriads of salmon and white trout fry, and are worked without any regard to close seasons'.[21]

The Erne was still a grand fishing stream. 'Where can an angler go to in Scotland between the middle of June and the middle of August and get any sport approaching that which the Erne offers?' exclaimed Grimble. However, drift-netting night and day in Donegal Bay, regardless of close time, and often unlicensed, under the noses of the police and coastguards, was dissipating the stocks. 'These drift or hang nets are the most destructive and wasteful that have ever been invented. They not only kill alike kelts and clean fish, but . . . numbers of fish become disentangled and sink to the bottom of the sea; while those that are brought into the boat are blown up to an unnatural size by having been hanged for hours and left dead in the water, and are as much unfit for human food as any drowned or strangled animal.'[22]

The Deele was famous for the quality and quantity of its salmon as far back as the days of Henry VIII. Up to about 1820, fish were so plentiful they were hawked round the neighbourhood for twopence a pound. Then flax cultivation began in the valley, and the washing of flax water destroyed all vestige of fish life. The river became worthless.

Fishing on the once-prolific Bann had declined considerably during the previous decade owing to many factors, such as poaching of fry and mature fish, pollution by flax water and by chloride of lime from bleaching and dyeing works on the banks of its tributaries, diversion of water to supply millraces, massacre of fry that were sucked into the unguarded intakes of turbine wheels, and depredations of gulls and other birds at the river's mouth. Salmon catches had decreased by about 50 per cent since 1885. Pollution was prohibited by law 'but the fines are so small [an average of thirteen pence halfpenny each for 100 convictions] while the disgrace is nil, that most of the flax growers and manufacturers habitually break the law rather than incur the small expense of making a settling tank'.

'Poor Bann!' cried Grimble. 'Never was there a river more suited to give large returns to legitimate netting, or to provide the best of sport for the rod. In all our experience we have never come across any river so unfortunate as this one. Others suffer from one or two, or perhaps even several, of the evils already enumerated, but for the unhappy Bann there exists in their strongest form every conceivable evil that is deadly to salmon life.'[23]

The unsullied Boyne remained one of the best salmon streams in Great Britain despite the fact that the runs were tapering off as a result of assiduous drift-netting. In 1860 only five nets worked the waters around Drogheda; at the end of the century there were over a hundred. Many of the netsmen paid no attention to the weekly closure. As one of the proprietors told the Irish Inland Fishery Commission of 1901: 'As the fish increased the nets increased, and then when the nets increased, the fish decreased.' Another burden to which the Boyne fish was subjected was that 'in the Dundalk Fishery District, lying to the north of the mouth of the river, the sea nets continue to work for just a whole month after the Boyne District nets had been withdrawn by law, and thus these nets are permitted to kill great quantities of fish that would otherwise ascend the Boyne'.[24]

The Liffey seemed to be a splendid stream. The best salmon reaches were between Maynooth and Lucan, 'but owing to the want of passes in the seven or eight weirs, fish can only ascend at the rare intervals when the water is exactly at a right height for a successful leap, and thus there are very few fish about these pretty reaches, while higher up the river the fall at Poulpahouca entirely hinders them from reaching the upper waters'.[25] Not only was there considerable looting at the mouth of the Liffey but the lawful nets blithely ignored the weekend ban. So scarce had salmon become that only six nets were still in operation in 1903, and when the flow was low the netter at Island Bridge, licensed by the Corporation of Dublin, could take every salmon that came up the river from Monday through Friday, so that only weekend migrants got by, and many of these were snatched by mill hands at the millraces or weirs upstream.

In contrast to the Liffey was the Slaney, where 75 nets were at work, presumably draft nets, for drift-netting had been outlawed in the estuary, which captured 12,000 to 15,000 salmon every season; in addition, there was considerable angling by local people, especially for kelts. It was not unusual for a fishmonger at Enniscorthy to sell 100 to 200 spawned-out fish in one week. A splendid angling river, the Slaney at that time was fished by prominent Irish and English sportsmen such as the Marquis of Waterford, Lord Ruthven, Sir Shirley Salt, E. E. Hall-Dare and others.

If the decrease in licensed netting and angling is a criterion then the Rivers Barrow, Nore and Suir were being depleted of fish. Total nets dropped from 284 in 1869 to 170 in 1898, and angling licences from 300 to 170. Protection was so poor that one could see a hundred nets fishing on any Sunday night in the season between Inistioge and Cheekpoint. The thirty miles of the Suir from Carrick to Duncannon lighthouse near the entrance to Waterford Harbour was 'simply a river of twine, fished by about ninety nets (mostly drift nets) wholly regardless of any close time'.

What of the noble Cork Blackwater? In recent times it had had a chequered career. By 1862 it was almost barren of fish chiefly because the Lismore weir had an inefficient free gap. Opening of the weir quickly restocked the river, but after 1883 a decline set in and became gradually more pronounced, owing, it was believed, to the hyperactivity of snap nets in fresh water and drift nets in the estuary, and to the closing of the weir by action of the current. A large part of the river was owned by the Duke of Devonshire who, though he had drastically reduced netting, still permitted the operation of 3 stake weirs, 18 draft nets, 89 drift nets and 27 snap nets over a 20-mile stretch of narrow water, an average of one salmon trap to every 250 yards! In addition, there were the nettings of Sir Richard Musgrave, Villiers Stuart and others. Grimble estimated the total salmon catch from Lismore to Youghal at about 30,000 fish yearly, making the Blackwater one of the most productive rivers in the British Isles at that time. Ironically, despite the wealth of fish, relatively few salmon were seen by the proprietors above Fermoy during the netting season, and their fishings consequently were virtually ruined. There was, however, desirable sport below Fermoy, notably on the famous Careysville water.

Grimble's survey showed that the Rivers Lee and Bann were being wrecked as fish havens by unconscionable poachers using the deadly spurge. Fines proved ineffectual in stopping them since there was much profit in the traffic. Hucksters with their donkey carts haunted the streams. They knew when salmon were being landed, by fair means or foul, and paid as much as two shillings a pound for a fat February-run fish.

The River Laune flows out of the rain-dimpled lower lake of Killarney, past Killorgin down to Dingle Bay. Salmon were fished both in the lake and river; in the twenty years 1872–92 the Killorgin nets took an average of 8,585 fish and the Killarney nets 1,360 per year. Yet these catches were but trifles compared with the hauls of 70 to 80 boats working draft nets in estuary waters. Since this was a public fishery a licence could be obtained for a nominal sum, and the Government did not attempt to adjust the number of nets to the capacity of the runs–a common occurrence in Ireland's coastal and estuarial fisheries.[26]

On the Shannon every salmon and peal had to run the gauntlet of an incredible number of nets and fish traps. The estuary was strewn with every type of gear, while in the river itself the fish were faced with the formidable Lax weir, snap nets above Limerick, anglers' rods and nets at Athlone and in the Boyle district. Grimble thought that poachers probably were 'a greater destructive power than the united captures of all the [other] methods put together, for they chiefly kill fish in the tributaries when they are about to spawn. The destruction is wholesale, from cartfuls to sackfuls.'[27] Bailiffs and inspectors worked hard to nab the villains and obtained many convictions, only to have the fines remitted on pleas of poverty.

Lax weir took up to 15,000 fish a year. Another unfavourable factor was the drainage works on Lough Derg which created fluctuations of flow in the river, and the resulting short-running floods were not sufficient in duration to bring the fish forwards. It was clear that the Shannon runs had declined materially in the previous thirty years.

Summing up, Grimble declared that overnetting and poaching were the major burdens inflicted on the Irish salmon stocks. There was a plethora of bailiffs–873 on the Moy, Foyle and Erne alone, as against 89 on the Tay, Spey and Aberdeen Dee–but they were poorly paid and wholly inefficient. The problem was almost nationwide. In some districts it seemed that nearly every man, woman and child was a salmon poacher, and local bailiffs could not be expected to arrest people well known to them, especially relatives. 'It is quite certain', said Grimble, 'that far better results would be obtained by employing one-fifth of the number [of bailiffs] who were properly paid and who were strangers to the district.'

Apart from control of poaching, there was urgent need to reduce the number of drift nets, abolish snap nets, and 'order the Coastguards and the Constabulary to help in the preservation of the spawning beds, and the enforcement of the weekly close time'. Were this done, 'all would soon be well with the Irish fisheries. . . . The evils of weirs, water abstraction, and pollution are not nearly so overwhelming in Ireland as they are in England and Scotland.'[28]

Dams and fish

The creation of an independent nation in 1922 marked a new era in Ireland's economic history. High on the list of objectives was the development of its rivers to provide the precious mechanical ingredient of modern life–low-cost electricity. The Shannon scheme was the first great hydro-electric project undertaken by the fledgling republic. It marked the beginning of an economic revolution. Five rivers have been harnessed up to now: in addition to the Shannon, the Lee above Cork, the Liffey at Leixlip (landmark of the Danes) and Poulpahouca, the Erne at Ballyshannon, and the Clady. The demand for electricity for domestic and industrial use is rising steadily.

With the coming of electricity a new world was opened to urban and rural inhabitants. In the remote sections of the country, where life has stood still for centuries, where many families dwell in whitewashed one-room cottages with thatched roofs and earthen floors, candles have been snuffed out and kerosene lamps doused as electricity has come to the area. Farm work can now be done with power to lighten the chores. Radios and television can be tuned in to the world's news and entertainment; water pumps, even small refrigerators and other appliances, installed.

Rural electrification did not get started until 1948, when 2,200 consumers were connected to the lines of the Electricity Supply Board, the nationalized electricity agency, and progress was slow for many years. Now some 300,000 rural families enjoy the boon of electricity and even the remotest settlements, on the bleak coasts, are receiving this service.

The Shannon project (Figure 27) is the largest in Ireland. It was completed in 1927 and involved the construction of a dam and power station at Ardnacrusha, 3½ miles above Limerick, and a dam at Parteen below Killaloe.

The three Shannon lakes, Loughs Derg, Ree and Allen, provide the main water storage for the Ardnacrusha station, and the main control at O'Brien's Bridge comprises a weir with three sluice gates across the old river-bed and the adjoining intake to the headrace canal, 7½ miles long, which conveys the water required for the turbines to a 100-foot head at the dam. The power is taken from the station for transmission to Dublin and other parts of the country. A tailrace over a mile long, excavated through rock, carries the water back to the Shannon River. Barges are lifted from the tailrace to the headrace through a navigation lock.

When the Government formulated the Shannon scheme in the 1920s it was known that the river had been overfished and the runs were but a fraction of earlier times. Further declines were forecast. 'It was hoped', says R. L. Williams, Fisheries Manager of the Electricity Supply Board, 'that salmon would continue to move upstream to their spawning grounds, through the old river channel, but unfortunately the absence of a fish pass in the power dam at Ardnacrusha, coupled with the small flow in the old river, resulted in the almost total loss of two salmon cycles which were completed in 1934.' The Government therefore 'decided that all the private fisheries in the river above Limerick City should be acquired by the Electricity Board which was given power to compensate the owners . . . and statutory responsibility for development of the fisheries, subject and without prejudice to its primary function of supplying electricity'.

Thus the Board found itself a commercial fishery owner at a time when the salmon stocks were at their lowest ebb and 'there was real danger that the species would disappear from the catchment'. Two principal measures were taken to conserve the stock: (1) various experiments, which were unsuccessful, to keep the salmon out of the tailrace area and ensure that they would move upstream through the old river-bed; and (2) a voluntary reduction in the commercial netting operations. A large counting fence, Thomond Weir, was built in 1939 which could be used as a commercial fishing weir where a portion of the run would be cropped. 'These measures, coupled with the build-up of stock in a tributary of the Shannon not affected by the project, ensured the survival of the stock in the critical years, but up to 1955 the fishery was only maintained at a relatively low level of production.'[29] In 1956 the Board decided that the time was propitious for embarking on a large-scale programme of expansion designed to reopen the major catchment area to salmon. This involved the construction of a Borland fish pass at Ardnacrusha dam to facilitate the migration of salmon and elvers, and a large rearing station for young salmon; cleaning the spawning streams and feeding grounds of the parr; ensuring the safety of the parr by reducing predation; and designing devices to ensure safe passage of smolts and kelts.

Smolts are now admitted to the headrace and find their way into the navigation lock, which is operated at night when the generating station is closed. Since the little fish as well as the kelts are reluctant to enter dark passages, they are shepherded through the lock by a battery of electric lights. The river is restocked with salmon bred at Parteen hatchery which has a capacity of six million fry and 200,000 smolts annually.

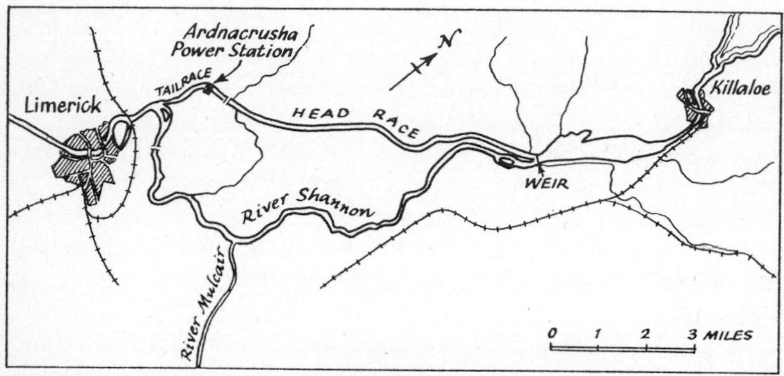

Figure 27

River Shannon hydro-electric development.

The weir at Thomond is a remarkable example of its kind, 480 feet across and anchored on 22 light concrete piers. One may watch the fish heading upstream, fresh from the sea, with the sea lice still on their bodies, travelling along its grid, to and fro, desperately seeking an opening. When they find it they may hover suspiciously in groups until one of them bravely ventures in. The others then follow, in single file, and are counted as they cross a white plate and head upstream. Another unique feature of this weir is the electrical installation which kills the fish for marketing.

The success of the project is shown in the rapid increase of fish passing the dam (Table 20). In the decade 1945–55 the average run counted at Thomond weir was 11,600 salmon yearly. A record horde of over 21,000 appeared in 1962; 23,300 in 1963; 14,000 in 1964; and 19,700 in 1965. The Board only takes 28 per cent of the run at this point. The bulk of the Shannon catches is still made by the 'public' fishermen in the long estuary, and by rodsmen. There is sport fishing at Castleconnell beside Limerick; on the nearby Mulcair tributary; in the Nenagh, Little Brosna and Suck Rivers; and

Table 20
Salmon counts at Shannon River installations
1959–1965
(*numbers of fish*)

Year	*Ardnacrusha*	*Thomond weir*
1959	1,132	11,518
1960	1,148	7,966
1961	1,216	5,455
1962	3,407	21,120
1963	4,873	23,322
1964	4,662	13,997
1965	7,178	19,704

Source: Electricity Supply Board.

up north as far as Athlone. Although a portion of the Shannon has been harnessed, pleasure boats still glide along the uncluttered, lazy river, operating out of old towns and calling at places with poetic names like Lanesborough, Shannonbridge, Banagher, Portumna and Dromineer.

Above Ardnacrusha dam is the Parteen weir where the Parteen hatchery is located. Here one-year-old smolts are bred for release mainly in the Shannon. The hatchery is based on the Swedish system but as yet there are no automatic feeders.

The Electricity Supply Board is engaged in rehabilitating the fisheries of the River Erne which were imperilled by the construction of two hydro-electric dams, one with a head of 94 feet and the other 33 feet. The harnessing of the river at Ballyshannon involved the excavation of a tailrace from the estuary to Cathaleen's Falls and the formation, above that, of a lake-reservoir of about 900 acres. A celebrated salmon leap has been drowned, but one may still see the fish –sometimes densely packed–waiting to enter the pool-type pass, similar to that at Pitlochry. As one stands at the power station of Ballyshannon, facing Donegal Bay, the horizon turns pink and then purple when the sun sets; the fish are slowly climbing the well-watered ladder, and go into the reservoir without any apprehension. Regulations ensure that 3,000 salmon are counted at the fish pass before commercial fishing is permitted. In 1965 8,715 salmon were counted and the limitation on fishing was removed for the 1966 season. In contrast, the commercial season comprised only thirteen days in 1961, while in 1963 the six draft nets licensed caught only 242 fish.[30]

On the River Lee, harnessed above Cork, salmon runs were seriously reduced after two power dams were built, at Iniscarra and Carrigadrohid, and the misty valley was flooded. In the decade 1949–59 the average annual catch was 8,200 salmon, but after that only a few hundred were taken each year, rising to 1,300 in 1963; the escapement dropped to 474 that year. This collapse appears to be due to complex factors such as the curtailment of spawning and nursery areas, an explosion of the pike population which preys on tiny salmon, maceration of smolts in the turbines, etc.

The Liffey has been dammed at Leixlip where a 60-foot drop in the flow between Celbridge, a picturesque village on the banks of the stream (home of Swift's ill-fated friend 'Vanessa'), and Leixlip provides a small amount of power. An ingeniously contrived fish pass, based on the principle of a canal lock, permits the salmon to move upstream to their spawning beds stretching almost as far as Golden Falls dam. The small runs on the Liffey have thus been preserved.

The salmon industry today

It is clear that Ireland's salmon resource which was declining around the turn of the century, according to Grimble's survey of the

---

17a. Parteen fish pass and hatchery, Ireland, showing temporary holding ponds and feeder pipe; also intake for fish-holding ponds and the exit drain into the mouth of the fish pass.

17b. Commercial fish trap at Thomond weir, Ireland, showing the electrodes which are used for electrocuting the fish taken for sale. Killing the fish in this way is preferable to the traditional 'knock on the head' in that it preserves the appearance of the fish and keeping qualities are enhanced.

rivers, has made a strong comeback in recent decades. This may be due partly at least to better management of the fishery. There are seventeen Boards of Conservators in the Republic, and three in Northern Ireland. The binational Foyle Fisheries Commission manages the lucrative fisheries in the Foyle district. These bodies are responsible for the protection and enhancement of salmon, trout and other freshwater fisheries. Each board consists of elected and representative members from the district. All holders of netting licences and most ratepayers are permitted to vote. The Conservators obtain their revenues from holders of fishing licences and from rates (taxes) levied on owners of private fisheries, and in some cases from state grants as well.

In Ireland fresh waters are owned privately but the public has a right to fish in most tidal waters and in the sea. Licences to fish for salmon are obtainable from the Boards of Conservators. The Fisheries (Consolidation) Act of 1959 is the basic statute for inland fisheries.

Salmon and grilse catches in Ireland (excluding Northern Ireland) showed a consistent uptrend in the last two decades (Table 21). The bulk of the salmon are landed in the Limerick, Ballina, Waterford, Kerry, Lismore, Letterkenny, Drogheda, Cork and Ballyshannon districts (Table 22).

A large part of the commercial catch is made by persons who fish under the common law right in the sea or tidal waters of rivers to which 'a valid claim to a several or exclusive fishery has not been established'. Many of these people have small farms or other low-income activities and are dependent upon salmon fishing to eke out their livelihood. Without opportunities to catch salmon their families would fall below subsistence standards.

The commercial fishery is also important to the economy of Ireland because it earns a sizeable amount of foreign exchange. The bulk of the catch is sold to eager foreign buyers, mostly in Great Britain. For instance, if you stand at Rosslare station you will see the trains run alongside the ships in the harbour and the cases of salmon, with other freight, loaded directly onto the vessel. Similarly at Fishguard Quay the fish are unloaded from the ship onto the train alongside. Salmon shipped via Dublin and Shannon airports are

---

18. Estuary stake weir trap used on the River Shannon, Ireland.

Table 21
Salmon and grilse catches in Ireland,* 1945–1965
(*1,000 pounds*)

Year	*Commercial methods*	*Rods*	*Total*
1945	905	114	1,019
1946	1,483	109	1,592
1947	1,514	150	1,664
1948	1,908	176	2,084
1949	2,020	173	2,193
1950	1,861	242	2,103
1951	2,580	250	2,830
1952	1,633	225	1,858
1953	1,640	211	1,851
1954	1,684	293	1,977
1955	1,014	247	1,261
1956	1,179	264	1,443
1957	1,491	309	1,800
1958	1,279	375	1,654
1959	1,364	260	1,624
1960	1,134	230	1,364
1961	1,153	193	1,346
1962	2,606	258	2,864
1963	2,495	342	2,837
1964	2,624	389	3,013
1965	2,453	416	2,869

* Excluding Northern Ireland.
Source: *Irish Fisheries Investigations*, Department of Agriculture and Fisheries, Series A, No. 1, 1965.

destined mainly for Continental markets. Much of the savoury salmon featured in London restaurants and gracing the bars of innumerable English pubs emanate from Irish waters. The number of boxes of Irish salmon delivered to Billingsgate Market is on

Table 22
Salmon catches (commercial and sports) in Ireland,*
by district, 1963
(*pounds*)

District	*Total*	*Nets*	*Rods*
Dublin	11,289	7,161	4,128
Wexford	73,461	43,894	29,567
Waterford	415,216	371,890	43,236
Lismore	299,689	259,826	39,863
Cork	115,960	87,077	28,883
Kerry	313,948	267,511	46,437
Limerick	406,773	358,956	47,817
Galway	60,342	52,661	7,681
Connemara	4,842	—	4,842
Ballinokill	35,637	28,225	7,412
Bangor	92,312	80,172	12,140
Ballina	391,625	374,039	17,586
Sligo	70,081	61,969	8,112
Ballyshannon	102,247	96,450	5,797
Letterkenny	230,455	212,673	17,782
Dundalk	77,245	70,250	6,995
Drogheda	135,608	122,347	13,261
Total	2,836,640	2,495,101	341,539

* Excluding Northern Ireland.
Source: The Sea and Inland Fisheries Report for 1963, Department of Lands, Fisheries Division.

the average almost equal to that delivered from Scotland. England takes about 90 per cent of the total salmon exports.[31]

Salmon angling

The demand for salmon angling is increasing swiftly in Ireland. This trend is reflected in the number of rod licences issued, which increased fourfold in the last two decades. In 1965 anglers took 14·5 per cent of the total salmon catch, compared with 12·9 per cent in 1964.

Sports fishing is an important income producer, for it creates jobs for persons who provide services to anglers, boosts hotel business and aids the economy in other ways. Went estimates that every visiting fisherman spends not less than £30 ($84) to catch a salmon and since in many cases he brings his wife and family–who may not fish–considerable income accrues. The Irish Government is advertising salmon fishing heavily as a tourist attraction. The rod catch tripled between 1945 and 1965.

The Irish Tourist Board lists the Liffey, Slaney, Barrow, Nore, Suir, Cork Blackwater, Bandon, Feale, Maigue, parts of the Shannon and some of its tributaries, Corrib, Moy, Ballisodare, Bundrowes, Boyne, Kells Blackwater, Glyde, and Dee as among the best salmon rivers.

The Irish salmon disease

In the autumn of 1964 diseased sea-trout were noticed in the Cummeragh River near Waterville in County Kerry; in November these were joined by diseased salmon. Next spring sick salmon were also found in other rivers in County Kerry and in the river Feale. In the autumn of 1965 many fish died in the Bandon, Lee and Blackwater rivers in County Cork and it was clear in the spring of 1966 that the disease had appeared in these rivers and in the Slaney, further east. It also infected the Shannon and, by the end of May, had spread up the east coast to the Liffey. It appeared in the Faughan and Bush rivers in northern Ireland during the summer and then in the Cumberland rivers Calder, Esk and Irt where many sea-trout also died. By the autumn it had spread to the Eden and to other rivers flowing into the Solway Firth and to north Lancashire rivers including the Lune and the Ribble. In 1967 the disease spread to North Wales and to the Tweed and other eastern Scottish rivers.

Establishing the cause of the disease has proved difficult. Badly affected fish have large patches of the fungus *Saprolegnia* but this is almost certainly a secondary infection. In May 1966 Dr. Margaret Brown, biologist to the Salmon and Trout Association, and her colleague Dr. Vera Collins provisionally diagnosed the primary infection as caused by a myxobacterium *Cytophaga columnaris* which is well known in North American Pacific rivers. But the situation seems to be complicated and it is possible that a virus or an unidentified fungus may be involved. The disease is now called Ulcerative Dermal Necrosis (U.D.N.), a name which describes the symptoms of heavily infected fish without indicating a cause.

Sick fish lose the urge to migrate upstream and tend to lie in sluggish waters where they are very conspicuous because of the white patches of fungus. Many are probably swept downstream by floods. The incidence of the disease becomes much less in the warmer summer months but so far it has always reappeared in autumn.

Future of the resource

The harvest of salmon has shown a healthy upward trend in Ireland in recent years–one of the few countries where this species is still found that can point with pride to its record.

As we survey the history of the Irish salmon resource we see that its relatively good fortune is due partly to the drastic reduction of fixed gear after 1863 and partly to the conservation measures initiated by the Government, proprietors, and others in recent years, especially the rehabilitation of derelict stretches of rivers and the large-scale restocking programme. A good example of the stream development work is on the Ennistymon River in County Clare. Salmon used to come up to the waterfall at the head of the tidal portion of the river and, during favourable periods of flow, manage to leap or climb a portion of the deeply-sloping rapids, but the last 15 feet usually proved to be impassable. Exhausted, the fish would drop back downstream and make their way to small tributaries which flow into the Ennistymon and presumably complete their spawning act. In 1963 a 'Denil' type of fish pass was installed, thus opening 27 miles of habitat in the upper river, where fry and adult fish had been planted by the local anglers' club. In the very first year of its existence some 500 adult salmon negotiated the Ennistymon pass and reports since then have been encouraging.

Government hatcheries now produce over 5,000,000 salmon ova and several hundred thousand smolts annually.

An important factor in the healthy state of the salmon population is the relative lack of industrial development. With few exceptions, the streams run clear, reflecting every colour of the sky; fish and insect life abound.

As industries spread, however, the purity of flowing waters will be imperilled. Even today many rivers are polluted, mostly with milky wastes from creameries. It is difficult to cause an established effluent to be discontinued, but there are now laws by which projected effluents may be controlled. Even the Cork Blackwater is in parts polluted from factories, dairies and with the sandy liquor from quarries. The domestic sewage problem is improving as local authorities build more disposal and treatment plants.

No longer is poaching a serious menace. Many a countryman may have a yen to snatch a fish or two from the river but the wardens are alert and the penalties severe. In his charming book, *Lovely is the Lee*, Robert Gibbings describes the fate of poachers nowadays, a strong contrast to Grimble's day:

> Do you remember Paddy Ryan and the way he was caught at the poaching? Out in the morning, early, he'd been, and a couple of nice salmon he'd brought back. Hid them in the hayrick in the haggard he did. And when the police came along there was Paddy sitting up at his breakfast rubbing the sleep out of his eyes. As innocent as you please. Every inch of his house they searched and not a sign of a scale. But what did they see as they were going down the lane from the house, only Paddy's two cats, and they with the fish between them. Dragged them out of the hayrick, they did. Twenty pounds it cost him. He couldn't bear the sight of a cat ever after.

Fishery conservation is now strongly rooted in Ireland; the Government budgets for this kind of work are increasing; and the number of biologists and engineers needed is also rising. The future of the salmon therefore looks fairly bright.

Northern Ireland

The six counties of Ulster, which form part of the United Kingdom, are studded with rivers and lakes in many of which salmon are found.

For the most part, the numerous rivers of Ulster are short and have a small volume of water. Only one, the Erne, which issues out of Lough Erne, has been harnessed for power generation, at Bally-

Table 23
Salmon and grilse catches in Northern Ireland
1960–1964
(*metric tons*)

Year	*River Foyle*	*Other rivers*	*Total*
1960	248	55	303
1961	193	54	247
1962	412	74	486
1963	424	74	498
1964	502	91	593

Source: Annual Reports of Foyle Fisheries Commission.

shannon just south of the border, thus transforming an anglers' paradise into a storage reservoir.

In the last few years Northern Ireland has become one of the world's leading producers of Atlantic salmon. It ranked fifth in 1963, and sixth in 1964, when almost 600 tons of salmon and grilse were landed (Table 23). Catches in the Foyle district, which includes all the rivers flowing into the sea between Malin Head in County Donegal and Downhill, rose from about 20,000 fish in 1920 to 100,000 in 1965 (Figure 28). Five-sixths of the catch comes from the River Foyle, managed by the Foyle Fisheries Commission.

Created in 1952 by the Parliaments of Northern Ireland and the Irish Republic, the Commission consists of four members, two nominated by the Irish Minister for Agriculture and Fisheries and two by the Ministry of Commerce in Belfast. This administrative mechanism not only ended the perpetual strife among owners and lessees of the valuable fisheries, including the venerable Irish Society which obtained fishing rights on the River Bann and Lough and the River Foyle by charter in the early seventeenth century, but made possible conservation and improvement of the runs. Since the fishery codes on two sides of the border differed in many respects, the two Parliaments agreed to enact a basic code in identical terms. There was also need to provide an absolute and indefeasible title to the fishery acquired by the two Ministries jointly from the Irish

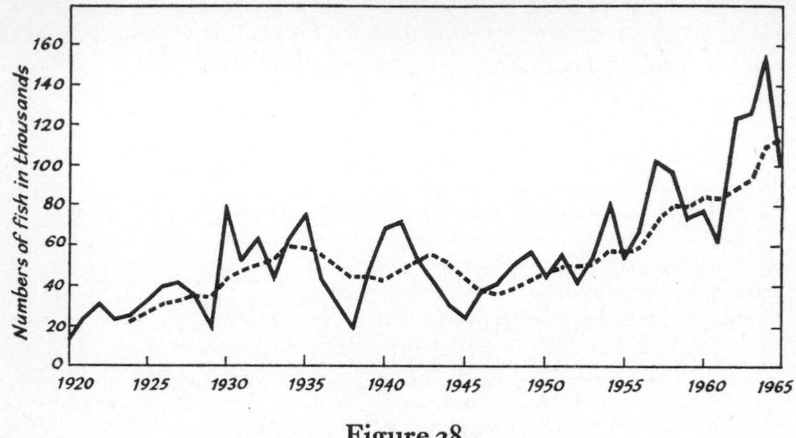

Figure 28

Catches in the River Foyle, 1920–1965. (Dotted line=actual catches; full line=5-yearly moving average.)

Society. The statutes of 1952 gave the Foyle Fisheries Commission the power to promulgate regulations which have the force of law.

The first major tasks of the Commission were to create a licensing system, establish sanctuary areas necessary to conserve fish stocks, and set up election machinery to bring an Advisory Council into being. Next came the formation of an enforcement staff and machinery for operating the Commission's own fishery.

Northern Ireland, like Southern Ireland, is becoming increasingly attractive to salmon anglers. Rod catches rose to a total of 9,300 fish in 1964 in the Foyle District: the best returns were reported from the Rivers Faughan, Roe, Mourne and Strule, Finn and Reelan.[32]

The official publication, *Angling in Ulster Waters*, lists hundreds of rivers and lakes open to rodsmen, and a high proportion are said to contain salmon in greater or lesser quantities. The main rivers favoured by salmon are:

County Antrim–Maine, Braid, Glenwherry, Clough, Bush and Dun
County Down–Shimna and Quoile (Mountains of Mourne district)
County Armagh–Arney and Colebrook (and Loughs Erne and Melvin)
County Tyrone–Mourne, Strule, Derg, Glenelly and Ballinderry
County Derry–Lower Bann, Moyola, Roe and Faughan.

Except for Lough Melvin, which receives spring salmon, the runs consist chiefly of grilse that enter fresh water around the middle of June, if the rains have been obliging; by the middle of July there are sufficient fish in the pools to provide excellent sport.

NOTES

1 Arthur E. J. Went, *Irish Salmon and Salmon Fisheries*, p. 74.
2 *Ibid.*
3 A. Demangeon, *The British Isles*, p. 119.
4 Stephen Gwynn, *From River to River*, p. 144.
5 Paul M. Hansen, 'Report on Recaptures in Greenland Waters of Salmon Tagged in Rivers in America and Europe'.
6 Most of the data on the natural history of the Irish salmon as well as some of the historical material in this chapter are taken with his permission from Dr. Went's numerous and exhaustive publications, especially his *Irish Salmon qnd Salmon Fisheries.*
7 Arthur E. J. Went, 'Fisheries of the Munster Blackwater', p. 130.
8 Arthur E. J. Went, 'Fisheries of the River Liffey', II, pp. 166–9.
9 Arthur E. J. Went, 'The Pursuit of the Salmon in Ireland', pp. 201–3.
10 Quoted by Went, 'A Short History of the Fisheries of the River Nore', p. 26.
11 Arthur E. J. Went, 'The Pursuit of Salmon', p. 225.
12 Arthur E. J. Went, 'Notes upon Some Fixed Engines for the Capture of Salmon, used in Ireland since 1800', pp. 155–6.
13 Constantia Maxwell, *Country and Town in Ireland under the Four Georges*, p. 35.
14 Helen Landreth, *Dear Dark Head*, p. 101.
15 Fynes Moryson, *Itinerary*, pp. 231, 320–1.
16 Alice Stopford Green, *The Making of Ireland and Its Undoing*, p. 48.
17 George O'Brien, *The Economic History of Ireland in the 17th Century*, p. 195.
18 Quoted by Went, 'Fisheries of the River Liffey', I, p. 48.
19 Cecil Woodham-Smith, *The Great Hunger*, p. 76.
20 Augustus Grimble, *Salmon Rivers of Ireland*, Vol. I, p. 80.
21 *Ibid.*, p. 110.
22 *Ibid.*, pp. 142–3.
23 *Ibid.*, pp. 200–1.
24 *Ibid.*, pp. 241–2.
25 *Ibid.*, Vol. II, p. 3.
26 *Ibid.*, p. 159.
27 *Ibid.*, p. 212.
28 *Ibid.*, p. 269.
29 R. L. Williams, Personal communication, March 11, 1966.
30 Bulletin No. 1, Inland Fisheries, Department of Agriculture and Fisheries, 1965.
31 Arthur E. J. Went, 'Review of the Irish Salmon Industry', *Irish Fisheries Investigations*, Series A, No. 1, p. 5.
32 Foyle Fisheries Commission, Annual Report for 1963–64, p. 25.

10

The American Disaster

In a year-end report issued early in 1966 Secretary of the Interior Stewart L. Udall gave Americans a frightening but not exactly new picture of the wildlife resources of the nation. 'Despite unprecedented conservation in 1965,' he said, 'we are still losing the overall battle to save America's endangered species of fish and wildlife from extinction.' He listed 78 species which were in danger of disappearing entirely from the American scene. Among them, along with the California condor, Florida Everglades kite, Key deer, whooping crane, bald and golden eagles, and Florida sandhill crane, was the Atlantic salmon.

It is hard for Americans who have never seen an Atlantic salmon, either in the market or the river, to realize that once they were as numerous as the salmon are now in Alaskan or Pacific North-west waters. Every suitable coastal stream from the Ungava Peninsula to the Housatonic River proliferated with salmon. The quantities taken from the rivers of Labrador, Quebec, Newfoundland, the Maritime Provinces, New England and upper New York state waters are beyond our comprehension today.[1] At times this fish was a drug on the market in some localities in the Colonial era and was used as fertilizer!

What is left of all this piscatorial wealth after three centuries of exploitation by the white man? Canada retains substantial stocks, although they are much reduced from those of the eighteenth century. Maine, which originally had a score of salmon rivers, some of which extend a hundred and more miles into the interior, now possesses only a few where any salmon appear, and the yearly catch in all of them is about 500 fish. All the other New England rivers, and those in northern New York flowing into Lakes Champlain and

Ontario, have been completely deserted by *Salmo salar*. No nation has frittered away its salmon wealth so completely.

How did a fisheries disaster of this magnitude occur? What were the processes of destruction of rivers and motivations behind them? The facts are not easy to uncover and weave into a significant pattern. They are buried in old government reports, in the memoirs of settlers and travellers, and in the logs and letters of fishermen. Scarcely any American historian has bothered to look into this subject.

Salmon in the wilderness

'I think in all the world the like abundance is not to be found', said the English sea captain, Arthur Barlowe, agent for Sir Walter Raleigh, shortly after he discovered Virginia in 1584, and by abundance he referred to natural resources, forests, waters, plants, wildlife, and rivers teeming with fish.

Salmon is the first fish mentioned in the chronicles of North America. The Norse saga of Eric the Red, which describes the voyage of the Icelander Leif Ericson and his band of Vikings about A.D. 1000, says they settled in a land where 'there was no lack of salmon there either in the river or in the lake, and larger salmon than they ever seen before'.[2] When the north-eastern coast of America was rediscovered by Europeans five centuries later they frequently remarked on the occurrence of this famous species of fish. Thus, when John and Sebastian Cabot sailed near Newfoundland on their return to England in 1497 they reported that 'the region abounded in large codfish, salmon, sole and seal'. The Portuguese Gaspar Cortereal as he passed north from Newfoundland in 1500 mentioned 'massimenti di salmoni', a fish which then inhabited Portuguese waters (where it is now extinct), while Jacques Cartier in his description of the great river St. Lawrence, the Gaspé Peninsula and the Bay of Chaleur which he explored in 1535, took note of waters teeming with *Salmo salar*, a species he knew at home.

When Richard Hakluyt, the Elizabethan geographer, composed his *Discourse on Western Planting*, a scheme of settlement in the New World, 'he quoted Cortereal and, listing the flora and fauna of North America by latitudes, placed salmon near the sixtieth degree as an attraction to ambitious emigrants'.[3] Henry Hudson, sailing into the palisade-lined river named for him, in 1609, observed many leaping fishes which he believed to be salmon, according to his mate Juet who reported the voyage, but there is uncertainty whether this species originally inhabited the river.

The rivers inhabited by *Salmo salar* flowed through one of the world's richest forest belts. The European explorers who touched the eastern coast of North America, coming from lands that had been largely deforested, were amazed and awed by the sylvan wilderness. Forests covered the undulating valleys and filled the hills and mountains, the margins of lakes and rivers. Here and there were sand barrens, swamps, savannas, balds, beaver meadows and areas cleared or burned by the Indians, but the dominant feature was the forest: pine, spruce and hemlock; birch, beech and maple; and occasionally oak and other hardwoods. This predominantly coniferous belt stretched from Newfoundland to New York state and sent an arm south along the main body of the Appalachian mountains.

For countless centuries the salmon and other denizens of the rivers had lived in perfect harmony with the primeval wilderness. Their cycles of birth and growth, of migration to the sea and return to the river, were as regular and undistinguished as the rhythm of surrounding forest life, where seedlings grew into slender saplings and saplings became sturdy trees that lived out their span of years. In this pristine world life and death jostled each other, sprightly young trees were nurtured on the rotting stems of the dead. The silence was broken only by the songs of birds and cries of passing animals, the soughing of the wind and murmur of flowing waters, the pelting of rain and crash of thunder, and occasionally the leap of a fish out of the water.

Salmon ran into nearly all the Atlantic coastal rivers, and sometimes into the shallow brooks that laced the wilderness north of 40-degree latitude. 'It is wonderful how well watered this country is', said Thoreau, exploring the Maine woods in the middle of the nineteenth century. 'As you paddle across a lake, bays will be pointed out to you, by following up which, and the tributary stream which empties in, you may after a short portage . . . get into another river, which empties far away from the one you are in.'[4] And most likely there would be salmon disporting in its cool rapid waters, at least before the white man came.

The most renowned river was the Connecticut, longest in New England, which originates in the Connecticut lakes near the Canadian border, forms the boundary between New Hampshire and Vermont, and flows through central Massachusetts and central Connecticut. The abundance of fish in its pristine waters is today unbelievable. Salmon came up a distance of about 300 miles, as far as Colebrook, New Hampshire, having scaled such impressive falls as those at South Hadley and Rockingham. They bred in the headwaters and in various tributaries.

The Merrimack, formed by the confluence of the Winnipesaukee, which issues from the New Hampshire lake of the same name, and the Pemigewasset, which rises near the notch of the White Mountains, courses through New Hampshire for a distance of 78 miles and, after dropping into Massachusetts, flows north-eastward for 35 miles to the sea. Originally salmon nosed their way past all obstacles for 150 miles along the main stem and into the Pemigewasset and even the sub-tributary, Baker's River. They also frequented the Contoocook in small numbers.

The richest salmon river in Maine was the Penobscot, which is about as long as the Connecticut, and receives the waters of numerous affluents, some of them substantial in length and flow. Its west branch follows an exceedingly tortuous course through many lakes, formed where glacial waters in the Ice Age were held back by deposits of gravel, sand and clay, until it joins the more regular east branch. After its confluence with its major tributary, the Mattawamkeag, the river flows southward in a wide valley towards Penobscot Bay. Samuel de Champlain in 1604 sailed up the Penobscot to the end of tidewater and was impressed by the wealth of its fish life as well as its clear waters.

The Kennebec rises in Moosehead Lake in central Maine, runs due south for 150 miles, picking up the flow of the Androscoggin 25 miles below Augusta, and after weaving around a lattice-work of coastal islands in the estuary of Merrymeeting Bay drops into the Atlantic. Salmon used to go up the main river as far as Carratunk Falls and some hardy fish climbed this 16½-foot obstacle to spawn in the main stem and its tributaries.

The Androscoggin drops 1,250 feet in a turbulent course from its source in Rangely, Richardson and Umbagog Lakes in northern Maine, close to the New Hampshire border, to the sea. It flows south-west and then south through New Hampshire and at Gorham swings into Maine, past rolling hills to the inner coastal lowland, and then south-east to join the Kennebec. In its unspoiled state the

Androscoggin was a magnificently-endowed river. It was limpid and swift, with many gravelly stretches where the fish like to lay their eggs. However, the numerous falls, like those at Lewiston, turned back many of the migrants, and those that scaled this barrier were confronted by insurmountable cataracts at East Rumford.

Such were some of the rivers harbouring salmon in New England. Salmon of the land-locked variety were found in Lakes Ontario and Champlain and their feeder streams.

The runs

Salmon entered the New England and New York rivers commonly in the spring when the ice had disappeared from the streams, the ground had thawed, the sun was warming up, and flowers poked their heads above the ground. They moved into the rivers from April through August, with the runs peaking mostly in June. In the Connecticut the majority arrived in April and May, although a few fish entered in July and even later, and odd individuals came in winter.[5] If they could surmount various natural obstacles, and this depended on the volume of flow, they would move rather swiftly to their spawning areas in the headwaters. Spawning occurred in the fall. The smolts went to sea in the second or third spring of their lives, and returned in two or three years. The large runs of grilse which are features of Canadian stocks were not observed in rivers of the United States. Thus, Alfred L. Meister, biologist for the Maine Sea-Run Salmon Commission, in sampling the small number of fish that now inhabit Maine waters, says that grilse account for but 2 to 3 per cent of the runs; 87 per cent are first spawners, and 11 per cent have successfully survived spawning and are returning for the second or third time.[6]

New light was thrown on the oceanic migrations of North American salmon by the recovery of two tagged fish from the Narraguagus River in the Greenland fishery. One adult, tagged on September 10, 1962, was recaptured in Amerdloq Fjord, Holsteinsborg, over a year later, while another, released on September 11, 1963, was recovered within 14 months in the same locality. The fish had swum at least 1,890 nautical miles and had almost doubled their weights. These were the first solid proofs that Maine salmon, like the Canadian, feed in the sub-Arctic waters.

The Indian fishery

From the scanty records available it appears that salmon were important items in the food supply of some north-eastern Indian tribes who taught the white men how to fish for them. Williamson, in his *History of the State of Maine*, says that 'the fish were caught by hook and line, by entangling them in weirs, by dipping with scoop nets, or by striking them with spears'. Indian fish lines and nets were made of deer's sinews, bark of trees, or tough grass spun into threads, while the hooks were made of bone. The aborigines also built stone weirs. Thoreau said that the remains of such weirs were still to be seen in his time on the Winnepesaukee, one of the headwaters of the Merrimack.

Commonly the Indians fished at the falls of the rivers where the salmon congregated. A man in a birch-bark canoe, standing erect with a wooden spear in his hand, would pin the fish as the craft skimmed over the surface of the water. This, of course, was but one way of taking them.

Bellows Falls on the Connecticut was a favourite camping ground for the Abnaki, partly because of the plentiful salmon and shad and other fish that came up to this point. Here the river descends in a foaming cataract for a considerable distance and is islanded with steep rocks. The falls of the Androscoggin were called by the Indians 'a place of much fish, fowl and beasts'. At the confluence of the Concord and Merrimack Rivers there was a fishing station, antedating the coming of the white men, where shad, salmon, lampreys, eel, sturgeon, bass and other fish were taken. Here in the seventeenth century an English magistrate used to come once a year, during the fishing season, accompanied by a minister who 'took the opportunity to spread the net of the gospel, to fish for their souls'.[7]

At what is now Manchester the Merrimack roared wildly over granite ledges and fell 80 feet in the course of half a mile in ceaseless spray to the rocks below. This was Amoskeag Falls where the Indians had a fishing village long before the colonists arrived.

Many other streams were exploited by the Indians in New England, a subject about which we know relatively little. Champlain found an Indian fishery when he discovered the Big Chazy River which empties into Lake Champlain, a treasure-house of salmon.

The Colonial fishery

The colonists preferred sturgeon to shad or salmon, although all of them were plentiful in the rivers. Sturgeon was caught in such immense quantities in the Hudson Valley that it was dubbed 'Albany beef', while shad swarmed in the early summer when a fisherman could take thousands in a few days and sell them for a penny each.

It does not seem that salmon was assiduously fished until about the end of the seventeenth century when families in the Connecticut Valley began to salt them in casks. However, they were seldom sold until the eighteenth century, for they fetched but little: a penny a pound in Hartford and other places, rising to between two and three pence a pound by the time of the American Revolution.

When salmon acquired some popularity as a food item they were captured at the falls with dip nets and in the rivers with seines. In Maine they were almost always taken by meshing nets, either stationary or drifting. 'At points where the shore was bold a net would be set directly from it, the end being made fast to a stake and the outer end being kept in place by killocks anchored off at a proper distance. On a gently sloping shore the fishermen would build a brush hedge to a suitable distance from shore and set the net at the end of that. The size of these nets was not uniform, but a common length was 40 feet, for use on a bold shore. . . . In 1814 the length of the nets set in the Penobscot River, including any other contrivance to which they might be attached, was limited by statute to one-third the width of the stream where used.'[8]

Drifting for salmon was practised in all the rivers, sometimes over almost the entire length of the stream, though the best spots were just below natural obstructions. As the runs diminished, drifting on the lower courses was gradually abandoned, and in the nineteenth century laws were passed in Maine forbidding fishing within 500 yards of a dam or fishway.

In the early days of the Maine fishery the bulk of the salmon was

---

19a. A low dam without a fishway, one of hundreds dotting the rivers of Maine, U.S.A., denies access of Atlantic salmon to spawning and nursery area upstream.

19b. Sheepscot River fishway, Cooper Mills, Maine.

either salted down or smoked. Salted salmon was mostly sold in distant markets: smoked salmon also became an attractive item of commerce.[9]

In 1729 we hear of petitions to erect salmon weirs in New Hampshire, thus indicating that the fish were regarded as worth catching in that area. There was a law in Massachusetts requiring permission from the Court of Sessions for building weirs or fishing dams. The fishery was already a reality by 1740 for a traveller named Bennet noted that in Boston there was plenty of salmon in the market and 'these they sell for about a shilling apiece which will weigh 14 or 15 pounds'.[10] In the second half of the century salmon and other freshwater fishing was an important economic activity in the Connecticut Valley. 'Shad, bass and salmon more than half support the province', wrote Peters in his *History of Connecticut* (1783). 'From the number of seines employed to catch the fish passing up the locks one might be led to suppose that the whole must be stopped, yet in six months' time they return to the sea in such multitudes of young ones as to fill the Connecticut River for many days, and no finite being can number them.'[11]

Sports fishing was not unknown in the Colonial era, but it was not the kind practised by Izaak Walton. Gentlemen sometimes indulged in the sport of spearing salmon, as we learn from the diary of Judge Matthew Patten of Bedford, New Hampshire, which covers the years 1754 to 1788. His favourite haunt was Amoskeag Falls, where salmon were not only speared but captured with fly nets set across the channel, or by fish traps called 'pots'. Patten apparently fished for the market as well and used all three methods. Colonel Theodore Atkinson, one of the richest men of the province, in contrast, came for sport alone, driving the 40 miles from Portsmouth purely for the thrill of spearing and gaffing the leaping fishes.

As the Colonial period came to a close the anadromous fisheries in some rivers were already diminishing, due to the custom of blockading streams to provide a supply of water for settlements or local

---

20. An example of restoration of salmon rivers. The Cathance Lake outlet dam and fishway control the water level in Cathance Lake and the water flows in Cathance stream, a major tributary of the Dennys River, in south-eastern Maine, U.S.A.

mills. Some towns, like Machias, Maine, saw the need for passing laws requiring by-passes for the fish, but increasingly dams were built without any means of fish passage, or if they had such gaps, they proved often to be ineffective. Many dams fell into disrepair in time and were abandoned, but they continued to obstruct the streams and made fish migration difficult or impossible.

In 1771 the colony of New York passed a law forbidding the taking of salmon for five years from the newly stocked Hudson River.

Demise of southern New England rivers

After about 170 years of colonization there were less than four million people in the United States in 1790 and beyond the fall line of the rivers settlements were generally sparse. There the Indians usually shared the land with fur trappers, traders and their entourages. Even along the Atlantic seaboard the wilderness was still dominant, except around the few colonial towns. But changes were coming. Population was to increase rapidly, the face of the land would be greatly altered, and some of the natural resources which seemed inexhaustible to the colonists would diminish and even disappear.

The decline of the salmon had already begun in some localities in the eighteenth century, not only because of the damming of smaller streams, but because of excessive pursuit of the fish with nets and spears and other implements. It was not, however, until the first half of the nineteenth century, when industrialists seized upon the water power of larger streams and some of their affluents, and blockaded nursery grounds, that the rivers began to lose their fisheries.

The American factory system for cotton spinning and weaving was born in New England. By 1840 there were 1,200 such establishments in the United States and two-thirds of them were in New England. For example, Francis C. Lowell, inventor of the first American power loom, established his factory on the Merrimack River in 1822 and named it Lowell. Woollen mills arose at Lawrence upstream around 1847. These two cities, pre-emptying much of the flow of the river, ruined the Merrimack fisheries. The same story was repeated on numerous waterways in Connecticut, Rhode Island,

Massachusetts, New Hampshire and Maine which were harnessed to factories that made firearms, furniture, wooden clocks, machine tools, shoes, paper and a great variety of other commodities.

The fate of the Connecticut River illustrates the process by which Americans, with their prodigal exploitation of natural resources and utter lack of a sense of conservation, at least until the late nineteenth century, deprived themselves of one of the major food fishes in the rivers. As late as 1790, according to Jeremy Belknap in his *History of New Hampshire*, salmon and other migratory fish ascended the Connecticut up to its farthest reach. There was at times such a plethora of fish that it was not uncommon to hear of bond-servants refusing to work unless their rations of salmon were reduced. Also, when a housewife went to purchase shad in the Connecticut Valley in the later eighteenth century, the fishmonger might stipulate that she take salmon as a tie-in sale. It was possible to catch 3,700 salmon in one haul in Old Saybrook's South Cove. Yet by 1814, according to Dr. Samuel Latham Mitchill, in *The Fishes of New York*, New York City was no longer able to get its salmon supply from the Connecticut but had to bring it, covered with ice, from the distant Kennebec. The Reverend David Dudley Field, writing in 1819, averred that *Salmo salar* had scarcely been seen in the Connecticut for twenty years. What had caused the precipitous decline?

In 1798 a corporation known as the Upper Locks and Canal Company built a 16-foot dam across the Connecticut at Hadley Falls. There was no law requiring the installation of a fish ladder. Later, other dams were built downstream without fish passes. For about the first decade of the new century many salmon made their way to the upper waters and vainly attempted to reach their spawning grounds. When Timothy Dwight, President of Yale, visited the Connecticut Valley around 1810, he noted that 'the waters . . . are remarkably pure and light. . . . The tributary streams, almost without exception, issue from hills, formed by stone, covered with gravelly soil.' But salmon had largely deserted the river. Shad, formerly taken as far up as Bellows Falls, were now stopped by a dam at Montague. Instead of shad and salmon the river was crowded with bass.[12] When a solitary salmon strayed into the Connecticut in 1872 the Saybrook fishermen, never having seen this fish, could not identify it!

In his report for 1872–73 the U.S. Commissioner of Fish and Fisheries said:

The most serious artificial obstruction in any of the American rivers to the upward movement of the salmon as well as other fish, so far realized, has proved to be Holyoke dam at South Hadley Falls; and persistent effort has been made for many years by the Commissioners of Massachusetts, aided by those of other states, to cause the powerful corporation owning the dam to introduce a proper fish-way. An act of the Massachusetts legislature requiring this to be done was contested by the company, the suit being carried successively to the supreme court of the state, and then to that of the United States. Beaten on all points, the company has finally yielded gracefully to the necessity, and is now engaged in erecting a fish-way, . . . in accordance with the unanimous recommendation of the commissioners of all the states through which the Connecticut River flows.[13]

Marshall McDonald, writing in 1887, commented that the costly fishway did not bring any results: 'certainly no shad have ascended it, and no salmon, if their capture above that point is to serve as a criterion'.[14]

Salmon fry were planted in the Connecticut by the state Fish and Game Department, but as the 1878 Report of the New Hampshire Fish and Game Department said: 'In addition to a large number of seines, an army of gillnets is permitted to patrol the river, day and night. And last, not least, a law has been passed allowing the capture of all adult salmon, which gives them no chance to reach their spawning grounds.'[15] Thus the fry reached the smolt stage, went to sea, and returned to the river, only to be netted at the mouth. No permanent brood stocks could be established and replanting ceased.

The fate of the Connecticut salmon was duplicated by the Merrimack. In 1839 Thoreau found this stream aesthetically enchanting but bereft of much of its fish life:

Salmon, shad and alewives were formerly abundant here, and taken in weirs by the Indians, who taught this method to the whites, by whom they were used as food and manure, until the dam and afterward the canal at Billerica, and the factories at Lowell, put an end to their migration hitherward; though it is thought that a few more enterprising shad may still be seen. . . . Perchance after a thousand years, if the fishes will be patient, and pass their summers elsewhere, meanwhile, nature will have leveled the Billerica dam, and the Lowell factories, and the Grass-ground River run clear again, to be explored by new migrating shoals.[16]

Salmon runs ended around 1860. Later a fishway was erected over the 27-foot dam at Lawrence but very few came back. In 1886 anadromous fish catches on the Merrimack were 2,139 shad, 32,400 alewives, and 3 salmon. Efforts to restock the Merrimack were futile.[17]

We know little about the history of other rivers in New Hampshire, Connecticut and Rhode Island. There were shoals of fish in the Housatonic, believed to be the southernmost limit of the salmon's range in North America, around 1750, but fifty years later they seem to have disappeared. What happened to the salmon in the Quinnipiac River is not clear, while in the Willamantic they were caught as late as 1822 when a dam without fishways, like most of those built in southern New England, permanently blocked their ascent. On the Thames, of which the Willamantic is a tributary, migration of fish ceased when dams were constructed in the 1830s. Salmon are believed to have been fairly numerous in the Pawtuxet and Pawcatuck Rivers. They vanished at an unknown date.[18]

Demise of the Maine rivers

The destruction of Maine's salmon rivers is at least partly associated with the voracious demand for timber and explosive growth of lumbering, and partly with the usurpation and blockading of the waterways by small manufacturing industries. The Maine woods were prized at first for their plentiful white pine. When this wonderful tree became scarce red pine, spruce and hemlock stands were felled, and later the cedar and fir. Maine's virgin timber wealth disappeared rather quickly.

From nearly every creek and tributary during the spring logs tumbled into the salmon rivers, such as the St. Croix, Penobscot, Androscoggin, Kennebec, East Machias and Machias, Saco and St. John, to form the grand drives, guided by nimble lumberjacks, heading downstream towards the sawdust towns. In 1840 Maine had about 1,380 sawmills, clustered mainly around tidewater. There were 250 sawmills on the Penobscot and its tributaries in 1837. The river was crowded with log booms and lumber rafts, and choked with slabs and other mill waste.

'Here is a close jam, a hard rub at all seasons,' said Thoreau, who visited the Penobscot in 1846, 'and then the once-green tree, long since white, I need not say as the driven snow, but as a driven log, becomes lumber merely. Here your inch-, your two- and your three-inch stuff begins to be, and Mr. Sawyer marks off the spaces which decide the destiny of so many prostrate forests.' He divined rightly that the aim of the lumbermen was to strip the state of Maine of its merchantable timber, 'to drive the forest all out of the country, from every solitary beaver-swamp and mountain-side, as soon as possible'.[19]

The rivers were slowly accumulating mountains of sawdust and other lumbering debris, creating sandbars and narrowing the channels, making fish migration difficult. In 1834 a state law was enacted prohibiting this practice of dumping on the Kennebec, and similar laws came later to protect other streams, but it is doubtful if they were enforced or did much good to abate pollution. Worse still, in the logging operations conducted during the nineteenth century, the era of 'cut out and get out' lumbering, no attention was paid to the impact on watersheds and watercourses. Clear cutting invited soil erosion by wind and water, and this in turn induced siltation of streams. Logs were flushed down the channels of larger streams by splash dams, the water and logs scouring the stream beds and removing the rubble needed by fish for their spawning beds. Protective cover and marginal aquatic plants were destroyed and as a result food for young fish diminished. Jams containing millions of logs, and sometimes stretching for miles, impeded the passage of fish.

The Maine lumber barons grew rich and founded potent dynasties but the forests were stripped and the streams gravely damaged. So far as one can discover, loggers rarely if ever gave a fleeting thought to the fisheries.

While logging must take part of the blame, the damming of rivers without providing fish ladders is the major factor in the destruction of Maine's anadromous fisheries. The survey of salmon rivers by E. M. Stilwell in 1872 revealed that the state was literally forested with mill dams. They served grist mills, cotton and woollen mills, sawmills, tanneries and ironworks, paper mills and other manufacturing operations. The majority were too high for salmon to negotiate and very few had efficient fish passes.

In the 1880s, only seven Maine rivers–the St. Croix, Dennys, East Machias, Penobscot, Sheepscot, Kennebec and Androscoggin–

continued to support regular salmon runs. At times, the fish were seen in six others, but in all the rest 'the ancient brood of salmon was long ago extinguished, and the rare specimens occasionally observed must be regarded either as strays from some of the better-preserved rivers, or as early returning members of the new broods established by artificial culture in several rivers', said Charles G. Atkins. 'The fishermen's nets and spears and pounds would hardly have sufficed to extinguish the brood of salmon in a single river. Commonly these two classes of destructive agents co-operated. The dams held the fish in check while the fishermen caught them out. In some rivers, the dams alone would have sufficed to exterminate the stocks.'[20]

Salmon used to ascend the St. John River, which is partly in Canada, as far as Grand Falls, where they were stopped by a huge cataract. Nearly all the tributaries below this point served as spawning and nursery grounds. The complete closing of some of these affluents by dams and partial closing of others tended to reduce the runs.

The Aroostook is fed by numerous brooks and creeks and meanders for about 140 miles through the province of New Brunswick and the state of Maine to join the St. John six miles east of Fairfield. Aroostook County is potato country and also wilderness. Where the flowering potato fields end the trees stretch illimitably to the west, clothing the low, rugged mountains and filling the valleys. Game abounds in the woods and fish in the rivers and lakes, but not salmon any more.

A century ago salmon were caught a hundred miles from the mouth of the Aroostook. The first dam on the river was built at Caribou about 1890; it had a usable fishway. Hundreds of salmon could be seen at times in the Caribou pool, clearing the dam on the way upriver. In 1906 the Tinker hydro-electric station was constructed to harness the energy of Aroostook Falls in New Brunswick. For thirty years it had no fish pass, thus stopping all migration. When a ladder was finally built it was so poorly designed that fish could successfully hurdle it only in low water.

Other forces contributed to the destruction of the Aroostook fishery, such as gross pollution with untreated domestic sewage, poisonous wash water from frozen-food plants and woollen mills, and wastes from numerous starch factories. Heavy cutting of the forests, especially along lake shores and the banks of brooks, seriously reduced the water-holding capacity of the soil and disrupted stream and lake levels. Moreover, clear cutting of the timber and bulldozing of hauling roads destroyed ground cover and induced quick run-off which generally resulted in lowering the water levels and also led to erosion and siltation. All this tended to impair the habitat of fish.[21] Eventually salmon vanished.

On the St. Croix River dams were built in the eighteenth century but they were provided with fishways. The chief fishery was at Salmon Falls near Calais, where the entire flow of the river is compressed into a narrow and steep chasm, so that shad, salmon and alewives used to jam the main channel and push into several side channels. Here they were readily caught with dip nets, elsewhere with trap weirs and gill nets. It was reported, for instance, that a man could procure 100 salmon in two days, while another person, standing on a log jam below the falls, dip-netted as many in one day. Daily catches of up to 100 barrels at this locality were sometimes made.

In 1825 the Union Mills dam was erected at Calais without a fishway and thus shut out all but the nimblest migrants that could surmount it at high tide. While waiting for favourable opportunities to enter, the salmon were mercilessly speared and netted. Is it any wonder that by 1850 the entire St. Croix River system, which is larger than any east of the Penobscot, yielded but 200 fish? In 1869 fishways were finally installed at the dams at Union Mills and Baring, and other improvements were made at various impoundments, but the damage was irrevocable.

In 1872 Atkins noted that the Dennys River produced about 1,000 salmon yearly, a small fraction of its eighteenth-century wealth. The principal obstacle to greater yields was outrageous fishing in the pools with set nets, dip nets, spears, and even stones and clubs. It is noteworthy that the use of spears, which had caused tremendous damage to salmon runs in the British Isles, was permitted on Maine rivers without restraint.

The 75-mile Machias and its three tributaries had so many salmon as late as the 1830s that a man with a dip net could take 60 in a day at the lower falls and a 10-pound fish could be bought for 50 cents. This bounty was due to the foresight of the town of Machias, situated at the river's mouth. Five years after its settlement in 1763 the stream was completely blocked by dams which not only barred the fish from the upper waters but altered the normal flow of the river. In 1780 the town passed a regulation that ensured passage of a portion of the fish runs through the dams, and both salmon and alewives became abundant. After industry entered the valley, however, new difficulties arose: two dams were built at Machias in 1841–42 and a third at Whitneyville in 1842. Dam owners and operators, as elsewhere, gave no consideration to the fish and controlled stream flow as their business or whims dictated. Fluctuations of flow can be detrimental to so sensitive a creature as the salmon in all phases of its freshwater life, and even where fish ladders are provided the vagaries of stream flow can inflict serious losses on the stocks. Expectedly, the anadromous fishes vanished from the Machias, but a small remnant was able to return after a pool-type fishway was installed at upper Machias dam and at Whitneyville in the 1870s.

Multitudes of salmon frequented the Narraguagus in the olden days. This river was fed by springs, lakes and streams with suitable spawning beds. There were people still living in 1872, when Atkins made his survey, who remembered taking 40 big fish in a night at Cherryfield. There were no close seasons, no patrols or wardens, and no licensing system anywhere in the United States. Fish in the rivers and lakes are public property and hence anybody could help himself to them. Small boats were used to load quantities of salmon in the Narraguagus just above the end of tidewater and at Beddington Lake 16 miles upstream. In time the low impoundments which were negotiable by salmon gave way to higher dams and the river became derelict.

'The works of man have interfered less with the migration of salmon in the Penobscot than in any other large river south of the St. John', said Atkins in 1872. 'Owing to its great volume and other favourable circumstances, dams, quite impassable by salmon, have never been in existence many years at a time.'[22] Considerable nursery areas then remained on the main stem and the upper tributaries, and the river system continued to account for the bulk of Maine's–and eastern United States'–salmon catches well into the twentieth century.

Fishing was carried on in Penobscot Bay with weirs, drift nets and 'pound nets'. The pound net was 11–12 feet deep and 18–20 fathoms long, supported by wooden floats, so that it rose and fell with the tide and was held in place by anchors planted at the end of long 'warps'. The fish were either caught in the mesh or trapped in the pound. The Penobscot type of fish weir was built of stakes and brush, loosely driven into the shore, to which was attached a pound made of netting. Weirs were set usually on the same site year after year, as early in the spring as the water would permit, and in the river a little later. Most commonly they were found on the west side of the bay from Orrington to Belfast and on the east side to Castine. In 1870 there were 160 salmon weirs in operation but the number fluctuated from year to year because of the varying runs, and some of them depended on the capture of menhaden and alewives to make a profit. In lower Penobscot Bay salmon were occasionally caught with hook and line.[23] In the river they were regularly netted between Oldtown and Castine.

Sawdust pollution abated in time but the Penobscot was ultimately ruined by overfishing and repollution from pulp mills and other sources.

About 15,000 salmon were harvested in Penobscot River and Bay in 1872; between 1873 and 1890 catches dropped to an average of 12,000 fish. Landings declined steadily, despite repeated plantings of hatchery stock. In 1947, when salmon weirs were finally declared illegal in Maine, the commercial take on the Penobscot was only 40 fish![24]

The chief fisheries on the Kennebec used to be within 20 miles of the mouth of the river, at Waterville 60 miles upriver, and at Carratunk Falls. At Carratunk it was easy for two men to take a boatload of salmon in a day, and at Ticonic Falls just below Waterville drift nets hauled out several thousand fish each season. Near the mouth of the Kennebec salmon were fished successfully with set nets and weirs. Until 1837, when a dam was built at Augusta, the fisheries flourished. In 1872 the river and its tributaries had 69 dams of varying heights, none of them provided with fishways. 'The dam at Augusta was 18 feet high and would be absolutely impassable were it not for the lock provided for navigation. Through this a greater or less number of salmon passes each year', said Atkins. 'Almost every summer a few of them pass the second, third and fourth dams and are seen at Skowhegan; and not infrequently they pass this point also.'[25] It is understandable that under the circumstances a river with the capacity of the Tyne or Tweed should yield only 500 fish in 1871 and 1,500 in 1873. Eventually it became derelict.

The Androscoggin, although a shorter river, was almost the peer of the Kennebec (which it joins at Merrymeeting Bay) as a salmon producer. However, the dams at Brunswick debarred the fish from their breeding areas early in the nineteenth century, and in 1872 Atkins reported that the Androscoggin salmon were 'utterly decimated' and the 'few specimens now and then seen . . . are no more than we should expect to stray into it from the Kennebec'.[26]

What about the Saco River, flowing down from the White Mountains? Salmon used to come up in goodly numbers as far as Hiram Falls and into the Great and Little Ossipee, its principal affluents. There were thirteen dams in this river system in 1872. Those at Saco and Biddeford rendered the falls at that point, which were always difficult, quite insurmountable. Salmon stocks, depleted in the previous century, became extinct around 1860. Between 1860 and 1873 four specimens were taken at the mouth of the river in shad nets.

Between 1873 and 1889 an average of 150,000 pounds of salmon were landed yearly in the rivers of Maine in addition to quantities taken by individuals for their own use. Very few salmon were caught elsewhere in New England. By 1890 the total commercial yield was only 60,000 pounds of fish. In 1925 Maine had only two salmon rivers left, the Dennys and Penobscot; a small number of fish ran up the St. Croix, where sawdust pollution had abated, and other streams. The deterioration of the resource could not be stopped. Since 1950 the total commercial catch has never exceeded 1,000 pounds a year. The rods take several hundred pounds of salmon annually nowadays.

Salmon in Lake Ontario

It may surprise many readers to learn that Lake Ontario and its feeder streams once possessed tremendous stocks of salmon. The Jesuit Fathers Le Moyne and Le Mercier on their diplomatic mission in 1654 for the French Government to the Onandaga Indians were astonished to see the red men come down the Oswego River in canoes filled with salmon. There were so many fish in the river that they could easily be speared or killed with paddles.

Rivers on both sides of Lake Ontario are known to have been originally inhabited by this species. According to Richard Follett, writing in the *Transactions of the American Fisheries Society* in 1932, probably as many as fifty streams between Hamilton and Kingston on the Canadian side were frequented by *Salmo salar* at some time of the year. The fish were caught as far west as the River Don. On the American side there were ample stocks in the Genesee, Salmon and Oswego Rivers and in smaller streams draining into Lake Ontario as well as the lake itself.

Elizabeth Simpson in her local history, *Mexico, Mother of Towns*, presents numerous quotations from early upstate New York settlers attesting to the abundance of salmon in Salmon Creek, a tributary of Lake Ontario.

The weight of the evidence now is that Lake Ontario salmon were a landlocked variety of *Salmo salar*–not the sea-going kind. From an examination of the scales of two specimens preserved in a museum the Canadian biologist A. A. Blair concluded that they had spent two years in the stream before becoming adults and spawned the next year as grilse, and had never been in salt water. Samuel Wilmot, the pioneer Canadian fish culturist, marked fish trapped at Grafton Creek in the fall of 1868. Many were recaptured by fishermen but none below Quebec. From this he concluded that the fish did not migrate to the sea. Indeed, it was logical to assume that if thousands of fish journeyed all the way to the Gulf of the St. Lawrence and back, some would have been observed by fishermen in the lower river. But none were ever reported downstream.

There was furthermore no evidence that salmon entered Ontario rivers or creeks east of Toronto at any other time than autumn, during the spawning season. Huntsman, who studied all the available historical and biological information about the Ontario salmon in 1944, concluded they must have been a landlocked species that used the lake (just as the salmon use the Baltic Sea) for their feeding migrations.

Salmon used to go up the Oswego River as far as its headwaters in Cayuga and Seneca Lakes. 'Seventy-five years ago,' said Follett, 'farmers near Baldwinsville, New York, actually threw salmon out of the Seneca River with pitchforks, so dense were the schools of fish at that time.' They were taken with gill nets at the mouth of the Oswego. De Witt Clinton, in a 'Discourse Before the Literary and Philosophical Society of New York' in 1815, stated that they were caught in the Seneca River in every month of the year, and sometimes they weighed as much as 37 pounds. They passed the town of Oswego and went up the river in April, and returned to Lake Ontario in September and October, 'much reduced in size and fitness'.[27]

In 1872 when M. C. Edmunds, Fish Commissioner of Vermont, toured the south side of Lake Ontario in his survey of salmon rivers in New York, he found that the fish were no longer seen in the Oswego River. A canal had been built from Oswego to Syracuse which followed nearly the entire course of the river, debouched into it, and rendered it unfit as a salmon stream.[28]

The Salmon River had provided lucrative fishing well into the nineteenth century. In fact, as late as 1836, according to an informant of George Brown Goode, U.S. Commissioner of Fish and Fisheries, two men in a skiff took 230 salmon one October night and two others caught an additional 200 between midnight and morning, presumably on spawning beds, using three-tined spears and a jack lantern. Some nights as many as 2,000 fish were landed at the bridge in Pulaski. 'We have had 1,500 fresh salmon in the fish house at one time', said a fisherman. 'The principal fishing time was September, October and November.'[29]

When Edmunds visited the Salmon River he was enchanted with it. 'A stream admirably adapted to the growth of salmon. There are several dams situated on the river, but so low and in such favourable localities as to give easy passage to the salmon.' It was in fact the only waterway draining into southern Lake Ontario that still harboured salmon, several having been caught both above and below the dams in the preceding year, although its former riches had departed. He recommended it as worthy of consideration for the establishment of a salmon hatchery.

Those who now visit the city of Rochester and gaze upon the placid Genesee River can hardly imagine that here men once fished for salmon as successfully as they do at Galway, Ireland. Prodigious numbers came up every spring, and migrated as far as the falls. But in 1817 Elisha Clark blockaded the stream with a dam at Rochester. Subsequently it was reported that over 10,000 salmon were killed with clubs, spears and pitchforks below the impoundment. 'This of course ended the salmon of the Genesee River for all time', said Follett.

Edmunds visited several small rivers between Syracuse and the Genesee at Rochester and went as far as Niagara River. Many of them 'once had been salmon streams of greater or less celebrity', but the fish had long ago said goodbye to them, and 'neither sawdust nor other foreign matter had aught to do with their extermination. . . . The trap and pound nets have entirely exterminated this fish from the south shore of Lake Ontario. They have been set in the mouths of nearly all the rivers emptying into the lake, and consequently the fish have become an easy prey to the fishermen.'

On the Canadian side they ceased to be regular inhabitants of all waters from Toronto westward in the 1860s, although surviving in some streams to the east that drained into Lake Ontario. Owing to considerable restocking from the hatchery on Wilmot Creek, there was a resurgence of the runs in some waters in the 1870s, but in 1879 a decline set in and eventually all the salmon disappeared. The hatchery was abandoned. The last specimen recorded on any feeder stream was observed in Wilmot Creek in 1896 and two years later a 7-pounder was netted off Scarborough Beach near Toronto.

Ontario fish disappeared for a variety of reasons. Wilmot, the pioneer fish culturist, spoke of 'murder on the fishing grounds'. There was unlimited trap-net fishing along the shores of the lake and in the estuaries. Settlement and clearance of areas around the lake stripped the vegetative cover and, allied with poor agricultural practices, induced erosion and siltation of streams. These forces radically altered the habitat and, coupled with the construction of mill dams, development of bars at the stream mouths and heavy netting, wiped out the salmon stocks of the Lake Ontario region. Repeated attempts to restock the tributary waters were unsuccessful.

Salmon in Lake Champlain

Lake Champlain lies in the broad valley between the Adirondacks and the Green Mountains and for about a hundred miles marks the boundary between New York and Vermont. It is connected with the St. Lawrence through the Richelieu River which drains the lake from the north, as Samuel de Champlain discovered. The cool and pure waters of the lake, fringed with forests, were an ideal habitat for salmon, which were once familiar in the lake, and in the lower reaches of the St. Regis, Chateaugay, Racquet and Grass Rivers in Canada and the Big Chazy, Little Chazy, Salmon, Saranac, Little Ausable, Ausable, Bouquet, Otter Creek, Winooski, Lamoille and Missisquoi on the American side.

We know very little about the biology and migratory habits of the Lake Champlain fish, for they are now extinct. It is believed that, like the Lake Ontario salmon, they were a landlocked variety of *Salmo salar* although a few tramp individuals might have made their way down the Richelieu River to the St. Lawrence and thence to the sea and returned. They reached a size of 20 pounds.

Lake Champlain salmon make their appearance in history with the discoverer of the lake who in 1608 marked on his chart a point, near the present village of Champlain, where an Indian fishery existed on the Big Chazy River. On a map published in 1777 the words 'Salmon Fishery' likewise appear at the north end of the lake. Benedict Arnold, who commanded the Continental forces in this region in 1776, made a notation that William Gilliland, a pioneer settler of Willsborough, New York, 'complimented the American army with fifteen hundred salmon in one year'–evidence enough of their plenitude. The 'extraordinary copiousness' of the fish was due 'to the coolness and purity of the streams which empty into the lake', said Winslow C. Watson, historian of Essex County, 'their short, rapid course with long stretches of gravelly beds, and, up to the middle of the eighteenth century, the absence of destructive human activities'.[30]

By 1842, when Daniel P. Thompson published his *History of Vermont*, the salmon, he noted, had become exceedingly rare. Thirty years later Edmunds found no trace of them in their well-known haunts such as Otter Creek which flows on the Vermont side of Lake Champlain; the Winooski River ('once a fine salmon-stream'); the Missisquoi which rises in Canada and empties into Missisquoi Bay at Swanton, Vermont; the Saranac and Salmon Rivers; and the Big and Little Chazy Rivers. The last run in the Ausable was said to have occurred in 1838.

Tales of their fantastic abundance still floated around the Champlain Valley in the 1870s. The proprietor of the Fouquet Hotel at Plattsburgh told Edmunds that his grandfather used to see immense schools of fish at the mouth of the Saranac River, 'rendering their capture by cartload an easy matter'. The last salmon was taken on this stream in 1824. An old resident on the Salmon River (not to be confused with the stream of the same name in the Lake Ontario region) related that when he was a boy the runs were so heavy his father used to collect enough fish with a pitchfork to fill a one-horse load in the morning before breakfast.[31]

Winslow added evidence of their incredible abundance: 'A record exists of five hundred having been killed in the Bouquet in one afternoon, and as late as 1813 about fifteen hundred pounds of salmon were taken in a single haul of a seine, near Port Kendall.' But they too disappeared. 'The secluded haunts they loved have been invaded; dams have impeded their wonted routes; the filth of occupied streams has disturbed their cleanly habits, and the clangour of steamboats and machinery has excited their fears. Each of these causes is assigned as a circumstance that has deprived the country of an important article of food and a choice luxury.'

'The subject', he concluded, 'is not unworthy the inquiry and investigation of the philosopher of nature.'[32] Salmon were planted in Lake Champlain in 1872 and 1873 but there is no authentic record of their return.

Salmon in the Hudson River

Was the Hudson River originally a salmon stream?

Although Henry Hudson claimed to have seen these fish when he arrived at Sandy Hook, on September 3, 1609, and eleven days later as he passed the Highlands, the weight of the evidence is that he was mistaken. Around 1770 the Colonial government introduced salmon into the Hudson, doubtless transplanted adults, but we do not know how successful this experiment was.

Dr. S. L. Mitchill, pioneer New York ichthyologist, argued that while the river originally harboured shad and sturgeon, it did not possess any salmon, for the following reasons: (1) schools of salmon were never observed in the Colonial period and there was a record only of solitary individuals who may have strayed from the Connecticut or other streams; (2) salmon favour cool, limpid waters whereas the Hudson tends to be discoloured and muddy; and (3) the Dutch word used by Juet, who reported Hudson's journey, is *salm* or *salmpie*, which might refer to trout, a member of the Salmonidae family known to have inhabited the Mohawk, a major tributary of the Hudson.[33]

The prominent fish culturist, A. N. Cheney, in a paper contributed to the *Bulletin of the U.S. Fish Commission* for 1886, conceded that salmon might have spawned in some of the smaller tributaries or in the main stem below Baker's River.

Between 1873 and 1876 the New York Fish Commission planted salmon eggs in Fishkill Creek and in Long Island streams. Some of them grew to smolt stage, went to sea and returned to the river. *Field and Stream* for July 5, 1877, reported that salmon were found in considerable numbers off the mouth of the Hudson and also as far as Hyde Park. One fish netted off Governor's Island weighed 27 pounds, and others were caught near Staten Island and at Seabright, Long Island.

In 1880 the state of Vermont made a small planting af Atlantic salmon fry in the Battenkill which flows from Vermont into the Hudson near Troy. These may have been the fish taken on their return to the river in 1884.

Between 1882 and 1886 over 500,000 fry were released by the U.S. Fish Commission. They reached smolt stage in two years and returned to the river two or three years later weighing 10 to 13 pounds. Many were captured below Troy dam which had no fishway.

The state of New York eventually constructed fish passes at Troy, Mechanicsville and Thompson Mills to facilitate fish passage to the spawning grounds. Dean Sage, a well-known angler, said in 1905: 'I have seen but one of them, that at Mechanicsville, which was built by some incompetent person on plans of his own, and utterly inadequate.' At this dam small numbers of fish assembled but were caught 'by hooks ostensibly baited with pieces of pork, and dragged along the bottom till the "sportsmen" at the other end could feel them against a fish, when a hard jerk sometimes fastened the hook in the luckless creature'.[34]

Thus, despite considerable efforts and expense by state fish and game commissions and the U.S. Fish Commission to introduce salmon into the Hudson River, their attempts came to naught. No subsequent plantings were ever made, apparently.

Angling for salmon

Salmon angling is a late nineteenth-century development in the United States. Several reasons may be advanced for its apparent neglect in contrast to Great Britain. 'The streams of Maine and those of northern and western New York', says Charles E. Goodspeed, historian of American angling, 'in which salmon were formerly abundant were, before the era of railroads, too distant to be frequented by anglers from populous districts of the east; and by the year 1830, when our sportsmen had to some extent become fly-fishers, the opportunity for salmon fishing was lost, for the fish had all [but] deserted those accessible rivers to which they were native.'[35] Obviously, the royal sport could make little headway in a country that was systematically destroying its salmon rivers.

Fly fishing was known to have been practised on the Penobscot and Dennys Rivers as early as the 1830s. Charles Lanman in his *Tour to the River Saguenay* (1848) mentions killing two salmon with a fly rod on the Aroostook and Kennebec. Charles Hallock tells us in *An Angler's Reminiscences* that he killed his first salmon in the deep pool below Aroostook in 1859 and that in the 1860s the Union and Dennys Rivers were the only ones where a fly fisherman could catch these fish in the United States. However, there were very few people of this breed, for Americans generally 'were too busy to while away time in fishing. They hardly knew a trout by sight.'[36]

In Colonial and pioneering days hunting and fishing were the most common ways of enjoying the outdoors but in New England, according to the Puritan ethic, they were only sanctioned when they were necessary for a livelihood. In parts of the United States where the tradition of sports for pleasure lingered, an inheritance of British culture, as in the South, New York and Pennsylvania, fishing was a pastime of the upper classes. 'Hunting and fishing, for mere sport, can never be justified', said *The Housekeeper's Manual* (1873), and for the generality of God-fearing Americans this taboo was effective.[37]

In 1886 Henry P. Wells published *The American Salmon Fisherman*, probably the first book of its kind. It opened with the statement: 'That where there was one fly-fisherman in the United States ten years ago there are ten now, is a general and perhaps unexaggerated belief.' Yet he could name only three rivers where salmon fishing might be obtained (the St. Croix, Dennys and Penobscot) compared with over a hundred in eastern Canada. He reported that over 50 salmon were caught on the St. Croix in 1885; the Dennys was 'a fine natural stream but much obstructed with nets, drift trash from saw mills, and other abominations', although it was believed that these abuses would end soon and 'the river would be well worth the attention of the angler'. The Penobscot offered the best sport because, though its stocks were greatly depleted, it was being restocked with fry from the Craig Brook salmon hatchery, the only one in the United States. From 1885 onwards the history of salmon angling in New England is virtually confined to the Penobscot and mainly to Bangor pool, although some fly fishing was provided on the St. Croix and at Caribou on the Aroostook from 1890 until the Tinker hydro-electric dam blockaded the river in 1906.

W. C. Kendall in his *History of Salmon Angling in New England*, published in 1935, offers a detailed chronicle of the sport in the Penobscot, drawn from newspapers and sport magazines. The belief, widespread in Maine, that salmon would refuse to strike at an artificial fly was overcome in 1885 largely through the feats of Fred W. Ayer, a Bangor resident. Anglers from New York and Boston flocked to Bangor. For about twenty years fishermen had success, although the catches were very small compared to those on the Tay, Wye, or Laerdal.

In 1907 the newspapers reported that the Penobscot sport was doomed because of overangling, pollution by pulp mills, poaching, insufficient restocking, and worst of all by weir fishermen in the bay working night and day, on every tide. In 1904 Dean Sage wrote that the Penobscot 'is fast going under', and the St. Croix was gradually growing worse. The Dennys had already faded out. By 1940 the Penobscot was a dead river–salmon were scarce and fly fishing was ended in Bangor pool.

Maine restoration–too little and perhaps too late?

No appreciable attempts were made to restore any New England salmon rivers until after World War II. A glorious opportunity was missed in the 1930s when ample public works money and labour were available.

Stimulated chiefly by sportsmen, the programme was started on a modest scale with the creation of the Atlantic Sea-Run Salmon Commission in Maine in 1948.

In addition to considerable research, the restoration programme has so far involved eight streams. The state has appropriated about $35,000 annually, while the federal government has expended the same amount in salaries and operational expenses at the modernized Craig Brook hatchery at East Orland. Salmon enthusiasts in Aroostook County and a few legislators teamed together in 1959 and obtained $45,000 of state money for special work on the Aroostook River. A hydro-electric corporation and a large timber company have contributed some funds for work on rivers where they have a special interest and obligation.

The major efforts of the programme are directed at restocking the rivers, removing obstructions, and erecting fishways. The inland waterways of Maine are littered with abandoned dams, even though state laws require that fishways be installed 'where practical, economical, feasible, and . . . needed'. At the mouths of some streams commercial fishing weirs and traps constitute other impediments. For example, a few salmon were still being taken in 1960 in mackerel weirs at the mouth of the Sheepscot River.[38]

Restocking began in 1954 and has continued on an accelerating scale on the main stem or tributaries of the Aroostook (Figure 29), Narraguagus, Dennys, Sheepscot, Penobscot, Machias, Pleasant and East Machias Rivers. At first the practice was followed of releasing only salmon fry. Since 1959 emphasis has been placed on rearing smolts and planting them in the streams where they linger for a few weeks before setting off for the ocean. Much better returns of adult fish have been the result.

Various projects have been completed to improve stream flow and fish passage. The fishway at Machias Gorge was improved and a water control structure and fishway were built on Pleasant River Lake.[39]

A Denil-type fishway was built at Cooper Mills on the Sheepscot, thus opening up new spawning areas. The Dennys, long plagued by low water during the critical period when fish enter the river, was ensured a stable flow with the construction of a water control dam at Cathance Lake. Two Denil-type fishways were installed on the international St. Croix River, one at the dam at Woodland, Maine, and the other at Grand Fall in Kellyland, Maine. Salmon, shad and alewives will now be able successfully to migrate upriver to their spawning grounds at the headwaters. If pollution from a pulp mill can be reduced in the river below Woodlands and the planting of young salmon results in successful and successive migrations up the St. Croix, it may mean that a magnificent salmon river, sterile for almost a century, has been reclaimed.

As a result of these and other improvements, small numbers of salmon have begun to reappear in the Dennys, Machias and Narraguagus, and occasionally in the Pleasant, East Machias and Sheep-

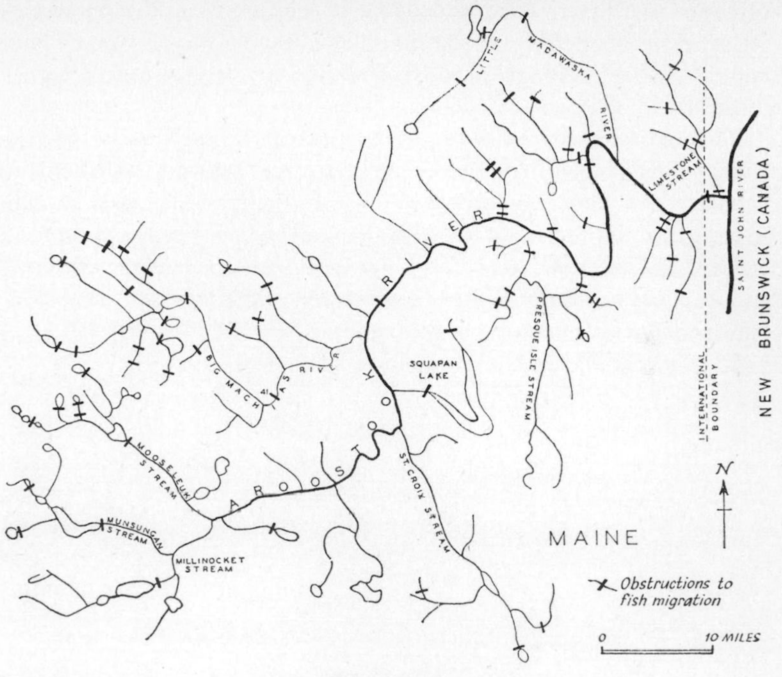

Figure 29

Obstructions to fish migration in Aroostook River drainage.

scot. The run in the Narraguagus is now said to be about 1,000 adult fish, comparable to the stocking of a small river in Canada.

Rod catches on all these streams are about 400 to 500 annually. There is virtually no netting.

In 1965 Congress passed the Anadromous Fish Act to be administered by the U.S. Fish and Wildlife Service. It is designed to enhance the supply of anadromous fish by making $25 million available to the states on a matching basis by 1970.

For the first time, a large sum will be spent to revive a river with considerable potential: namely, the much-abused Penobscot. The Federal Government's allotment for the fiscal year 1966–67 is $125,000. Dr. W. Harry Everhart reports in a personal communication of November 28, 1966:

We plan to spend the money to help build two fishways on the main Penobscot River in the summer of 1967. These fishways will be at Great

Works and at Milford. Then, depending on the allotment of Anadromous Fisheries money in 1968, we plan to remodel the fishways in the Bangor dam (the city of Bangor has already voted $20,000 help) and build a fishway at Veazie on the main Penobscot. This will provide fish passage clear into the headwaters of the Piscataquis and its tributaries. Then in 1969 we plan to build fishways in the West Enfield dam and remodel the fishway in the Mattaceunk dam. This will then open up the important East Branch for spawning and nursery areas. The Bangor Hydro-Electric Company, owner of the dams at Milford and Veazie and the Penobscot Chemical Fibre Company at Great Works, have agreed to furnish half the cost of the fishways in each case.

The U.S. Fish and Wildlife Service plans to build a major Atlantic salmon hatchery in Maine capable of producing 600,000 smolts annually.

If all these plans, which will cost several million dollars, are realized, an annual run of 1,200 to 3,000 fish may eventually be established in a river that once teemed with salmon. Such a run could provide, says Everhart, an angling harvest of 200 to 750 fish each year. No netting will be permitted.[40]

It is often true in the United States that the prick of conscience, sometimes termed 'the conservation ethic', occurs too late or almost too late. This seems to be a valid interpretation of the efforts to resuscitate some of Maine's salmon rivers.

The question is often asked, 'Will the Atlantic salmon ever reach its former abundance?' The U.S. Fish and Wildlife Service replies: 'Probably not, but wise management may some day make them more than the token resource they are today.' The St. Croix alone, according to fishery biologists, can potentially support annual runs of 9,000 to 18,000 salmon.

NOTES

1 The anthropologist Erhard Rostlund who made an exhaustive study of freshwater fish and fishing in native North America concludes that 'there is theoretical reason for thinking that Atlantic salmon, per unit area, was at least as plentiful as Pacific salmon. The Atlantic salmon was only one of several anadromous species on the east coast, but the other fishes - shad, alewife, eel, sturgeon, or striped bass - did not compete with the salmon for spawning grounds. Hence, if the eastern rivers were proportionately as well provided with suitable spawning beds as the western rivers - and I

see no reason to doubt it – and utilized by the salmon to about the same extent in both regions, then the salmon population per unit area could have been as large in the East as in the West. And if the unit area in mind is not water surface but square miles of territory, the salmon population in the East was probably denser than in the West, because there is on the average more water per average square miles of territory in the East than in the West.' (*Freshwater Fish and Fishing in Native North America*, p. 26.)

2 *Vinland History of the Flat Island Book*, p. 51. On the basis of this statement Hjalmar R. Holand, in *Westward from Vinland*, places the Norse settlement on Cape Cod. More likely it was the Labrador coast of Newfoundland. There is no certainty.

3 W. L. McFarland, *Salmon of the Atlantic*, p. 16.

4 H. D. Thoreau, *The Maine Woods*, p. 336.

5 *Frank Forester's Fish and Fishery of the United States and British Provinces of North America*, published in 1850, says that the fish enter American waters rarely before the middle of May, and are taken in the estuaries as late as the end of July.

6 Alfred L. Meister, 'Salmo Salar's Future in Maine', *Atlantic Salmon Journal*, Fall 1965.

7 Daniel Gookin, writing in 1674; quoted by C. E. Goodspeed, *Angling in America*, p. 65.

8 C. G. Atkins, 'The River Fisheries of Maine', p. 679.

9 *Ibid.*, p. 680.

10 Alice Morse Earle, *Home Life in Colonial Days*, p. 123.

11 Quoted by George B. Goode, *Game and Food Fishes of North America*, p. 443.

12 *Travels of Timothy Dwight in New England and New York*, Vol. II, p. 307.

13 *Report of the Commissioner of Fish and Fisheries*, p. lxvii.

14 In G. B. Goode, *The Fisheries and Fishery Industries of the United States*, p. 663.

15 Quoted by C. E. Goodspeed, *op. cit.*, p. 262.

16 H. D. Thoreau, *A Week on the Concord and Merrimack Rivers*, pp. 39–40.

17 C. E. Goodspeed, *op. cit.*, pp. 262–3.

18 C. G. Atkins, 'Local History of Salmon and Salmon Fishing in New England Rivers', pp. 325–7.

19 H. D. Thoreau, *The Maine Woods*, p. 4.

20 C. G. Atkins, *op. cit.*, p. 290.

21 See 'Aroostook River: Salmon Restoration and Fisheries Management', Fishery Research Bulletin No. 4, Maine Dept. of Inland Fisheries and Game.

22 C. G. Atkins, *op. cit.*, p. 302.

23 *Ibid.*, pp. 307–8.

24 'Maine Salmon Survey', conducted in 1959 for the Boone and Crockett Club by the Wildlife Management Institute, Washington, D.C. (unpublished).

25 C. G. Atkins, *op. cit.*, p. 322.

26 *Ibid.*, p. 323.

27 Quoted by C. E. Goodspeed, *op. cit.*, p. 246.

28 M. C. Edmunds, 'Obstructions in the Tributaries of Lake Champlain', pp. 628–9.

29 G. B. Goode, *The Fisheries and Fishery Industries in the United States*, pp. 473–4.
30 Quoted by C. E. Goodspeed, *op. cit.*, p. 250.
31 M. C. Edmunds, *op. cit.*, pp. 624–5.
32 Quoted in the *Report of the Commissioner of Fish and Fisheries for 1872–1873*, p. lxviii.
33 See C. E. Goodspeed, *op. cit.*, p. 247.
34 *Salmon and Trout* by Dean Sage and others, p. 39.
35 C. E. Goodspeed, *op. cit.*, p. 244.
36 *Ibid.*
37 See Hans Huth, *Nature and the American*, p. 55.
38 'Maine Salmon Survey', Boone and Crockett Club, pp. 15–16.
39 Atlantic Sea-Run Salmon Commission, *Biennial Report for July 1, 1960 to June 30, 1962.*
40 *Penobscot River*, *Atlantic Salmon Restoration*, Orono, Maine, U.S. Fish and Wildlife Service, March, 1967.

11

The Varying Fortunes of *Salmo salar* in Canada

The Italian John Cabot, after discovering Newfoundland in 1497, reported that 'the sea there is swarming with fish', and the brothers Cortereal a few years later confirmed this news. Thus the imagination and greed of fishermen of several countries were aroused and the trek to the outlands of Canada began, in the hope of making fortunes from the garnering of massive quantities of fish that could be sold in European countries.

Around the coast of Newfoundland and Labrador, the stepping-stone islands of the Gulf of St. Lawrence, and the peninsula of Nova Scotia, the Bay of Fundy and the Gulf of Maine, the sea teemed with life. Hundreds of rivers poured their pure waters into the ocean. In few areas on the globe was marine life so abundant. Seals (born on the drifting ice) and whales lurked in the waters, feeding on the multitudes of cod, herring and other fishes dwelling in the stratified layers of the sea. Great colonies of sea birds, gannets, gulls, murres and others, nested on the rocky coast, and especially around the Gulf of St. Lawrence, swooping out by day in sky-darkening flocks to fish in the sea, and returning at night to their rocky perches.

South of Newfoundland are shallow areas of the ocean, really plateaux, called 'banks', sunken remnants of the northern Appalachian Highlands and Atlantic coastal plain which in the remote geologic past had extended past Nova Scotia and Newfoundland. In these waters the shoals of cod shed their eggs, their larvae fed on the plankton and the fry on tiny crustaceans. As they grew to maturity they followed their food supply, mainly herring, capelin and squid, wherever it led them. In the wake of the cod came the far less numerous anadromous fishes, salmon, shad, and others, heading for the multitudinous rivers from Ungava Bay to Maine.

The seemingly inexhaustible supplies of cod made it the pre-eminent prize to fishermen. The most favourable fishing conditions were found in the sea extending from the coasts of Labrador and Newfoundland to Cape Cod, and especially around the banks south-east of Newfoundland and Nova Scotia. French and Portuguese fishermen were established in this region early in the sixteenth century. Englishmen, mainly from the West country, settled on the shores of Cape Breton, Nova Scotia, the Gaspé and the Gulf of St. Lawrence. Although the rivers and estuaries abounded with salmon, a commercial salmon fishery did not arise until the eighteenth century. Ancillary to cod, it was destined to make the fortunes of many people, including the partners of the Hudson's Bay Company.

Life cycle and migrations

Young salmon stay in Canadian rivers from two to four years, sometimes longer. In New Brunswick streams for which information is available about two-thirds of juveniles spend three full years in the river and the remaining one-third two years. In warmer waters the majority of the salmon have only two years of premigratory river life. In some streams, like parts of the Restigouche system, one- to two-thirds of the runs spend four years before going to sea as smolts.

Salmon return to Canadian rivers in the spring and the runs continue throughout the summer and into late autumn; but all the fish wait till October or later to spawn. This pattern naturally varies among rivers. Few salmon return to the Margaree River on Cape Breton Island before June, and there may not be many in the pools until September or October. In the St. John River of New Brunswick the fish appear to enter at least from May to December, the last being in reality very early-run fish of the next year. The rivers of the outer coast of Nova Scotia may have salmon as early as February, 'due to the warm influence of the Atlantic Ocean acting on the coastal waters in which the salmon presumably stay'.[1] They appear in force in early April in the Medway and other Nova Scotia rivers, and in late April in the St. Lawrence and Bay of Chaleur, waiting until the snow water has run out before attempting the upstream journey.

In the Miramichi system, which is the focus for the largest Atlantic salmon fishery in Canada, a modest run of large fish enters fresh water commencing about the middle of May. These are followed about mid-June or early July by a larger run of grilse. By August both grilse and older salmon runs peter out. A fall run starts in September and ends in early November, and consists of fewer grilse and more big fish than the early run.[2] Salmon emanating from other rivers are also taken in the Miramichi fishery.

Salmon enter the rivers of the St. Lawrence coast early in June, are taken at Hamilton Inlet in Labrador in July, but do not ascend the Koksoak and other rivers flowing into Ungava Bay until mid-August.

As a general rule first-time spawners returning to Canadian rivers after an absence of about a year weigh up to 6 pounds, two-sea-year fish may scale from 8 to 15 pounds, and older specimens much more. The average size of a mature salmon is about 15 pounds, although 30- and 40-pounders are not uncommon.[3] In recent years grilse have become prominent in catches on many rivers and along the coast whereas in 1930 F. Gray Griswold, in his book *Life-History of the Salmon*, averred that only certain Canadian streams, like the Godbout and Restigouche, contained grilse.

The Canadians have conducted tagging experiments for many years in an effort to learn where the salmon wander when they leave fresh water, and have obtained interesting insights into their movements. For instance, a group of 68 salmon and 386 grilse were fin-clipped in 1940 at Bonavista on the east coast of Newfoundland and sent to sea. Many were recaptured that year and next in various places–in northern Newfoundland, the coast of Labrador, off Cape Breton Island, eastern Nova Scotia, eastern New Brunswick, and in the Bay of Chaleur. The longest distance travelled (on a straight-line basis) by any fish was 783 miles in 33 days, averaging 24 miles per day. The average distance covered was 322 miles and quickest rate of travel 26 miles per day. The smaller grilse made somewhat shorter journeys than the big salmon, yet one of them completed a voyage of 727 miles in about 32 days, at an average speed of 23 miles a day.[4]

Salmon tagged at Francis Harbour Bight near the southern end of the Labrador coast headed in either a southern or northern direction. Those fish that went north averaged 98 miles before being recaptured while those that went south averaged only 47 miles. One fish was caught at Hamilton Inlet, 186 miles away. The speediest travel was 17 miles per day and the average was 10 miles per day.[5]

These movements are greatly overshadowed by the jaunts of

marked Canadian salmon recaptured in the Greenland fishery. Smolts weighing 13 to 15 centimetres when tagged travelled 1,500 to 1,800 nautical miles in 16 to 18 months while the grilse averaged somewhat over 1,800 miles in 14½ months, and the two mature salmon 1,265 miles in 12½ months.[6]

Studies by A. G. Huntsman of the salmon in the Maritime area led him to conclude that, in contrast to these trans-oceanic migrations, the bulk of the fish 'remain in the sea not many miles from the mouths of the rivers to which they belong, the distance depending upon local conditions, food being probably the most important.'[7] The older fish, particularly males, scatter more widely than the younger. Scarcity of food and extreme temperatures probably lure them to distant pastures.

The salmon industry of New France

In New France, as in the mother country, salmon enjoyed a high reputation. They were not only caught by the colonists for domestic consumption but were the object of regular trading in Quebec City. Religious houses made ample use of the species. In the archives of the Seminary of Quebec, the oldest institution of learning in Canada, we find numerous references to barrels of salted salmon purchased for the monks. Local markets in sparsely settled New France, however, were insignificant and the salmon taken in the eighteenth century were mainly sent to Europe, particularly to Catholic lands.

Among the earliest exploiters of the salmon in Newfoundland was George Skeffington. Financed by New Englanders, he acquired in 1708 a 21-year monopoly on the fishery at Freshwater Bay, Rugged Harbour and Gander Bay. The fishery reached a considerable level within 30 years for the Colonial Office reported in its annual 'Schemes of the Fishery of Newfoundland' the export of 1,000 tierces[8] of salmon yearly in 1736–39. In 1743 over 1,000 tierces were shipped to Italy and Spain, and by 1757 the volume jumped to 4,848 tierces. Newfoundland then had but one industry, fishing, in which the bulk of the 10,000 inhabitants, swelled by visiting fishermen, were engaged. In 1765, following the Seven Years War, and the defeat and withdrawal of the French from Canada, Newfoundland exported 1,172 tierces of salmon.

With the English in control of the Maritime areas, a brisk trade in fish developed with the West Indies. Schooners were loaded at Canadian ports and sent to Dominica and other places and returned with cargoes of salt, sugar and molasses. The volume of Newfoundland salmon shipments fluctuated considerably but remained fairly high, as follows: 1764, 2,320 tierces; 1770, 649 tierces; 1773, 3,543 tierces; and 1784, 725 tierces.[9]

In 1786 salmon fisheries were conducted on the Exploits River, at Halls Bay, Loo Bay, Indian Arm and Dog Bay, Ragged Harbour, Freshwater Bay, Indian Bay and Gander Bay. About 1,160 tierces were produced that year but subsequently operations must have expanded greatly since almost 18,000 tierces are reported to have been shipped to Madeira, Spain, Portugal and Italy in the years 1787–91. Trinity Bay, noted for its seal fishing, also became a lucrative source of salmon in Newfoundland.

The cold waters of Labrador, amply stocked with salmon, began to attract fishermen after the Seven Years War. One of the first to go into the business was the colourful Captain George Cartwright, brother of Edmund Cartwright, inventor of a prototype power loom. George Cartwright had been an aide to the Marquis of Granby and after the war visited Newfoundland and the north. He formed a partnership with three Bristol merchants, bought a 50-ton vessel and sailed it across the Atlantic to Fogo Island. In 1771 he sent boats north to Cape St. Francis and Point Spear to fish for salmon. Difficulties arose and the partnership was dissolved but he persisted, on his own or with new partners. Operating from several trading posts along the Labrador coast from Cape St. Charles to Sandwich Bay, his men took furs in the winter, salmon when the ice had broken in the rivers, and cod later in the year.[10]

Cartwright's interesting *Journal* throws considerable light on the salmon fishery of Labrador. We learn that in 1774 the Alexis River was completely barred by nets, and soon after the Eagle and other streams were similarly blockaded. In July 1775 Cartwright wrote: 'We have 140 tierces ashore (from the Eagle River), but have had to take up two nets, as fish get in too fast.' At times the pools were so full of salmon 'you could not fire a ball without injuring some'. It was not unusual to see a dozen black and white bear fishing along the banks and the remains of hundreds of salmon strewn in the vicinity. In five days, August 7 to 11, 1776, Cartwright took 1,230 fish from one pool. 'Few escape there', he boasted. 'My ten nets, each forty fathoms long, fastened end to end, stretch right across the stream.' His men were killing salmon faster than they could pack them.

On July 17, 1779, he wrote in his *Journal*:

> In Eagle River we are killing 750 salmon a day, or 35 tierce, and we would have killed more had we more nets. Three hundred and fifty tierce ashore already at Paradise. If I had more nets, I could have killed a thousand tierce alone at this post, the fish averaging 15 to 32 pounds. At Sandhill Cove two men have 240 tierce ashore, and would have had more, but we had no more salt.

That year Cartwright landed on Eagle River, one of the richest salmon streams in North America ('comparable to the Fraser', said Wilfred Grenfell), 12,400 salmon, making 300 tierces, from June 23 to July 20. Yet in 1782 we find in the *Journal* the comment: 'Little or no salmon at Cartwright.' In 1786 the runs improved: 'We have 420 tierces in White Bear River and Paradise River, and 165 tierces at Charles Harbour.'[11]

The Maritime colonies

The earliest settlers in Nova Scotia found the rivers full of salmon and other fish, and sometimes town sites, like Liverpool on the Medway, were selected near the mouths of such streams in order to exploit the fishery. The salmon runs were heavily fished and the catches were sold in England. By the late eighteenth century commercial salmon fishing provided a source of revenue for many persons, and there is evidence that depletion of stocks in this area caused fishermen to go to the Gulf, Newfoundland, and even to Labrador, for salmon.[12] However, the runs restored themselves in due time.

In 1764 we hear of a salmon fishery established by William Davidson on the banks of the Miramichi. He caught and cured from 1,400 to 1,800 tierces annually for several years.[13] The Jersey firm of Robin, Piper and Company was also active on this river, and their vessel, the 101-ton *Hope*, carried 70 tierces of salmon to Bilbao, Spain, in 1769. There was a similar operation on the Restigouche, where the fish 'were speared by the Indians and were consequently fit only for the West Indies, whereas the use of nets would make it easy to build up a European market'.[14]

During and immediately after the American Revolution the fishing industry of the Maritime colonies expanded rapidly, particularly that of Nova Scotia and Cape Breton. Cod was always the main prize but mackerel, herring and salmon were taken in huge quantities. Salmon were caught in drift nets in offshore waters, trap nets along the shore, and trap and gill nets in the estuaries. Barrington and Port Medway became prominent centres of salmon fishing. Schooner loads of this fish were sent to United States markets, chiefly Boston, from the entrepôt at Halifax and other ports.

Records of catches in Canada go back to 1870, and while the figures for this period, as in other countries, may not be very accurate, they indicate that some 2 to 2½ million pounds of salmon were taken yearly in Nova Scotia in the 1870s, declining to less than half a million pounds in 1881 and rising to nearly 1·75 million pounds in 1887. Increased demand from the United States induced a great acceleration of fishing. Indeed, by the time of the American Civil War the bulk of the salmon consumed in the eastern part of the United States was being supplied by Canada. 'The only fresh salmon we get now', said Thad. Norris in *The American Angler's Guide*, 'come from Montreal, and from St. John, New Brunswick: from the latter by steamer to Boston, packed in ice, where they are repacked and sent to cities further south.' At Chatham, Bathurst and several other places in the southern British Provinces there were salmon canneries, while smoked and salted salmon came from points farther north.[15]

Hudson's Bay Company

In the nineteenth century the Hudson's Bay Company was active in the salmon industry in Labrador and southern Quebec, an enterprise fitting well into its general scheme of operation in the wilderness. In 1831 the Mingan District consisted of four trading posts and nine salmon fisheries along the north shore of the St. Lawrence River; the most important fisheries were at St. John's, Great Romaine, Washicouté, Natasquem, Kikaska, Washisou and Little Romaine Rivers. Donald A. Smith (Lord Strathcona), the first High Commissioner from the Dominion to Great Britain, as a young man served the Hudson's Bay Company at Tadoussac and later at Mingan. From 1847 to 1860 he was chief factor in Labrador where he distinguished himself, among other things, in expanding the profitable salmon fishery.

The Company was the largest buyer of salmon on the Labrador coast and owned not only nets but houses or 'posts', as they were called, on all the best points of land in the long inlets which the 'planters' used, turning in half the fish they caught as rent and obtaining goods from the Company's store for the rest. Most of the fishermen were also fur trappers and when the Labrador salmon industry declined at the end of the century for lack of fish many of these people were in distress. They had 'neither traps, safe guns, ammunition, nor even clothing and food to enable them to get out and face the Arctic cold of winter', said Wilfred Grenfell.

Like other enterprises, the Company may have overfished the salmon runs, or rather, since it did not directly engage in fishing, encouraged excessive netting. Yet in *Fishing in Canada*, published in 1860, Sir James E. Alexander observed that while the salmon streams of the north shore of the St. Lawrence were being wastefully handled, 'the protection the company affords is the only present safeguard for the existence of salmon in Canada. Were the protection withdrawn for one summer without the substitution of some other as effective, this noble fish would be utterly exterminated from our country. Fishermen from everywhere would swarm up our rivers, and with nets, spears, torches and every other engine of destruction, would kill, burn and mutilate every fish that ventured in.'[16]

Genio Scott in *Fishing in American Waters* (1875) provides contrary evidence. Embarking with a party of fishermen in a steamer from Quebec that was employed by the Government to provision the lighthouses along the shores of the Gulf of St. Lawrence, he had an opportunity to see the rivers of the north shore 'which come rushing and tumbling down every few miles from mountain heights to swell the tides of the Gulf'. He conversed with Government agents who superintended the fisheries, some of whom had formerly been employed by the Hudson's Bay Company. 'All agreed that the Company had greatly depleted the rivers of salmon, and necessitated the exercise of wisdom and care on the part of the Government to restock them with a supply as ample as would be required for rendering them profitable, besides supplying the needs of the growing population.'[17] Scott saw fishing huts and stations belonging to the Company standing idle and decayed.

Decay of the fishery

Although detailed information is scanty, there is some proof that the salmon populations in some areas declined appreciably during the nineteenth century and later. When Richard Nettle, coming from England, settled in Quebec in 1840, he was appalled that salmon were being slaughtered freely on their upstream journeys. He and others made their protests heard and at length an Act of Parliament was passed which provided for the appointment of a Superintendent of Fisheries in both Upper and Lower Canada, with authority to investigate and prosecute violators of existing laws and be responsible for drafting new ones. Nettle was appointed Superintendent for Lower Canada and is said to have prosecuted offenders so zealously that he antagonized powerful landowners on the lower St. Lawrence. In 1864 he was removed from his position.

It is obvious that freshwater fishery conservation was virtually non-existent at that time and for a considerable period afterwards, not only in Quebec but in all the provinces of the Dominion. In fact, the major reasons that Canadian stocks of *Salmo salar* did not suffer the same dire fate as those in New England was that human settlement was sparse in most of the region inhabited by the fish and industrialization rather negligible, although lumbering, as in Maine, had already adversely affected some watersheds, particularly in New Brunswick.

Observers reported rivers depleted of salmon or practically deserted by them. In *The American Salmon-Fisherman* (1886) Henry P. Wells listed for the benefit of sportsmen many well-stocked streams as well as a few poorly stocked or ruined Canadian rivers. In the latter category were south-shore streams like the Quelle (blocked by four mill dams), the Rimouski ('run down'), and the Matane ('badly poached'); among north-shore rivers were the Sault-au-Cochon and Grand Escoumains (which had once been 'very good' and was 'destroyed by lumbering'), the Mistassimi and Blanche ('run down'). The Miramichi was 'very much run down' although some of its affluents had recently been restocked by the Dominion Government (including the Little and Big Sevogle entering the North-west Branch, and the Bartholomew, Caius, Dungarvon, Taxis, Rock Brook and Clearwater flowing into the South-west Branch). Although the Government was engaged in a restocking programme, noted Wells, no efforts were made to curb netting at the mouths of the very rivers which had been restocked. 'Indeed, the casual observer would think any escape impossible from the labyrinths of nets which, for miles below the head of the tide and in close proximity to one another, bar the ascent of the salmon to their spawning grounds.' The law forbade netting from Saturday evening until Monday morning but one could not be sure how well it was observed. 'Of the many fish I saw', said Wells, 'which had been taken with the fly on the Restigouche River during June and July, 1885, hardly more than one in ten was free from wounds unmistakably due to the meshes of the nets.'[18]

Illegal fishing was seemingly widespread. In Labrador, according to Wilfred Grenfell, writing at the turn of the century, nearly every trap net used in the cod fishery caught salmon in its leaders, and these were salted, smoked and taken to Newfoundland where they were sold at high prices. Moreover, 'the trap leaders specially used for salmon are set out from points exactly as cod-trap leaders are, and being four inches instead of six inches in mesh, stop much smaller fish. In this way a very large number of small salmon are taken every year, and in the opinion of many people, the traps do more damage to the salmon than the river nets.'[19] Grenfell added that practically all Labrador streams of any value were illegally netted; in fact, to fish in defiance of the law had become a prescriptive right.

In its annual report for the year 1902 the Newfoundland Department of Fisheries underscored Grenfell's accusations. If the salmon resource were managed as it should be, said the Department, it 'would be a valuable gold mine for our population'. The main causes of decline of the catches were obstruction of the rivers by nets and mill dams and pollution by mill refuse. 'The famous Gander River – one of the most splendid salmon streams in North America – affords an object lesson as to how a great fishery can be ruined.' Eighty years before the Gander produced 2,000 tierces of salmon annually, and even fifty years earlier the catch averaged 1,000 tierces; now it was down to less than 30 tierces. The fishermen in early summer and spring planted their nets along the sides of the estuary; during July or earlier they moved up into the main river and barred the migration of any fish.

A new deal apparently was inaugurated in 1902 when nets were not allowed to be placed below Salt Island during the peak season, and all nets were removed from the Humber and other rivers. As a result, the netters' catches had increased. 'If the present regulations are maintained by efficient and well-paid river wardens not only the Gander will again become a great salmon river, but all the net fishermen on the coast will have their catch increased.'[20] The Department believed that with proper care of the rivers the total salmon output of Newfoundland could be multiplied tenfold. This prediction was not too far from the mark, although it took many years to overcome the impact of unrestricted fishing and to institute and effectuate a programme of rehabilitating some of the best rivers in the province.

A survey of Nova Scotia rivers conducted in 1881 and 1882 by F. H. D. Vieth revealed the destruction of the salmon fisheries by forces similar to those which ruined New England streams. Extensive logging had caused quick run-off, higher water temperatures in summer that salmon cannot tolerate, and silting of stream beds by the deposition of eroded material. Almost every river and its tributary had one or more dams without fishways. 'The only exceptions on the mainland of Nova Scotia were the Mersey and Medway with good fishways, a portion of the St. Mary's, and several smaller rivers such as Nine Mile and Pennant [which were] unobstructed.'[21] Heavy freshets on Cape Breton Island made construction of dams on the large rivers unfeasible but all the tributary brooks were barricaded with dams. Sawmills blithely dumped sawdust and other wastes into the waters and ruined spawning areas below the dams.

The 1890 report of the Nova Scotia Department of Fisheries disclosed that of 27 salmon rivers emptying into Northumberland Strait, only four were unobstructed, and all the others were blocked by mill dams without fishways! Inspector Hockins reported that in his district, the eastern mainland of Nova Scotia, 90 per cent of the fishways were not in a condition to allow fish to pass.

The only reason the Nova Scotia salmon fishery did not completely collapse was that mill dams and driving dams allowed salmon to pass at certain times of the year. Many were low structures with a spillway or sluice gate, and they impounded very little water. Operations were confined to a few months in the year and then the gates were opened; or because of a low head, water flowed over the dams during freshets and the salmon managed to reach their spawning grounds. Usually the losses consisted of fish entering the rivers very early in the year, March or even February, when there was not enough water to permit them to negotiate the obstructions. Although salmon catches rebounded in Nova Scotia at the end of the 1880s, the potential was by no means fully exploited.

A survey of Quebec rivers was published by E. T. D. Chambers in 1911. On the north shore of the St. Lawrence there were scarcely any salmon streams left west of the Saguenay. Nearly all the waters as far as Lake Ontario were now barren. A few specimens still ascended the Murray River which flows into Murray Bay. Mill refuse choked Grand River which enters the St. Lawrence a few miles below Ste Anne de Beaupré. The Jacques Cartier, some thirty miles west of Quebec, attracted a few fish and 'if the Dominion regulations concerning the location and mesh of salmon nets were properly enforced in the St. Lawrence, there is every reason to believe that so clean a stream . . . would, in the course of a few years, become once more an excellent salmon river'.[22] Other rivers east and west of Quebec could be successfully restored, said Chambers, if pollution were eliminated, the runs protected, and fishways built at all dams below the spawning grounds.

The salmon rivers flowing into the Saguenay such as the Mars, Eternity, Shipsaw, Chicoutine and Ste Marguerite, as well as the best of the accessible streams emptying into the St. Lawrence and the Gulf, to the eastern boundaries of the Province, were leased to private individuals and clubs and therefore were usually carefully protected, at least from early spring until the close of the spawning season. Others were in poor condition. East of the Saguenay 'one passes in succession estuaries of Grand Bergeronnes, Petit Bergeronnes, Escoumains, Portneuf, Sault-au-Cochon, some of which formerly contained salmon'. The Escoumains, from which an old fisherman told Chambers he used to take 75 barrels of salmon a year a half-century earlier, was blocked by a mill dam and ruined by pollution. Many small streams in this part of the Province could be used by the salmon if natural falls were laddered.

On the Bersimis River, which was part of the Montagnais Indian Reserve, destructive fishing had reduced the catch from 80,000 to 20,000 pounds of salmon annually. The Moisie and St. John were still productive, and the Godbout and Trinity were literally alive with fish during the open season. The St. John was then leased to James J. Hill, the American railroad tycoon, for $3,300 annually, and the Moisie, famous for its large fish, for $6,300 for net fishing. Other good angling rivers in eastern Quebec, said Chambers, were the Eskimo (which at one time yielded 50,000 salmon a year), St. Augustine, Mecatina, Etamamiou, Coacoacho and Kegashka. Most of them, however, 'were difficult of access to anglers and just as difficult for the netters to protect. They are, consequently, at the mercy of the netters.'[23]

On the south shore of the St. Lawrence the most westerly rivers that still contained salmon were the Rimouski (which was in private hands and therefore carefully tended), the Bic and its neighbour the Cap Chat. The most important rivers flowing into the lower St. Lawrence were the Matane, Ste Anne-des-Monts, Dartmouth, York and St. John's falling into Gaspé Bay. Into Chaleur Bay flowed some of the richest salmon streams in eastern North America, such as the Cascapedia (leased by the Province for $12,000 annually), Bonaventure, and the fabulous Restigouche. A small army of canoe men, guides and wardens were employed on the Restigouche, Cascapedia and other rivers to protect the waters and cater to the wealthy sportsmen, accompanied by their friends, wives and cronies, who fished these waters.

Figure 30 shows the productive salmon rivers of eastern Canada at the end of the nineteenth century.

Rise of sport fishing

Canada's swift rivers rising in distant, unexplored hinterlands, rushing and tumbling undisturbed to the welcoming sea, began to attract many anglers in the nineteenth century, especially Americans.

Consider, for example, a river which flows along the northern shore of the Strait of Belle Isle:

> From the air, this is a land of fog and blowing clouds and jumbled, rounded rock formations, valleys dark with forests, hilltops green with lichen. Innumerable pot holes and lakes stretch away to the horizon. Rivers with white water and falls wind to the sea, and for hundreds of miles there are no signs of habitation. The hills climb to the sky, the timber stopping near the summits, the green mosses going on, and against the naked skyline great boulders are silhouetted, monuments to the prodigious forces of the bygone ice ages. In the summer, icebergs, whitish

blue and translucent, float upon the sea. Here runs the Pinware River of Labrador, the waters pure enough to drink, filtered only through hundreds of watershed miles of rock and spruce and balsam fir, lichen and sphagnum moss, slightly tinted by the peat.[24]

This is Shangri-la, deep in the wilderness, where a man may escape the madding crowds, urban noises, mundane cares, and shout or sing or pray, and come close to the secrets of creation. This is sublime fishing country.

There are scores of rivers in Canada like the Pinware, and their names send thrills of anticipation down the spines of anglers. In 1950 there were 222 rivers with 3,400 miles of fishable waters on which salmon anglers could cast their lines with reasonable chances of success; 55 were in Quebec, 28 in New Brunswick, 31 in Nova Scotia and 108 in Newfoundland.[25]

In the nineteenth and early twentieth centuries few fishermen could achieve their ambition of pitting their skill and tackle against the battling salmon on wild Canadian rivers because they were difficult of access and the cost of fishing was prohibitive. It was necessary to take a long train ride, or venture by ship for hundreds of miles, and then by canoe for several days to reach salmon water. Three weeks or a month were needed for the trip. But the rewards were ample.

'To spend a summer month on one of the great rivers which empty into the Gulf of St. Lawrence', said Genio Scott in 1875, 'is to rest the mind by the most absolute exclusion from the world. When I essayed the ascent of one of the great rivers . . . north of the island of Anticosti, the world was tranquil. For a month I admired the grandeur of the mountains, the majesty of the broad and rapid river, the elegant play of salmon, and the dexterity of the seals; and at night the brilliancy of the northern horizon and gorgeousness of the lunar bow enraptured me.'[26]

Nowadays super highways and airlines have brought most of Canada's rivers within relatively easy reach of any part of the continent. Many of the waters are privately held or leased to angling clubs. A few, in Quebec, are Crown preserves, managed by the Provincial Department of Game and Fisheries. There are five public rivers in Quebec, including the Matane, Little Cascapedia and Romaine. In Nova Scotia there are no closed waters. Most of New Brunswick's salmon rivers are under lease (as in Quebec) but there are many fishing camps from which one can hire a beat. Labrador remains a fishing paradise, although accommodations are scarce and guides (usually desirable in Canada) not readily available. Here are no privately owned or restricted waters. Newfoundland, the richest in salmon, has much public water.

Fluctuation of harvests

Although the salmon still inhabits hundreds of rivers in eastern Canada, it is estimated that more than 75 per cent of the stocks are now found in six principal river systems in Newfoundland and New Brunswick. The populations of Nova Scotia and Quebec have suffered particularly heavy losses in the past century or more.

Commercial salmon fishing occurs at the mouth of the St. John River, along the Miramichi, in the Bay of Chaleur to the north, along the coasts of Newfoundland, and elsewhere. The gear includes gill nets, drift nets from motor-boats, trap nets, pound sets and weirs. Federal regulations prescribe the maximum size of the nets and minimum measure of the meshes as well as the fishing season and time of weekly closure (36 or 48 hours, depending on the locality). No salmon may be retained if it weighs less than five pounds. In New Brunswick there is a legal fishery for kelts, called 'black salmon', in the spring, and about 5,000 are taken in an average year in the Miramichi River.

What is the current status of the Atlantic salmon fishery? J. L. Kask, chairman of the Fisheries Research Board of Canada, said in 1957:

> Most of the rivers that formerly supported salmon runs and no longer do, have lost their runs more from adverse changes in the very restricted and demanding fresh water environment in which they are born and spend the first half of their life, than from overfishing. . . . Agricultural, urban and industrial pollution (including spraying forests and waters with DDT) contribute substantially. Removal of adjacent forest cover with attendant fast run-offs and exposure of critical river areas to increases in light and temperature can have deleterious effects. Multiple water uses for irrigation, power, navigation, etc. and physical interference with the river itself such as often accompanies logging, mining or road building all can, and do, affect the river as an environment for living organisms.

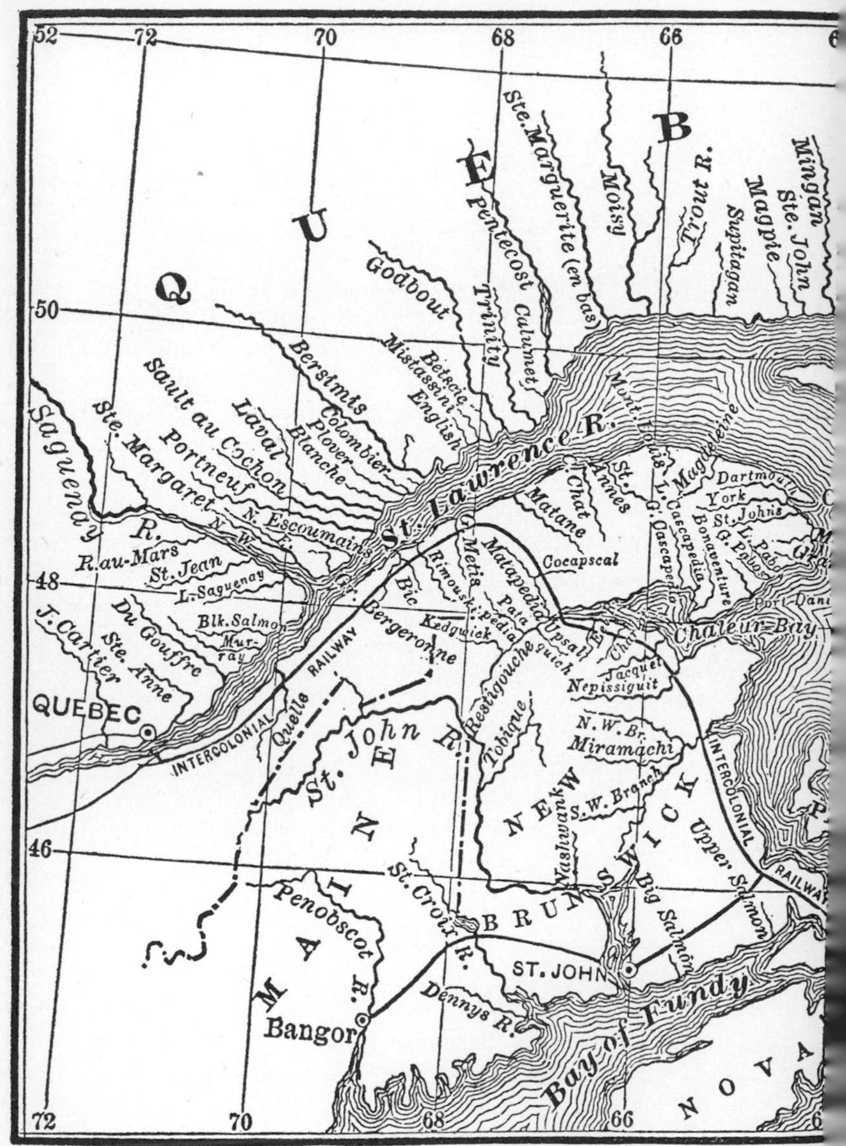

Figure 30
The salmon rivers of eastern Canada at the end of the nineteenth century.

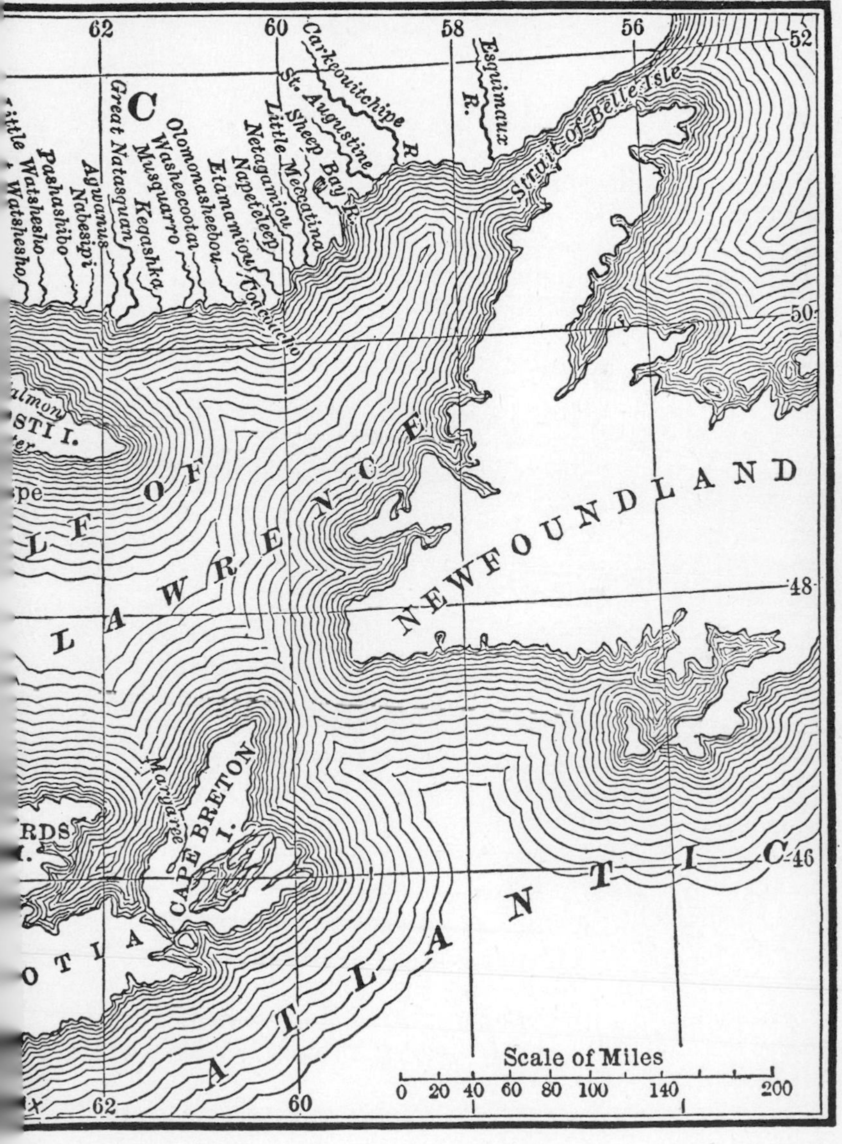

62
60
58
56
52
50
48
46
C
Carkeouitchipe R.
Esquimaux R.
St. Augustine
Sheep Bay R.
Little Mecatina
Netagamiou
Napeteleep
Etamamiou
Coacacho
Olomonasheebou
Washeecootai
Musquarro
Kegashka
Great Natasquan
Agwanus
Nabesipi
Pashashibo
Strait of Belle Isle
NEWFOUNDLAND
L F O F
L A W R E N C E
Margaree
CAPE BRETON I.
O T I A
A T L A N T I C
Scale of Miles
0 20 40 60 80 100 140 200

Concern for the future of the resource led to the formation in 1949 of a Federal-Provincial Co-ordinating Committee on Atlantic Salmon which has resulted in stepped-up conservation efforts and expanded research by both the federal and provincial governments.

It is worth noting that while man-made forces closely affect the abundance of a 'domesticated' species like the salmon, the phenomenon of periodicity in animal numbers cannot be ignored. In his study, *The Maritime Salmon of Canada*, published in 1931, Huntsman suggested that there was a regular cycle of 9·6 years in swings of abundance and scarcity whose cause or causes remain mysterious. He found a correlation of salmon populations, as evidenced by catches, with those of Canadian fur-bearing animals such as the Arctic fox, hare, lynx and marten, as shown by returns of the Hudson's Bay Company.[27]

The Russian ichthyologist Leo S. Berg found that fluctuations in salmon harvests in the Barents and White Sea basins over a period of fifty years coincided with the maxima and minima of salmon catches near the coasts of Norway, in England, and in Canada. He pointed out that 1928 was a very poor year in the fishery of the Soviet north, Finland, Norway and Scotland as well as Canada but 1924 was a good year in the U.S.S.R., Norway and Canada. Sometimes there is a difference of one year between the maxima and minima in Russia and Canada. In the period since 1875, the lowest take of Atlantic salmon in Russia was in 1882 and in Canada in 1881. Generally the years 1879–82 were quite poor in Russia and the years 1880–83 equally unproductive in Canada. More recently, the catch was low in Russia in 1921 and in Norway, Scotland and Canada in 1920.[28] A comparison of Canadian with Scottish salmon catches led Menzies to conclude that 'whatever man does, these fluctuations in salmon stocks cannot be avoided. Conservation in the most approved manner, and, apparently, based on the soundest principles, may assist the peaks, but will not avoid the troughs.'[29]

What may be the cause of periodicity? Berg asserts that while reproduction in the rivers is influenced by dry-land factors, abundance in the sea is affected by: (1) fishing; (2) predators about which there is scant information as yet; and (3) fluctuation in abundance of organisms on which salmon feed. The latter two factors, in their turn, depend on changes in the water temperature which are estimated as occurring in 8–9-year cycles. 'It can thus be seen', concluded Berg, 'that the fluctuations in the abundance of salmon follow a general pattern covering most areas of oceans and continents. The initial cause of these fluctuations can only be found in large-scale climatic fluctuations.'[30] As we have seen, Lindroth came to the same conclusion, after studying the trend of catches in many Baltic rivers.

Although Canadian catches have fluctuated widely in the past century, overall production of Atlantic salmon compares favourably with that of any other country in recent years.

As in other countries, sports fishing for salmon is booming in eastern Canada and nowhere perhaps are anglers more vociferous and active in promoting their sport and attempting to obtain access to more salmon waters. There has not only been a considerable increase in the number of anglers but their catches have mounted in greater proportion than the generally improved harvests would indicate. In 1958 C. J. Kerswill reported that about 75,000 fish were being taken annually by sportsmen. In 1963 the rod catch jumped to almost 124,200 and in 1964 to 115,700. New Brunswick provided 73,000 rod-caught salmon in 1963 and 54,000 in 1964; Newfoundland 33,400 and 42,500 respectively; Quebec 15,000 and 14,400; and Nova Scotia 2,800 and 4,800.

It is estimated that in a typical year, such as 1959, the 'Atlantic pool', representing the number of fish caught by rods and nets in the four Atlantic provinces and Quebec, was 760,000.[31]

Table 24 shows Canadian landings of Atlantic salmon in the years 1953–65.

Angling for salmon is regarded by sportsmen as more important economically than commercial fishing in the provinces of Quebec, New Brunswick and Nova Scotia. The Atlantic Salmon Association has sponsored studies which purport to prove this assertion.

There is a rising demand in Canada for public access to salmon waters. This grass-roots movement was described by T. B. Fraser, president of the Atlantic Salmon Association, in his report for the year 1964:

> We are living in an age and a country now rapidly becoming more and more socialistic. The man on the street wants a higher and higher standard of living. . . . You have in this electing public many freshwater fishermen. . . . Very few can belong to a private salmon club where fish cost $192 or up, depending upon who you are and where you are. Some salmon fishermen, who cannot afford or do not have the opportunity to join a private club,

Table 24
Landings* of Atlantic salmon in Canada, 1953–1965
(*1,000 pounds*)

Year	*Total*	*Newfoundland and Labrador*	*Maritime Provinces*	*Quebec*
1953	4,533	3,088	919	526
1954	3,676	2,153	1,079	444
1955	2,669	1,752	474	443
1956	2,669	1,645	558	466
1957	3,117	1,964	708	445
1958	3,553	2,154	889	510
1959	4,155	2,345	1,159	651
1960	3,714	2,089	993	632
1961	3,612	2,093	1,010	509
1962	3,940	2,239	1,200	501
1963	4,119	2,677	1,010	432
1964	4,530	2,790	1,293	447
1965	4,807	2,757	1,493	557

Sources: Figures for Newfoundland-Labrador and Quebec from *Fisheries Statistics of Canada*; Maritime Provinces from Maritime Region Headquarters, Department of Fisheries of Canada.
* Includes sports catch.

fish on outfitters' waters where a salmon costs about $91. But there is another group . . . who cannot afford . . . even the outfitters' rate and these men want open or government controlled waters where they can fish easily and cheaply. Some even want to fish without a guide. There is being added to this group, at an ever increasing rate, trout fishermen who never killed a salmon but who are simply crazy to do so.[32]

In Quebec, where only five salmon streams are open to the public (1966), the province's policy is under fire, and politicians are listening. As a consequence, provincial officials are suggesting a new approach to river management, 'one which is of necessity more modern and better attuned to the changed sociological atmosphere', as Wilfred Carter of the Quebec Department of Fisheries says. Basic to the proposed new deal is 'acceptance of a responsibility to provide controlled public salmon fishing', such as exists in British Columbia.

This would involve restoration of rivers which, like the Petit Pabos in the Gaspé, were once attractive to migratory fish, but are now deserted by them, and others on which artificial or natural obstacles can be removed, as on the Rimouski, Métis, Madeleine, Escoumains, Franquelin, and others. Also, rivers or parts of rivers leased to clubs that are now unable or unwilling to provide good management and proper maintenance would be repatriated. Finally, on streams in which the fishery is not now being fully utilized additional outfitter clubs would be created either by individuals or the government, or fishing seasons would be adjusted to take full advantage of the runs. 'As these different rivers become available over a period of time,' says Carter, 'it will be the government's responsibility to decide the type of fishing arrangement which is most adaptable to each . . . situation.' This does not mean that 'all existing rivers should be opened to public fishing', but that 'there can be private clubs, controlled public fishing, commercial fishing and salmon too'.[33]

Future of the resource

The landings of Atlantic salmon in Canada have increased substantially in recent years. Whether due to cyclical causes or man-made, this relatively favourable state of affairs leaves no room for complacency. Powerful forces are arrayed against the species, as in most countries, for man continues to tamper with its environment, sometimes in a new and quite disastrous manner, and his greed leads to overfishing, as in Greenland waters.

Through 1966 the bulk of the tagged fish recovered in the nets of fishermen in Greenland, as we have seen, emanated from Canada. While conclusive evidence is not yet available, we may logically assume that the Greenlanders are taking mainly Canadian salmon, and this will be reflected in coming years in the homeward migrations and, probably, in the catches. This situation is creating serious apprehension among all those who have an interest—vested or not—in Canada's Atlantic salmon resource.

Examples of wanton (and) needless destruction of salmon stocks occurred in New Brunswick and Quebec, both of which are heavily dependent on pulp and paper manufacturing for economic prosperity. One of the new tools of foresters is to spray woodlands and streams with deadly concentrations of DDT in order to combat insect pests, especially the spruce budworm which defoliates and ultimately kills the trees.

Heavy forest spraying began in the spring of 1952 when about 200,000 acres on the Upsalquitch headwaters of the Restigouche system were treated. The next year about 2,000,000 acres were treated in the Restigouche and Tobique watersheds, and in 1954 over 1,000,000 acres in northern Miramichi headwaters. As the spruce budworm epidemic widened, more areas were treated, sometimes for the second or third time. About 2,000,000 acres were treated in 1958. Spraying was then halted for one year, and was resumed on a scale of about 2,000,000 acres annually.

The effects of applying DDT in forests which shelter waters rich in fish life became quickly apparent. Fingerlings and small parr exposed to heavy and repeated dosages dropped by aeroplanes died by the millions. Older parr also suffered tremendous mortalities but were better able to survive, while adult salmon apparently were not affected. Fatalities occurred not only immediately after spraying but up to four months later. The spray also killed most of the immature aquatic insects which comprise the food of young fish.

Until 1960 the sprayers used one-half pound of DDT to the acre. At this strength the dosage killed nine-tenths of the fry, three-fourths of the small parr around one year old, and one-half of the large parr that would have migrated as smolts the year after spraying. After 1960 the standard dosage was reduced, at the insistence of fishery men, to one-quarter pound of DDT to the acre, but even then half or more of the fry were killed.

Summing up in 1964 the consequences of what has been called the world's most extensive forest-spraying (and fish-killing) experiment, the biologists P. F. Elson and C. J. Kerswill said: 'Considering all available information it can be concluded that spraying of northern New Brunswick forests with DDT between 1953 and 1958 has been responsible for a substantial portion of the recent severe depression in salmon fishing success, particularly in angling, in the province, between 1959 and 1962. The complete absence of spraying in 1959 played a large part in the improved angling for grilse in

1963.'[34] If DDT spraying had not occurred commercial and sports catches would have increased by 500,000 to 1,000,000 pounds per year at the end of the 1950s. The Tobique River, for instance, had only one-sixth of its former stocks in the decade 1953–63.

The catastrophe in New Brunswick and Quebec may be blamed on the failure of forest entomologists (and their employers) to gauge the full impact of their spraying programme on life in the streams, and their unwillingness to co-operate with biologists in agreeing on a plan that would protect and save the trees and also minimize damage to the valuable fish populations–a condition which, since 1960, is improving.

There are other serious difficulties in maintaining salmon abundance. Jack H. Fenety, president of the Miramichi Salmon Association, points out that New Brunswick's water pollution problems are becoming serious. 'As elsewhere, the causes and sources . . . are well known. The major offenders are industrial plants and operations, municipalities dumping raw sewage, woodland operators, farmers and countless other individuals and groups.'[35]

The manufacture of pulp and paper is one of eastern Canada's leading industries. In fact, Canada supplies over half the world's newsprint, and the pace of reducing its magnificent forests to paper for printing worthless as well as worthwhile publications mounts every year. 'In many cases, unfortunately, the intensive and extensive cutting of trees has not always taken into account protection of water courses as a vital medium indispensable to salmon', says Alexandre Marcotte of the Quebec Department of Fisheries. This has resulted in pronounced deforestation near the rivers and its consequences: soil erosion, filling of river-beds, destruction of natural spawning grounds, flash floods, and often inundations followed by the partial drying up of watercourses. The irony is that nine-tenths of the forest area is owned by the Crown and is administered by the provincial governments from whom the pulp and paper mills lease woodland tracts, but there is no insistence usually on logging practices that would safeguard river flow and purity.

With the increase of population, wilderness areas are being tamed, forests removed, and rivers encroached upon by towns and other settlements. 'Matapedia not so long ago was a magnificent water course,' says Marcotte, 'bordered right up to its source by rich and heavy forests. But the same river, today, is populated along both its banks and important agglomerations of people are established in certain localities.' Fish populations must necessarily suffer, for civilization and salmon do not mix well, unless extraordinary precautions are taken to protect their habitat.

Hydro-electric programmes, usurping salmon-rich rivers, also threaten the fishery. Almost all of Quebec's and 90 per cent of Newfoundland's electricity is derived from water power. In New Brunswick the proportion is 53 and in Nova Scotia 20 per cent. Many salmon streams have been partly or wholly sacrificed to kilowatts, although countervailing measures are believed to be offsetting natural fish losses, at least to some extent. The latest major scheme is Mactaquac dam to be built on the St. John River in New Brunswick to supplement two dams already in existence. Since there is no assured technique for passing adult fish over a structure the height of Mactaquac, it is proposed to trap upstream migrants below this dam and from them produce smolts in hatcheries for release in the river. Surplus salmon and migrating trout trapped at Mactaquac will be taken by truck to prearranged release sites upstream in order to provide angling opportunities on the main stem and above Tobique Narrows.

It is anticipated that those fish that escape the anglers' hooks will spawn principally in the Tobique River and their progeny will run to sea as smolts. However, only about half their number will probably reach safety below Mactaquac dam. It is recognized that the entire scheme, including the production eventually of 500,000 smolts annually by artificial propagation, is experimental and represents a brand-new approach to the salmon maintenance problem in Canada. In justifying this plan the provincial government, which will build the dam, points to Sweden, 'where an important commercial salmon fishery is entirely dependent on the output of smolts from a number of these hydro-electric river hatcheries. It is expected that the Mactaquac fisheries proposal will be capable of producing a sufficient number of salmon to maintain populations at a level equal to present-day St. John River runs.'

---

21. One of the best Atlantic salmon rivers in Canada is the Jupiter on Anticosti Island, in the Gulf of St. Lawrence. Noted for its exceptionally clear water, it produces from 1,500 to 1,800 salmon each year.

However, many people, principally anglers, oppose further development of the St. John River. Their point of view is well summarized by A. Lassel Ripley, writing in the *Atlantic Salmon Journal*, Spring 1965:

> I disagree that there is any real necessity for an increase in electric power in New Brunswick and that the building of the Mactaquac is critical to the economy of the Province. . . .
>
> If no nuclear plants are being built in Canada . . . it's high time they started, because at the present time they are more economical according to the best nuclear authorities today. . . .
>
> If Mactaquac is built, fifty miles of the most beautiful and most fertile valley in New Brunswick is destroyed, a major salmon river is all but destroyed along with one of the greatest tourist attractions in the Province, and all by the most expensive method. A nuclear plant destroys nothing.
>
> . . . With the building of more hydro-electric dams such as the Mactaquac, increased lumbering devastation, unrestricted lethal pollution from mines and other sources, and increased fishing and tourist propaganda, the salmon is on his way out.

Canada now produces on the average about as much Atlantic salmon as any European country (Table 1). The tide of depletion has been turned. Whether this record can be maintained in the face of so many inimical forces is a question that cannot be answered.

NOTES

1 A. G. Huntsman, *Return of the Salmon from the Sea*, p. 12.
2 P. F. Elson and C. J. Kerswill, 'Studies on Canadian Atlantic Salmon'.
3 F. H. Wooding, *Canada's Atlantic Salmon*, p. 10.
4 A. A. Blair, 'Atlantic Salmon Tagged in East Coast Newfoundland Waters at Bonavista', pp. 227, 231.
5 A. A. Blair, 'Salmon Tagging at Francis Harbour Bight, Labrador'.
6 Paul Hansen, 'Report on Recaptures in Greenland Waters of Salmon Tagged in Rivers in Europe and America'.

22a. There are two types of commercial fishing for Atlantic salmon in Canada: by shore nets and by drift netting. Picture shows netsmen in the Bay of Chaleur.

22b. An adult salmon counting fence on a Canadian river provides information for managing the fishery.

7 A. G. Huntsman, *The Maritime Salmon of Canada*, p. 99.

8 A tierce was said to weigh 300 pounds, but a portion of this, perhaps as much as one-third, consisted of water and brine. Probably the average tierce of salmon contained 200 pounds of fish.

9 These figures are taken from Harold A. Innis, *The Cod Fisheries*.

10 *Ibid.*, p. 198.

11 Quotations from Cartwright's *Journal* are taken from Wilfred Grenfell *et al*, *Labrador: The Country and the People*, Chapter XII.

12 Norman H. Morse, *Economic Value of the Atlantic Salmon Fishery in Nova Scotia*, Acadia University Institute, 1965, p. 7.

13 A. G. Huntsman, *The Maritime Salmon of Canada*, p. 56.

14 Innis, *op. cit.*, p. 278.

15 Thad. Norris, *The American Angler's Guide*, p. 207.

16 Quoted in *Atlantic Salmon Journal*, March 1962, p. 18.

17 Genio Scott, *Fishing in American Waters*, p. 216.

18 Henry P. Wells, *The American Salmon-Fisherman*, p. 19.

19 Wilfred Grenfell *et al*, *Labrador*, p. 338.

20 *Annual Report of the Newfoundland Department of Fisheries for the Year 1902*, p. 23.

21 N. E. J. MacEachern and J. R. MacDonald, 'The Salmon Fishery in Nova Scotia', p. 52.

22 E. T. D. Chambers, *Game Fishes of Quebec*, p. 199.

23 *Ibid.*

24 Aaron B. Stevens, 'The Pinware River of Newfoundland', *Atlantic Salmon Journal*, March 1964.

25 Data provided by the Atlantic Salmon Association.

26 Genio Scott, *op. cit.*, p. 204.

27 A. G. Huntsman, *The Maritime Salmon of Canada*, p. 96.

28 Leo S. Berg, *Freshwater Fishes of the U.S.S.R. and Adjacent Countries*, p. 232.

29 W. J. M. Menzies, *A Report on the Present Position of the Atlantic Salmon Fisheries of Canada*, p. 11.

30 Berg, *op. cit.*, p. 233.

31 These figures were given in a brief presented by the Atlantic Salmon Association, the foremost salmon anglers' organization in Canada, to the Tourist Council of the Province of Quebec in June 1963.

32 *Atlantic Salmon Journal*, Winter 1964–65.

33 Wilfred M. Carter, 'Quebec's Salmon Rivers', *Atlantic Salmon Journal*, Winter 1964–65.

34 P. F. Elson and C. J. Kerswill, 'Forest Spraying and Salmon Angling', *Atlantic Salmon Journal*, October 1964.

35 J. T. H. Fenety, 'The Struggle for Clear Water', *Atlantic Salmon Journal*, June 1964.

12

The Explosive Greenland Fishery

On July 5, 1965, Lord Balfour of Inchrye rose in the House of Lords to ask Her Majesty's Government whether it was aware that exports of Atlantic salmon from Greenland had skyrocketed from 2 metric tons in 1957 to 1,400 metric tons in 1964, 'due to growth of intense netting using improved methods', and that, since Greenland possesses but one river known to breed salmon, the increase constituted a grave danger to stocks in the rivers of Europe and the eastern American seaboard? Lord Hughes, Joint Parliamentary Under-Secretary of State for Scotland, replied that the Government was indeed cognizant of the potentially perilous situation which had been revealed for the first time at the annual meeting in the previous June of the International Commission for the North-west Atlantic Fisheries, and that 'the Danish authorities were . . . asked through their representatives at the Commission to consider whether means could be found of curbing further expansion of the fishery'.[1]

From the agitated discussion in Parliament, as reported in the press, the people in Great Britain and other countries learned of a new threat to the survival of what is certainly the world's most harried fish. For it appeared that man had wrested yet another secret from this inscrutable species by discovering its luxuriant pastures in Greenland waters. Salmon were originally Arctic fishes that entered the rivers of the temperate zone in Europe and North America in recent geologic times, when the Ice Age receded. Therefore it is natural for them to spend part of their lives in the ice-cold Arctic seas, as Menzies of Scotland and Huntsman of Canada long ago surmised. Yet the salmon industry was stunned at the exploitation by the Danes of the throngs of fish assembling from many countries in Greenland waters. Some 430,000 salmon were caught in 1964, eviscerated, frozen and dispatched to Copenhagen, where they were sold for high prices to buyers in several countries. Catches were considerably less in 1965 but reached almost the 1964 level in 1966.

The setting

To see the Greenland fishery in proper focus we must look at the land and its history. Greenland is the world's largest island, extending from 60 to 84 degrees North latitude, and jutting closer to the North Pole than any other land mass. From the air Greenland is a panorama of glaciers and mountains, buried in densely-packed snow, in places rising to 10,000 feet, with occasionally granite domes–called *nunataks*–peeking through the white mass. Far below, gigantic icebergs, most of whose bulk lies under water, move like white, many-spired cathedrals through the fjords and out to sea. Greenland is a desolate and mostly silent world covered by the inland ice which occupies 85 per cent of the island. Only in the coastal rim and along some of the deep fjords does the soil support vegetation. Trees grow, but only to dwarf size; the willow birch never reaches more than ten feet and the alder only three feet.

In the south summer unfolds a surprisingly luxuriant vegetation in the sheltered valleys away from the coast, while scattered over the interior are thousands of lakes where reindeer and other animals slake their thirst. Sheep and cattle are raised in south Greenland. In an area about the size of India, there are only 25,000 people who dwell mainly in settlements along the south-west and south-east coasts.

Greenland was first inhabited about 4,000 years ago by Eskimo who came from eastern Siberia and crossed the frozen top of North America to reach this forbidding land. Around A.D. 985 a band of Vikings from Iceland led by Eric the Red colonized the southern tip of the island. In time a flourishing civilization developed which endured for five centuries when it was overwhelmed, perhaps by adverse climatic changes, and disappeared. Denmark and Norway rediscovered the island beginning in 1721, gradually extended settlement, and created a new civilization. Denmark now owns Greenland and the population is a mixture of Scandinavians and Eskimos.

The native salmon

As far as can be determined, there is but one river, the Kapisigdlit, which flows out of the inner harbour of Godthaabfjord (64° 26′ North latitude), where salmon are known to breed. The Danish entomologist, Johann Christian Fabricius, in his book, *The Fauna of Greenland*, published in 1780, identified this stream as a salmon river. Here, says Jørgen Nielsen, salmon fishing 'has been carried out as far back as the memory of now-living Greenlanders goes'.[2] Salmon have also been caught in two other rivers, the Kugssuaq in Tasermuitfjord in the Nanortolik district, and the small Isersuitigdlit in Godhaabfjord, but it is not certain that the fish breed there.

Paul Hansen in 1940 revealed that the salmon were becoming more numerous than they had been; fairly large schools were seen in the Julianehaab, Godthaab and Sukkertoppen areas. Adolf Jensen in 1948 gave the following localities where salmon were caught in addition to the Kapisigdlit River: Sarfanguaq in the Holsteinsborg district; Tasermuitfjord and Lichtenau; Julianehaab; Fisknaesset in the Godthaab district; Ikserasak; Napassoq with nearby fjords; and Agpamiut in the Sukkertoppen district. In a 1951 publication Hansen reported salmon at Umanak, far up the north-west coast. No measure of the quantities taken were given in these reports, except that an occasional haul of 500 salmon was made in the Frederikshaab district. There was also a small salmon fishery on the east coast.

Considering the long Scandinavian habitation, it is surprising that so little information is available about the Greenland salmon, which, with char, are the most important of the country's freshwater fishes.

The Eskimos as well as the Danes made use of the fish that inhabited the short, swift rivers. V. Borum, describing the daily life of a nomadic hunter, says that 'he caught salmon in the rivers, shot eider-duck and rounded off the carefree summer life by going far into the mountains hunting reindeer. When he returned to his winter hut, he was full of adventures and good food.'[3] We may picture these Eskimos, dressed in sealskin, pursuing the fish in their kayaks, those light skin boats that float over the surface of the waters like gusts of wind.

Greenland salmon spawn in early November or late October, before the ice closes the river, or in spring or early summer, a

Figure 31

Greenland, showing areas of large-scale salmon fishing.

phenomenon observed in Scotland that may well occur elsewhere. The fish ascend the river from about May, when the bay into which it flows is still ice-covered, until September. Juveniles stay in the river mostly four and even five years. In fact, a migration age of six is not unknown. An unusually large proportion of the male parr are sexually mature, and some of these dwarf males more than ten years old have been captured in the Kapisigdlit.

Very little is known about the migrations of the native salmon. Studies conducted by the Greenland Fisheries Investigations under Jørgen Nielsen's direction in 1952–58 yielded meagre results. Of about 1,670 parr and smolts tagged one was recovered two years later as an adult at Sukkertoppen, about 170 miles from the place of tagging, and another, three years old, as a kelt in its home river.[4]

The invaders

It is evident that the commercial fishery was confined virtually to the Sukkertoppen district and was on a small scale until the late 1950s. As far back as 1945 salmon were found occasionally in the nets of French, Icelandic and Faroese trawlers fishing for cod on the rich banks of Davis Strait. As a rule, the trawls contained only a few salmon but sometimes as many as 50 were found. Salmon were also caught from time to time off the east coast, where no breeding rivers exist; for instance, in the autumn of 1957 many specimens were taken with the jig in the cod fishery at Skjoldungen (63° 14′ North).[5] In 1955 and 1956 Nielsen examined the scales of salmon caught at Napassoq and concluded that many of them must have originated in non-Greenland rivers because their parr life was much shorter than had been ascertained for Kapisigdlit fish. This was a remarkable bit of knowledge, published in 1961, which foreshadowed events to come. In 1956 the first of many fishes tagged in distant countries was found in the catches. This evidence suggested that Greenland waters known to be rich in food salmon like, might be one of the long-sought feeding grounds of the salmon of Europe and eastern North America.

Gill-netting for salmon started in 1959 near Napassoq, where a freezing plant was built; in that year 13 tons were produced for export. In 1960 the catch totalled 55 tons; it doubled in 1961 when the fishery spread to Holsteinsborg, Godthaab and Fredericksborg districts; jumped to 220 tons in 1962, 460 tons in 1963, and almost 1,400 tons in 1964. Cod fishing, which the Greenlanders had pursued for many years, reached a peak in 1962, but in the following two years the shoals of cod were much reduced. In order to take up the slack, the government-owned Greenland Trading Company doubled the price it paid for salmon, thus starting a stampede. Almost everybody who owned a motor-boat, or even a row-boat, purchased a net and began to ply the inshore waters where shoals of salmon were seen. Monetary returns to the fishermen were phenomenal.

In 1965 the Government-owned Greenland Trading Company, which markets most of the fish reduced the prices paid for salmon, and as a consequence–and perhaps because of greater runs of cod–the catch fell to 857 tons, including 52 tons taken by a Faroese drift netter and a Norwegian fishing boat. In 1966 the catch rose sharply, totalling 1,147 tons in the shore fishery and 88 tons offshore.

Fishing in Greenland (Figure 31) begins in August and ends in November, but about 90 per cent of the landings are made in September, October and November. The task is arduous. To fish from a small boat in cold waters, with a net set from the shore, is a tough job but the Greenlanders are tough and they have the qualities which make good fishermen. Equally tough, though very profitable, is offshore fishing.

No attempts are made by the Danish Government to set up conservation regulations. Fish of any size are caught; operations continue night and day. An analysis of the 1964 catch reveals that 47 per cent of the weight of the catch were salmon of 2·2 to 7·7 pounds. No grilse were found in the nets, and all the salmon sampled had remains of food in their stomachs. Furthermore, most of them were sexually immature, indicating they had one or more years of growth before they would have returned to their home countries.

Impact of the Greenland fishery

The salmon caught in Greenland seem to belong mostly to Canada. Ireland, Scotland and England contribute nearly all the remainder. It is clear that the stocks in the British Isles and Canada will in time be seriously affected by heavy netting offshore and on the high seas around Greenland.

The Danes, who chiefly profit from the windfall, seem to be on the defensive and tend to minimize the problem. In an article in the Danish magazine *Grøenland*, January 1966, prepared at the request of the Danish Foreign Ministry, Paul Hansen asserts: 'If the salmon's visits to the Greenland feeding grounds have any decimating influence on salmon stocks in the rivers on either side of the Atlantic, it is . . . more logical to seek the explanation in the many dangers with which the journey of 3,000 nautical miles is fraught, rather than in the few scattered nets set by the Greenlanders along their far-flung coastline.' He points out that the salmon fishing industry is subject to large fluctuations from year to year, and that the schools of fish may vanish from Greenland seas as suddenly as they appeared. Yet he told newspaper reporters in Copenhagen that 'even though there really was a possibility of making considerable inroads on the salmon resource he could not imagine how, in fairness, this could be prohibited'.

The Greenland salmon fishery was deemed a matter requiring urgent attention by the proper international fishery organizations in an effort to ascertain the facts and assess the impact of the stocks of the contributing countries. In addition to the International Council for the Exploration of the Sea (ICES), the International Council for Northwest Atlantic Fisheries (ICNAF) has taken up the matter and the two bodies have jointly set up a scientific working party to examine the available data and co-ordinate plans for further research. Meetings have been held from time to time since 1965 and reports issued. However, the continual depredations by the Danes (who control Greenland) and others on the feeding stocks of salmon have as yet precipitated no action by the responsible officials.

Unlike herring, cod and other marine species fished in large volume, salmon are regarded not as the common wealth of the sea but as belonging to the nations in whose rivers they breed. This attitude has in the past created many knotty international problems. Conflicts erupted in the Pacific Ocean and in the Baltic Sea long before the large Greenland fishery began.

Off the Asian coast, the possession of salmon from Russian rivers has been disputed since 1905 at least. The Russians claim that these fish belong to them while the Japanese ardently capture them. Treaties between Russia and Japan have attempted to settle the conflict. The latest agreement, embodied in the 1956 North-west

Pacific Fisheries Convention, covers the north-west Pacific generally west of 175 degrees West and north of 45 degrees North latitude, including the Sea of Okhotsk, parts of the Sea of Japan, and the Bering Sea. Although other species are involved, this convention provides a *modus operandi* for regulating the lucrative salmon fishing. Similarly, the International North Pacific Fisheries Convention between Canada, Japan and the United States provides a mechanism for regulating the capture of millions of salmon feeding in the mid-Pacific, a goodly portion of which, it is alleged by the Americans, originate in streams flowing into Bristol Bay, Alaska.

The latest international agreement concerned with salmon fishing on the high seas is the Baltic Sea Convention of March 1, 1966, ratified by Denmark, Sweden and West Germany. Here too Danish fishermen are the chief beneficiaries.

Since the Greenland dispute is of recent development, it is too early to predict the outcome. Additional facts must be gathered, and protracted negotiations will be necessary. The Danes, who are now sitting tight, as it were, may have to taper off their Greenland operations. However, the vessels of other nations may come in, as the Russians do along the coast of the United States, to capture the salmon outside territorial limits.

Measured by similar conflicts in various parts of the world, the Greenland dispute involves relatively small numbers of fish and a minor economic asset. It has, however, stirred up national passions, as salmon usually do, on a large scale. And they will not die until some kind of *modus operandi* is developed which is agreeable to all affected countries or, as is possible, the fish have fled to new pastures beyond the ken of rapacious fishermen.[6]

NOTES

1 *Parliamentary Debates* (*House of Lords*), July 5, 1965, p. 1136.

2 Jørgen Nielsen, 'Contributions to the Salmonidae in Greenland', p. 8.

3 V. Borum, 'Greenland Daily Life', in *Greenland*, Danish Ministry for Foreign Affairs, p. 90.

4 Nielsen, *op. cit.*, p. 21.

5 *Ibid.*, p. 12.

6 See the article, 'Greenland Salmon', by W. M. Shearer and K. H. Balmain, *Salmon and Trout Magazine*, September, 1967

13

The Controlled Icelandic Fishery

Iceland lies in 63 to 66 degrees North latitude. The ice-cold waters of the Arctic wash the north-east coast, but the rest of the island is warmed by the Gulf Stream. In the south the climate is humid and temperate, with rare periods of frost. 'Warm and cold air are constantly striving for mastery in the sky above and around this northern island. Fronts of depression swing to and fro, collide, occlude and fill up in endless succession.'[1]

Vulcanism and glaciation–fire and ice–have moulded the shape of the country. One-eighth of Iceland is under ice, and one glacier, the Vatnajökull, which is 3,000 feet thick in places, is the largest in Europe. The interior is for the most part a plateau of volcanic rock, rough and bleak-looking, yet picturesque in its own way. Volcanic peaks and smaller plateaux interrupt the horizon. There are numerous hot springs and many geysers which intermittently send up unbroken jets of boiling water and steam.

There are also slumbering volcanoes, some with ice caps, and occasionally they burst into action. When these outbreaks occur, glaciers melt under the flow of lava, explosions rock the countryside, and deluges of ash turn day into night.

The rivers

A small country, Iceland is richly endowed with rivers and lakes. Numerous mountain streams flow down from the glacier-covered interior and leap in large falls down to the sea. Except in the desert region, the rivers are rapid and large, fed by heavy precipitation and summer melting of the glaciers. The longest streams flow towards the south, south-west and north.

The coastline is greatly indented except in the south-west, where a majority of the 180,000 inhabitants live. As in Norway, many of the rivers flow out into fjords, some of which are bordered by high cliffs. Waterfalls abound and often reach great heights, like the famous Gullfoss which drops in two steps into a deep gorge several miles long. Nearly all the rivers have a foss somewhere along their course beyond which migratory fish cannot go.

The landscape is treeless except for birches here and there, and mountain ash which seldom attain 30 feet. A large part of Iceland presents a grey and sombre spectacle, broken by narrow, meandering streams with blue water, and framed by turquoise mountains laden with snow even in summer. There is a vast grassland along the coastal plain, green and lush. Alongside the glaciers one may see green meadows embroidered with colourful wild flowers in summer, and populated with sheep, cattle and horses. There are few roads in the interior.

Iceland is rich in bird life, particularly shore birds. Along the seashore grey seals may be seen poking their heads above water, perhaps searching for that dainty morsel, the salmon. There may be a consortium of turnstones, purple sandpipers, glaucous gulls, mandarin ducks and eider ducks, shepherding their large broods. Amid this assembly the schools of silvery salmon, returning from their feeding grounds in the ocean, attempt to slip unobtrusively into the rivers. Salmon run up nearly 60 Icelandic rivers; in some they penetrate only a few miles and in others up to 60.

The best salmon streams are in the south-west, in the Reykjavik area, where two-thirds of all the fish are caught. In the Árnessýsla district there is the great Ölfusá-Hvitá river complex, the main tributaries being the Sog, Brúará and Stóra Laxá (Great Salmon River). In the Borgarfjördur valley there is another Hvitá River with important tributaries like the Grimsá, Thverá and Nordurá. One of the most famous salmon rivers in this region is the Ellidaá, now owned by the city of Reykjavik, which flows in the outskirts of the capital. North of Reykjavik is the Laxá i Kjös.

The Dalasýsla district in the north-west has several admirable streams. In the Húnavatnssysla district the best rivers are the Midfjardará, Vídidalsá, Vatnsdalsa, Laxá[2] and Blandá. Only a few salmon streams are found in the north-east, of which the largest are

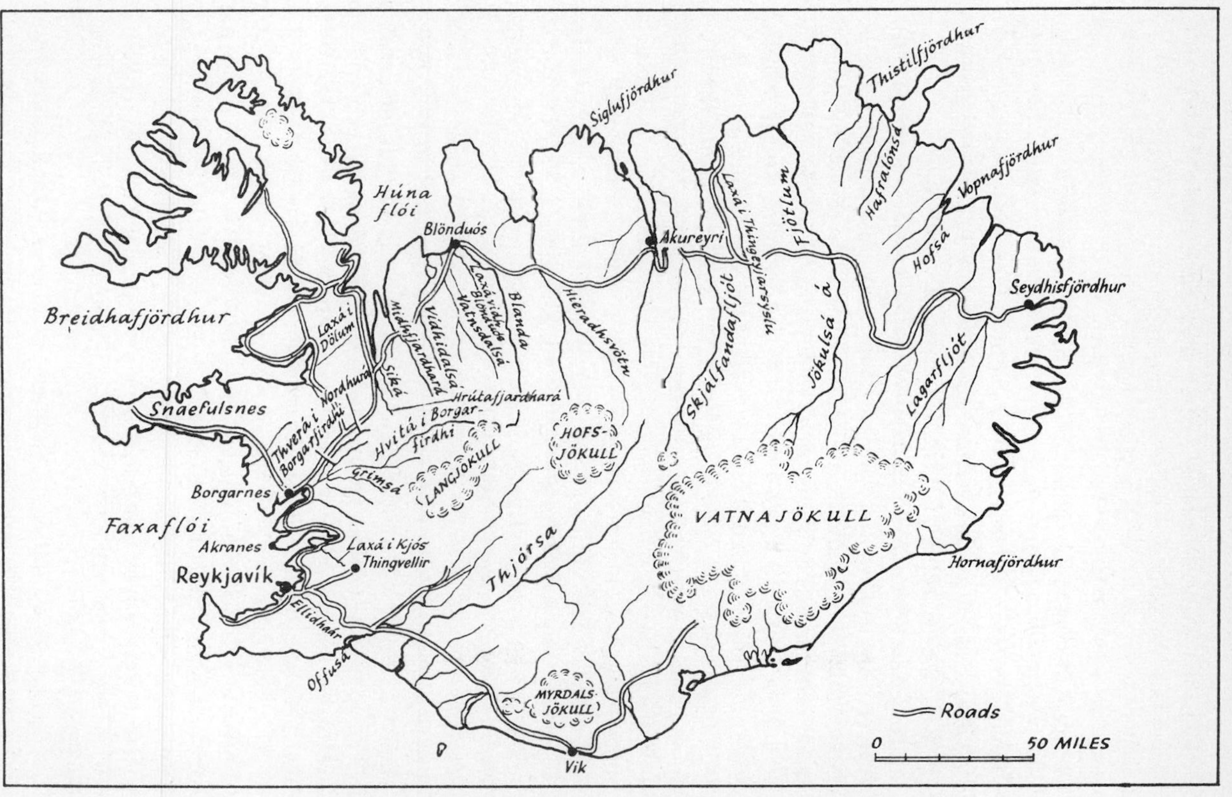

Figure 32

Important rivers in Iceland, including major salmon streams.

Laxá in the Thingeyjarsýsla district and three rivers flowing into Vopnafjördur. A map of salmon rivers is given in Figure 32.

Biological characteristics of Icelandic salmon

Icelandic salmon run true to the pattern of more northern countries. The fish arrive after the river ice has melted, which may be as early as May. The runs are at their height in July and August. Big fish come first, in May and June, while the smaller may not arrive until summer.[3] In northern Iceland drift ice may delay the appearance of the runs. For example, in Hrútafjardará River salmon do not enter until the middle of June, and spawning begins about the middle of September and is over by mid-October. In the Ellidaá spawning may sometimes be observed at the end of August.

The premigratory life of Icelandic salmon is normally three or four years and sea life one or two years. In the Ellidaá the smolts are commonly three years old when they head for the ocean and return mainly as grilse. However, though in some years there are good runs of grilse, the bulk of the fish are mature, yet small in weight. In the Ölfusá the majority of the salmon spend three years as parr but about half of them return as grilse and the remainder in two years. Females tend to have a longer ocean life than males.[4]

Major-General R. N. Stewart, who has fished Icelandic rivers over a period of more than fifty years, says that the small streams have many small fish which spent five or six years as parr. In one river 38 per cent of the salmon examined bore this record on their scales. He thinks that development to the smolt stage is delayed because the rivers are overstocked and there is an insufficient food supply.

The proportion of fish which spawn twice varies considerably among rivers. Fridriksson found that in the Ellidaá 4·6 per cent had one spawning mark; in the Ölfusá 18·4 per cent; in its tributaries, Stora Laxá and Litla Laxá (Little Salmon), 10·1 per cent and 15·3 per cent respectively; in the Nordurá 6·7 per cent; and in Laxá in Adaldal 8·8 per cent. Fish returning to spawn for the third time were quite rare.[5]

In general Icelandic salmon run from 4 to 12 pounds, since they are rarely more than two-winter fish. On the basis of a sample of 1,500–2,000 specimens, the Ellidaá salmon averaged about 5 pounds, and very few of them were grilse, according to General Stewart. In a study reported by Fridriksson on the same river, only 11 per cent of 585 salmon examined in 1938 and 1939 scaled over 7 pounds and only 3 per cent over 11 pounds. Thor Gudjonsson, Director of Freshwater Fisheries, says that only nine fish over 40 pounds are known to have been caught in Iceland. The largest weighed 49 pounds after being bled.

The life of Icelandic salmon in the sea remains a mystery. None has been found in the Greenland catches but at least one wandered as far as Canadian waters.

Use of the resource

Iceland has been inhabited since the ninth century and had a flourishing civilization throughout the Middle Ages, comparable to that of any western European country. Many festivities were held throughout the year, often culminating in sumptuous banquets at which great quantities of food and drink were consumed. Feasts celebrating weddings, funerals and other notable occasions often lasted several days. While records are scant about the kind of fare that was served, we may be sure that freshwater fish like salmon graced many a table. The salmon were caught by the farmers for home consumption and eaten fresh, salted or smoked. An export business in salmon did not start until about 1860, but it has continued to this day, with Reykjavik at the centre of the trade.

The customary method of harvesting salmon was by netting in the estuaries or along the coast. 'When I first visited the country in 1912,' says General Stewart, 'no Icelander that I heard of fished for sport, except a few boys. This was partly due to the fact that few of them had much leisure, partly to the consideration that fish were food and the less time lost in securing food, the more time there was for attending to more urgent problems.'[6]

That salmon were plentiful in past centuries is certain. As an example, Terkel M. Terkelsen, writing in *Trout and Salmon* (May 1965), quotes the following passage from a history of the Grimsá Valley as translated for him by an old farmer: 'In the autumn the ford is sometimes so tightly packed with salmon that the traveller cannot force his horse across.' The Ellidaá was always apparently rich in fish. 'In days gone by,' says General Stewart, 'it used to be let to visiting anglers and I have heard of one party catching over 2,000 fish in the season, average weight about five pounds.'

After 1930 some rivers were overfished, so the Icelandic Government stiffened the Freshwater Fishery laws before World War II, while additional support for conservation was provided by local regulations. Salmon was declared a 'freshwater fish' and netting in the estuaries and salt water forbidden. Only glacial rivers can now be netted and this is done by fixed nets similar to the stake nets used in Scotland. In recent years, according to the statistical bulletin of the International Council for the Exploration of the Sea, Iceland has reported a harvest of about 200 tons (440,000 pounds) annually.

In addition to the curtailment of netting, a programme of stream improvement has been carried out, particularly the laddering of waterfalls to permit the use of additional nursery grounds. In 1937, for example, a ladder was constructed at the foss on the Fitjá River which enters the Vídidalsá some 15 miles from its mouth, thus opening 25 miles of good spawning water.

Artificial breeding of salmon was tried on the Laxá in Kjos and Laxá in Dölum in the years 1886–90, and then ceased. It was resumed in the 1920s, and has been employed as a means of bolstering waning stocks, as in the Ellidaá, where a hydro-electric plant interferes with the natural runs. After the installation of the barrage, salmon were netted in this river and put into tank trucks and released above the dam.

'The State Directorate (of Freshwater Fisheries) does everything in its power by word and deed to protect and improve the fishing', says Thor Gudjonsson, Director of Freshwater Fisheries. 'Obstructions to the movement of fish in the rivers are removed where possible. . . . In many rivers the fishing is controlled and inspected. Electrification or industrialization has–compared with neighbouring countries–had little effect on fishing in Iceland.'[7]

---

23. Salmon fishing in Greenland. This photo was taken in September 1965 in Sukkertoppen. It shows a gill-net operation of the type conducted along west Greenland coastal waters. The buoy in the photograph marks the outer end of the net which is attached to the rocks on the shore. The fisherman in the skiff is overhauling the net and removing salmon and seaweed from it.

Iceland is one of the few countries that now has as much salmon in its rivers probably as it did a century ago. This fortunate situation is due to the fact that it 'has looked after its salmon fisheries better than any country that I know', says General Stewart. 'Thus, it has had a better chance, as there are no great industries and pollution is almost unknown, and the market for salmon is small.'[8]

Nearly all for sport

Understandably Iceland is a fishers' haven within the limits of its resource. Angling is well managed and therefore is as good as natural conditions permit. Beats are in great demand and rents have soared. 'The river I used to fish', said General Stewart in 1950, 'has risen from £75 in 1936 annually to £1,700. Another river which was £300 in 1936 is now £10,000.'

As in Norway, intrepid British anglers introduced the sport of rod fishing. One of the earliest visitors in the nineteenth century was Ackroyd, who fished the Laxamyri River on the north coast, bringing gillies and boats from England. 'Visiting anglers were considered most peculiar. The fact that they were prepared to spend good money and much time, in performing an everyday and rather tedious act, although welcome, appeared very odd to Icelandic eyes.'[9] General Stewart, who contributed a great deal to the development of salmon angling in Iceland, had a lease on the Hrútafjardará River and its tributary, the Síká, for twenty years, and at one time or another fished a total of seventeen Icelandic streams.

Most of the rivers are now leased to angling clubs that build accommodations along the banks, employ watchmen, undertake restocking, and generally manage the waters for full production. The number of rods allowed on any river is determined by the Directorate of Freshwater Fisheries, and is kept within reasonable bounds. Normally only a few rods are permitted on the shorter streams, so that every fisher has plenty of water to himself. Fishing is allowed

---

24a. The foss on Hrútafjardará River, Iceland. Here a fish pass could be built at no great cost to increase the runs.

24b. The Sog, Iceland. A south coast salmon river, tributary of the Hvitá, a large glacier river.

from 7 a.m. to 10 p.m., with a break of two or three hours at midday, and the season runs from June 1 to September 15. No licence is required and beats may be obtained at rates varying from $3.00 to $20.00 per day, averaging $12.00. Anglers are usually permitted to retain their catches.

With the growth of the Icelandic economy there has emerged a larger leisure class and an increasing army of fishermen. In 1950 there were probably no more than 800 persistent anglers in the country. Today one club in Reykjavik alone has 700 members, and each man must plan his sport months ahead, drawing lots in midwinter for days on club waters.

Not only the natives but many foreigners are learning the value of the country's rivers. Perhaps no better testimony may be given than that of Joseph W. Brooks, Jr., an American who has pursued the sport in many countries. 'Iceland', he says, 'has more fish per foot of river than any place I've ever fished.'

And it is in Iceland that the old rhyme seems peculiarly fitting:

Old men will tell tall stories
As we may seem to do,
But we have found a river
Where most fish lies come true.

NOTES

1 Gudmundur Thorlaksson, *A Brief Geography of Iceland.*
2 'Laxá' means salmon river.
3 Bjarni Saemundsen, *Fiskarni*, p. 346.
4 Arni Fridriksson, 'Salmon Investigations in the Years 1937–1939', p. 59.
5 *Ibid.*, p. 64.
6 R. N. Stewart, *Rivers of Iceland*, p. 145.
7 Thor Gudjonsson, *Salmon and Trout Fishing in Iceland.*
8 R. N. Stewart, personal communication, April 6, 1966.
9 R. N. Stewart, *op. cit.*

Epilogue

Once upon a time the Atlantic salmon roamed over half the northern hemisphere, as the map on page 24 shows, in the numerous straits, gulfs, bays and fjords of the Arctic and Atlantic Oceans and entered thousands of rivers stretching far into the interior of Europe and North America. The fish has a long history of human association for it was familiar to the Lapps of northern Scandinavia, the Eskimo of western Greenland and Labrador, and the Indians of the Connecticut Valley and Lake Ontario long before these peoples ever set eyes on the white man.

The salmon has provided man with food at least as far back as the Old Stone Age, longer probably than cattle or sheep or other domesticated animals. It has served man well but now, it seems, man is bent upon exterminating it, at least in some parts of its withered range. Indeed, in many lands the salmon has been pursued so relentlessly and so many barriers have been strewn along its migratory routes that the fish, so to speak, have said, 'Hail and farewell!' and are seen no more.

There is no possibility of the salmon's return, for instance, to the rivers of Portugal, Holland or Switzerland, even if there were any desire on the part of the people to restore them. In other countries the runs have been reduced to a trickle because the inhabitants didn't care enough to save them. Even in lands where substantial stocks remain, as in Norway, Sweden, Russia, the British Isles and Canada, there is no assurance of their continuation for new problems and dangers constantly arise. Apart from the difficulties of keeping rivers inviolate, the fishes' life in the sea is now threatened by the discovery of at least part of its feeding haunts and migratory routes in the north Atlantic.

While the tide of depletion continues, however, there is a countermovement of conservation. A great deal of research and investigation has enabled us to save large remnants of the stocks in various countries. Yet the question is still asked: how can the future of the species be assured? The answer is not easy but a few conclusions may be drawn from the facts presented in this book.

It seems that the nations which have fared the best in retaining their salmon have followed certain principles of conservation–and those which have fared the worst have basically ignored these principles.

Conservation requires first of all conservative exploitation of the runs in order to assure a perpetual crop. This is the guiding principle of the management agencies on the Columbia River, where all the salmon are counted as they cross a series of high dams and regulation of the catch can be based on more scientific data than is available anywhere else in the world.

Secondly, rivers must be kept clean and free of impassable obstructions. This requires a ceaseless war on pollution and rigid control of impoundments in order to assure the provision of effective fish passes or lifts or the like. Nations like France and Spain which have paid little heed to what was happening on their rivers have seen their salmon stocks dwindle away.

Thirdly, the quantity and quality of streamflow must be safeguarded in order to meet the exacting requirements of the sensitive salmon. For instance, raising the temperature of the water in summer can create an epidemic of furunculosis that is fatal to the salmon. Serious drawdowns of flow for agricultural purposes or power generation must be averted. Fish passes must not be permitted to run dry. Radiation introduced into rivers is inimical to the fish. All this means that competing uses for water require careful adjudication and fishery interests must have an effective voice in the management of a stream.

Fourth, we know that salmon runs can be increased by opening up new spawning territory through the laddering of waterfalls and removal of obstructions, and reclamation of impure waters. Norway has been outstanding in this endeavour.

Fifth, it is now recognized that artificial production is an invaluable tool of fishery management. The Swedish smolt-rearing programme has proven successful in bolstering the salmon populations of the Baltic Sea, thus assuring good harvests in the ocean as well as rivers, and plans are under way to build Swedish-type hatcheries in Norway, Canada and possibly Finland. In the Columbia River where very high dams and pollution have jeopardized an exceedingly valuable fishery, the runs are being sustained with the help of twenty hatcheries, each producing hundreds of thousands of fingerlings per year.

Continuous research is essential for perpetuation of the salmon. There is much to be learned about its life history and migrations, about the techniques of artificial production, and especially about getting both the adults and smolts safely past high dams. Scotland and Sweden are conducting the most ambitious research programmes in Europe; Ireland and Norway are doing important work and Russia too (so far as can be learned). Outside of these countries there is little interest in salmon research in Europe. I met no fishery biologists in my tour of France and Spain. Canada has made outstanding scientific contributions to our knowledge of *Salmo salar*.

So far we have discussed the measures taken to protect the salmon during its riverine phase of existence–its premigratory and post-feeding stages over which man has some control. What happens to the fish in the ocean remains mostly a mystery although some of its secrets–unhappily–have been pierced. However, man cannot control its oceanic wanderings any more than he can alter, however much he would like to do so, its inflexible habit of returning to spawn in the river where it was born or released as a juvenile. Ironically, the more we learn about the fishes' life in the sea the greater becomes the danger to their survival, as the upsurge of the Greenland (and more recently Norwegian) fishery proves.

Pessimists may argue that the salmon disease U.D.N. is about to decimate stocks in the British Isles but we may hope that the history of this will be similar to that of the salmon disease of the last century and that its virulence will decrease in a few years' time. Even at present, commercial fishing in the estuaries continues almost as usual since symptoms do not appear until the salmon come into fresh water. It is rod fishing in rivers, particularly in the lower reaches, which has been disastrously affected in spring and early summer. At least some fish have spawned in infected Irish waters and we may hope that immune stock will result from these spawnings and that salmon may be as numerous in British rivers in the 1980's as they were in the early '60s.

EPILOGUE

The preservation of the salmon rests almost entirely with man. He alone can exterminate the species or help to save what is left of the rivers and stocks. This is a truism.

It may be noticed that where the salmon have fared best there has been a partnership, or at least an *entente cordiale*, between the exploiters of the fishery and the management agencies; between the government, proprietors, commercial and sports fishermen, hydro-electric agencies, and others who have a vested interest in the rivers. Where there has been no such partnership or *entente*, or where 'the conservation ethic' has been absent, as in the United States during the nineteenth century, the resource has been grossly abused or destroyed.

It is clear that while conservation in the river is essential to the species' survival, there must also be conservation in the sea. The next urgent step in the attempt to save what is left of the vast populations of salmon involves oceanic fishing. Some restrictions on the catch during their feeding years is needed if the stocks of Europe and Canada are not to decline even further.

The convention of March 1, 1966, signed by the Baltic nations to limit and prescribe conditions for taking salmon in the Baltic Sea offers a model. At the present time our eyes are on Greenland. Unless some kind of curb on the incredible slaughter in this area is quickly put into effect the stocks of the countries which supply this fishery must suffer.

Bibliography

This bibliography is a list of the works actually used in the preparation of the book.

The most complete bibliography of the Atlantic Salmon is that of Julien Bergeron, *Bibliographie du Saumon de l'Atlantique*, published in 1962 by the Department of Game and Fisheries, Province of Quebec, Quebec, Canada.

Introduction

Bulletin Statistique des Pêches Maritimes, ed. Arni Frederiksen, Vols. XLV, XLVI, XLVII, International Council for the Exploration of the Sea, Copenhagen.

Hoek, P. P. C., *Propagation and Protection of the Rhine Salmon*, Bureau of Fisheries, Washington, D.C., Bulletin 28, 1910.

Le Danois, Edouard, *et al.*, *Fishes of the World*. Woodstock, Vt., Countryman Press, n.d.

Power, G., 'The Evolution of the Freshwater Race of the Atlantic Salmon (*Salmo Salar* L.) in Eastern North America', *Arctic*, Vol. II, No. 2 (1958).

Report of the Inspector of Fisheries for England and Wales for 1886, London, 1887.

Thomazi, A., *Histoire de la Pêche: Des Ages de la Pierre à Nos Jours*, Paris, Payot, 1907.

Standard Encyclopedia of the World's Rivers and Lakes, ed. R. Kay Gresswell and Anthony Huxley, New York, Putnam, 1965.

Chapter 1

Balmain, K. H. and Shearer, W. M., 'Records of Salmon and Sea Trout Caught at Sea', Scottish Home Department, H.M.S.O., Edinburgh, 1956.

Berg, Magnus, *Salmon and Salmon Fishing*, Bergen, Universitetsforloget, 1963, English translation unpublished.

Bibliography

Blair, A. A., 'Atlantic Salmon Tagged in East Coast Newfoundland Waters at Bonavista', *Journal Fisheries Research Board of Canada*, 13 (2), March 1956.

Brett, J. R., 'The Swimming Energetics of Salmon', *Scientific American*, August 1965.

Carter, Wilfred M., 'The Reproduction of Salmon in Scandinavia and the British Isles', *Atlantic Salmon Journal*, June 1964.

Elson, P. F., 'Predator-Prey Relationships between Fish-Eating Birds and Atlantic Salmon', Fisheries Research Board of Canada, Ottawa, 1962.

— 'The Importance of Size in the Change from Parr to Smolt in Atlantic Salmon', *Canadian Fish Culturist*, No. 21, December 1957.

Hagen, William, Jr., *Pacific Salmon*, Circular 24, Fish and Wildlife Service, Washington, D.C., 1953.

Hansen, Paul, 'Report on Recaptures in Greenland Waters of Salmon Tagged in Rivers in America and Europe', International Council for Exploration of the Sea, Salmon and Trout Committee, 1965.

Hardy, Sir Alister, *The Open Sea*, Vol. II, *Fish and Fisheries*, London, Collins, 1959.

Hasler, A. D., 'Odor Perception and Orientation in Fishes', *Journal Fisheries Research Board of Canada*, Vol. II, 1954.

Hasler, A. D. and Wisly, W. J., 'Discrimination of Stream Odors by Fishes and Its Relation to Parent Stream Behavior', *American Naturalist*, Vol. 85, 1951.

Hayes, F. R., 'Artificial Freshets and Other Factors Controlling the Ascent and Population of Atlantic Salmon in the La Have River, Nova Scotia', Fisheries Research Board of Canada, Ottawa, 1953.

Huntsman, A. G., *Return of Salmon from the Sea*, Biological Board of Canada, 1936.

Huntsman, A. G. and Hoar, W. S., 'Resistance of Atlantic Salmon to Sea Water', *Journal Fisheries Research Board of Canada*, 4 (5), 1939.

Jones, J. W., *The Salmon*, London, Collins, 1959.

Lindroth, Arne, 'Mergansers as Salmon and Trout Predators in the River Indalsälven', Institute of Freshwater Research, Drottningholm, Report No. 36, 1955.

Malloch, P. D., *Life History and Habits of the Salmon, Sea Trout, and other Freshwater Fish*, London, Black, 1910.

Menzies, W. J. M., *The Stock of Salmon*, London, Edward Arnold, 1949.

Mills, D. H., 'The Goosander and Red-breasted Merganser as Predators of Salmon in Scottish Waters', Department of Agriculture and Fisheries, H.M.S.O., Edinburgh, 1962.

— 'The Ecology of the Young Stages of the Atlantic Salmon in the River Bran in Ross-shire', Department of Agriculture and Fisheries, H.M.S.O., Edinburgh, 1964.

Netboy, Anthony, *Salmon of the Pacific Northwest: Fish vs. Dams*, Portland, Ore., Binfords and Mort, 1958.

Nielsen, Jørgen, *Contributions to the Biology of the Salmonidae in Greenland*, I–IV, Copenhagen, Bianco Lunos Bogtrykkeri, 1961.

Pope, S. A., Mills, D. H. and Shearer, W. M., 'The Fecundity of Atlantic Salmon', Department of Agriculture and Fisheries, H.M.S.O., Edinburgh, 1961.

Power, G., 'The Evolution of the Freshwater Races of the Atlantic Salmon (*Salmo Salar* L.) in Eastern North America', *Arctic*, Vol. 11, No. 2 (1958).

Pyefinch, K. A., 'A Review of the Literature on the Biology of the Atlantic Salmon', Scottish Home Department, H.M.S.O., Edinburgh, 1955.

Roule, Louis, *Fishes: Their Journeys and Migrations*, New York, Norton, 1933.

Stuart, T. A., 'The Leaping Behaviour of Salmon and Trout at Falls and Obstructions', Department of Agriculture and Fisheries, H.M.S.O., Edinburgh, 1962.

Vibert, Richard, 'Voyages Maritimes des Saumons et Retour à la Rivière Natale', *Bulletin Français de Pisciculture*, No. 170, 1963.

Walton, Izaak and Cotton, C., *The Compleat Angler*, London, Cassell, 1909.

White, H. C., 'Bird Control to Increase the Pollett River Salmon', Fisheries Research Board of Canada, Bull. LVIII, Ottawa, 1939.

— 'Factors Influencing Descent of Atlantic Salmon Smolts', *Journal Fisheries Research Board of Canada*, 4 (5), 1939.

Wooding, F. H., *Canada's Atlantic Salmon*, Department of Fisheries, Ottawa, 1956.

Chapter 2

El Salmón y su Pesca en España, Madrid, La Dirección General del Turismo (Spanish State Tourist Bureau), 1945.

G.-Camino, Enrique, *La Riqueza Piscicola de los Ríos del Norte de España*, Madrid, La Dirección General del Turismo, n.d.

— *El Salmón: Fuente de Riqueza*, Madrid, La Dirección General del Turismo, n.d.

Gallichan, Walter M., *Fishery and Travel in Spain*, 1904.

Muñoz Goyanes, Guillermo, *Informaciones Estadísticas Sobre la Pesca Continental en España*, Madrid, Dirección General de Montes, Caza y Pesca Fluvial, 1959.

Nagel's Travel Guide to Spain, Paris, Les Editions Nagel, 1954.

Pardo, Luis, 'A Modo de Síntesis: La Riqueza Salmonera en España', *El Salmón y su Pesca*, 1945.

Reeve, M. R., 'Where Salmon Fishing Reigns Supreme', *Country Life*, February 28, 1963.

Chapter 3

Bachelier, Roger, 'Situation Actuelle du Saumon en France', Paris, October 24, 1962; Memorandum, unpublished.

— *L'Histoire du Saumon en Loire*, *Bulletin Français de Pisciculture*.

Beall, George, 'Fishing in the Lower Pyrenees', *The Field*, April 21, 1960.

— 'La Saison de Pêche 1962 dans les Basses-Pyrénées', *Au Bord de L'Eau*, March 15–April 14, 1963.

de Boisset, L. and Vibert, Richard, *La Pêche Fluviale en France*, Paris, Librairie de Champs Élysées, 1944.

Boyer, Henri, *Le Saumon dans le Haut-Allier*, Paris, 1930.

Felix, R., *Le Saumon: Sa Vie, Sa Pêche dans l'Allier*, Nevers, Syndicat d'Initiative, n.d.

Lacroix, Paul, *France in the Eighteenth Century*, New York, Ungar, 1963. (Chapter XV, 'The Kitchen and the Table'.)

Commandant Latour, *Le Saumon dans le Courses d'Eau Bretons*, Paris, 1928.

Moreau, Émile, *Histoire Naturelle de Poissons de la France*, Paris, Masson, 1881, Vol. 3.

Roule, Louis, *Fishes: Their Journeys and Migrations*, New York, Norton, 1933.

— *Étude sur le Saumon des Eaux Douces de la France*, 1920.

Thomazi, A., *Histoire de la Pêche: Des Ages de la Pierre à Nos Jours*, Paris, Payot, 1907.

Le Veritable Guide de Pêcheur, par l'Uncle Pierre, Paris, Librairie Taride, n.d.

Vibert, Richard, 'La Regression du Saumon du Rhin', *Bulletin Français de Pisciculture*, No. 156.

— 'Les Poissons Migrateurs dans l'Economie Piscicole du Sud-Ouest', *Bulletin Français de Pisciculture*, No. 136 (1945).

— 'Dommages Piscicoles des Usines Hydroelectriques', *Bulletin Français de Pisciculture*, Nos. 148–9 (1948).

— *Recherches sur le Saumon de l'Adour*, Annales de la Station Centrale d'Hydrobiologique Appliquée, Vol. III, 1950.

— 'Voyages Maritimes des Saumons et Retour à la Rivière Natale', *Bulletin Français de Pisciculture*, No. 170 (1953).

Chapter 4

Alm, Gunnar, 'The Salmon Catch and the Salmon Stock in the Baltic during Recent Years', Svenska Vattenkraftforeningens Publikationer, Stockholm, 1954.

Bibliography

Andersson, Ingvar, *Introduction to Sweden*, Stockholm, The Swedish Institute, 1951.

Berg, Leo S., *Freshwater Fishes of the U.S.S.R. and Adjacent Countries*, Vol. I, 4th ed., Washington, D.C., National Science Foundation, 1962.

Bossi, Robert, *The Lapps*, New York, Praeger, 1960.

Carlin, Borje, 'A Swedish View of the Value of Stocking Rivers with Salmon', London, *Salmon and Trout Association*, 1960.

Carter, Wilfred M., 'The Reproduction of Salmon in Scandinavia and the British Isles', *Atlantic Salmon Journal*, June 1964.

Christensen, O., 'The Danish Salmon Fishery in the Eastern Baltic in the Season 1964–65', International Council for Exploration of the Sea, 1965, Salmon and Trout Committee.

Chrzan, F., 'The Movement and Growth Rate of Tagged Drawa Salmon', I.C.E.S., 1964, Salmon and Trout Committee.

Hansen, Paul M., 'Report on Recaptures in Greenland Waters of Salmon Tagged in Rivers in America and Europe', Int. Council for Exploration of the Sea, 1965.

Hurme, Seppo, *The Anadromous Fishes in the Baltic-Side Rivers of Finland*, Helsinki, Department of Agriculture, 1962.

— 'Concerning Salmon and Trout Bearing Rivers in Finland which Empty into the Baltic', *Fiskeritidskrift for Finland*, No. 4, 1963.

Institute of Freshwater Research, Drottningholm, Sweden:

Report No. 33, 1951—Arne Lindroth, 'Salmon Tagging Experiments in Sundsvall Bay of the Baltic in 1950'.

Report No. 36, 1955—Gunnar Svärdson, 'Salmon Stock Fluctuations in the Baltic Sea'.

Report No. 38, 1957—Arne Lindroth, 'Baltic Salmon Fluctuations: A Reply'.

Report No. 44, 1962—Arne Lindroth, 'Baltic Salmon Fluctuations: 2. Porpoise and Salmon'.

International Council for the Exploration of the Sea, Charlottenlund, Denmark:

Rapports et Procès-Verbaux des Réunions

Vol. 73—H. Henking, 'Untersuchungen An Salmoniden', Part II, April 1931.

Vol. 92—Gunnar Alm, 'Salmon in the Baltic Precincts', December 1934.

Vol. 101, 3rd part—M. Siedlicki, 'Fluctuations in the Number of Individuals Belonging to Different Age-groups in the Catches of European Salmon (*Salmo Salar*)', July 1936.

Vol. 119—T. H. Jarvi, 'On the Periodicity of Salmon Reproduction in the Northern Baltic Area and its Causes', April 1948.

Vol. 147—Borje Carlin, 'Results of Salmon Smolt Tagging in the Baltic Area', August 1959.

Vol. 147—'Measures for Improving the Stock of Demersal Fish in the Baltic', August 1959.

Vol. 148—Borje Carlin, 'Salmon Conservation in the Baltic', October 1959.

Vol. 148—'Contributions to Symposium on Salmon and Sea Trout, 1958', October 1959.

Journal du Conseil

Vol. IX, No. 1—Boris Dixon, 'The Age and Growth of Salmon Caught in the Polish Baltic, in the Years 1931–1933', April 1934.

Vol. XXIII, No. 3—Gunnar Alm, 'Seasonal Fluctuations in the Catches of Salmon in the Baltic', July 1958.

Vol. XXIII, No. 3—'Notes on Recent Atlantic Salmon Investigations in the U.S.S.R.'

Salmon and Trout Committee, 1963

A. P. Mitans, 'Food Composition of Young of Salmon (*Salmo Salar*) in Lithuanian Rivers'.

S. Zarnecki, 'Times of Entering into the Vistula River of Summer and Winter Populations of Sea-Trout and Atlantic Salmon in the 1952 Year-Cycle'.

Lindroth, Arne, *Fluctuations of the Salmon Stock in the Rivers of Northern Sweden*, Svenska Vattenkraftforeningens Publikationer, Stockholm, 1950.

— 'Salmon Conservation in Sweden', *Transactions American Fisheries Society*, Vol. 92, No. 3 (July 1963).

— 'The Baltic Salmon Stock: Its Natural and Artificial Regulation', *Mitteilung. Internat. Verein. Limnol.*, Stuttgart, August 1965.

Menzies, W. J. M., 'The Atlantic Salmon Fisheries of Canada', Atlantic Salmon Association, Montreal, 1951.

Montén, Erik, 'Salmon Fishery in Spite of Hydroelectric Developments', Swedish State Power Board, Stockholm, n.d.

Nikolskii, G. V., *Special Ichthyology*, 2nd ed. translated from the Russian, National Science Foundation, Washington, D.C., 1961.

Power Supply in Sweden, Swedish State Power Board, 1961.

Svärdson, Gunnar, *Goda Laxar-Och Daliga*, Stockholm, Norstedt, 1957.

Sweden, Ancient and Modern, Swedish Traffic Association, Stockholm, 1938.

Webster, Dwight A., 'Notes and Observations on Trip to Norway, Sweden, England and Scotland', Cornell University, Dept. of Fisheries, December 1961.

Chapter 5

Angling in Norway, Oslo, Norway Travel Association, 1958 and 1962 edns.

Berg, Magnus, *Laks og Laksefiske* (*Salmon and Salmon Fishing*), Universitetsforlaget, Bergen, 1963, tr. Sven Karell (unpublished).

— *Nord-Norske Lakseelver*, Olso, Tanum Forlag, 1964 (English Summary).

Calderwood, W. L., *Salmon and Sea Trout*, London, Edward Arnold, 1930.

Cooper, Gordon, *Your Holiday in Norway*, London, Alvin Redman, n.d.

Dahl, Knut, *Salmon and Trout: A Handbook*, London, Salmon and Trout Association, 1914.

Dahl, Knut and Sømme, Sven, *Experiments in Salmon Marking in Norway, 1935*, Oslo, 1936.

— *Salmon Marking in Norway, 1938, 1939, and 1940*, Oslo, 1942.

Dahl, Knut and Dahl, Eyvind, *Norges Lakseelver: Deres Utbytte i Tabeller og Grafer*, Oslo, Agriculture and Fisheries Department, 1942.

Fiskeriinspektørens Aarsmelding om Fierskvannsfisket for Arene, 1951–1962, Oslo, January 22, 1965.

Gathorne-Hardy, A. E., *The Salmon*, London, Longmans, Green, 1898.

A Geography of Norden, tr. Axel Strømme, Oslo, Cappelens Forlag, 1960.

Lov om Laks-og Gjø-ørretfiskeriene (Law Concerning Salmon and Sea Trout Fishing), February 27, 1930, Oslo 1954.

Lov ar 6 Mars 1964 om Laksefiske og Innlandsfiske, Oslo, 1964.

Major, Harlan, *Norway: Home of the Norsemen*, New York, David McKay, 1957.

Medill, Robert, *Norwegian Towns and People*, New York, McBride, 1924.

'Report on Industrial and Hydroelectric Power Developments in Norway and Sweden', Senate Committee on Public Works, 87th Congress, 1st Session, 1961.

Rosseland, Leiv, 'Salmon and Salmon Fishing', in *Havet og Nare Fisker*, ed. Gunnar Rolefsen, Eides Forlag, Oslo, n.d.

Rothery, Agnes, *Norway*, New York, Viking Press, 1939.

Skaun, Sigurd, *Lakser og Lorder in Stjørdalselven* (Salmon and Lords on the Stjørdal River), Trondheim, 1925, tr. Sven Karell (unpublished).

Sømme, Sven, 'Inland Fisheries', in *Industries of Norway*, ed. Alge J. Adamson, Oslo, Dreyers Forlag, 1952.

Chapter 6

Ashton, John, *Social Life in the Reign of Queen Anne*, New York, Scribners, 1929.

Ashworth, Thomas, *The Salmon Fisheries of England*, London, Longmans, Green, 1868.

British Field Sports Society, Map of the Trout and Salmon Waters of England and Wales, London, 13th ed., 1964.

Brookes, R., *The Art of Angling*, London, 1770.

Calderwood, W. L., *Salmon and Sea Trout*, London, Edward Arnold, 1930.

Cutting, Charles S., *Fish Saving: A History of Fish Processing from Ancient to Modern Times*, London, Leonard Hill, 1955.

Daniels, W. B., *Rural Sports*, London, 1800.

Day, Francis, *Salmonidae of Britain and Ireland*, London, Williams and Norgate, 1887.

— *Fisheries of Great Britain and Ireland*, London, Williams and Norgate, 1880–4.

Defoe, Daniel, *A Tour through England and Wales*, Vol. I, London, Everyman's Library, 1928.

Dempster, J. W., *Our Rivers*, Oxford University Press, 1948.

Derry, T. K. and Jarman, T. L., *The Making of Modern Britain*, New York, New York University Press, 1956.

Fort, R. S. and Brayshaw, J. D., *Fishery Management*, London, Faber, 1961.

Gathorne-Hardy, A. E., *The Salmon*, London, Longmans, Green, 1898.

Grimble, Augustus, *The Salmon Rivers of England and Wales*, London, Kegan Paul, 1913.

Hansen, Paul M., 'Report on Recaptures in Greenland Waters of Salmon Tagged in Rivers in America and Europe', I.C.E.S., 1965.

Hardy, Eric, 'That Other Eden', *Salmon and Trout Magazine*, September 1955.

Hassell, W. O., *How They Lived, 55 B.C.–1485*, Oxford, Basil Blackwell, 1962.

Hawke, Jacquetta, *The Land*, London, Penguin Books, 1959.

Jones, J. W., *The Salmon*, London, Collins, 1959.

The Journeys of Celia Fiennes, ed. Christopher Morris, London, Cresset Press, 1949.

Lennard, Reginald, *Rural England, 1086–1135*, Oxford, Clarendon Press, 1959.

Magri MacMahon, A. F., *Fishlore*, London, Pelican Books, 1946.

Mantoux, P., *The Industrial Revolution in the Eighteenth Century*, London, Cape.

Mascall, Leonard, *A Booke of Fishing*, London, Simpkin Marshall, 1894.

Moore, Stuart A. and Moore, Hubert Stuart, *The History and Law of Fisheries*, London, 1903.

Oke's Fishery Laws, 2nd ed. by J. W. Willis-Bund, London, Butterworth, 1878.

Pentelow, F. T. K., *River Purification*, London, Edward Arnold, 1953.

Radcliffe, William, *Fishing from the Earliest Times*, London, Murray, 1921.

Report of the Inspectors of Salmon Fisheries (England and Wales) for 1868, London, H.M.S.O., 1869.

Report of the Inspectors of Fisheries (England and Wales) for 1887, London, H.M.S.O., 1888.

Report of Committee on Salmon and Freshwater Fisheries, Cmnd. 1350, H.M.S.O., London, May 1961.

Stewart, R. N., *Salmon and Trout: Their Habits and Haunts*, Edinburgh, W. and R. Chambers, 1963.

A Treasury of English Wildlife, ed. W. J. Turner, Hastings House, New York, n.d.

Turing, H. D., *River Pollution*, London, Edward Arnold, 1952.

Waters, Brian, *Severn Tide*, London, Dent, 1947.

Wheatley, Henry B., *London Past and Present*, Vol. III, London, John Murray, 1891.

Young, Archibald, *Salmon Fisheries*, London, Stanford, 1877.

— *The Natural History and Habits of the Salmon: Reasons for the Decline of the Fisheries*, London, 1854.

Chapter 7

Ainger, William D. and Barclay, John S., *Freshwater Fisheries in Rivers and the Impact of the Water Resources Act of 1963*, London, Salmon and Trout Association, n.d.

Ashley-Cooper, John, 'Standards in Salmon Fishing', *The Field*, November 21, 1963.

Bibby, Cyril, *T. H. Huxley*, New York, Horizon Press, 1960.

Calcott, Ian, *The Art of Salmon Fishing*, Edinburgh, Oliver and Boyd, 1963.

Day, Francis, *Salmonidae of Britain and Ireland*, London, Williams and Norgate, 1887.

Day, J. Wentworth, *The Angler's Pocket Book*, London, Evans Bros., 1961.

Denton, C. R., 'A Regency Angling Club', *The Field*, August 26, 1965.

Fort, R. S. and Brayshaw, J. D., *Fishery Management*, London, Faber, 1961.

Grimble, Augustus, *The Salmon Rivers of England and Wales*, London, Kegan Paul, 1913.

Herbert, H. A., *Tale of a Wye Fisherman*, London, 1953.

Holliday, F. W., 'Teifi through the Centuries', *Salmon and Trout Magazine*, May 1964.

Houghton, A. T. R., *The Ribble Salmon Fisheries*, John Sherratt, Altrincham, 1952.

Hutton, J. Arthur, *Wye Salmon and Other Fish*, John Sherratt, Altrincham, 1949.

Hutton, J. Arthur, *Development of Our Salmon Fisheries*, Manchester, Sherratt and Hughes, 1917.
— 'Norwegian and British Salmon Fisheries', *Salmon and Trout Magazine*, 1934.
Klein, Louis (ed.), *Aspects of River Pollution*, Academic Press, New York, 1957.
Lancashire River Board, *Annual Reports for 1957 to 1961*, Preston.
— *Fishery Officer's Report for Year ended March 31, 1960.*
Maxwell, Sir Herbert, *Salmon and Sea Trout*, Routledge, London, n.d.
Northumberland and Tyneside River Boards, *Annual Reports for 1957 to 1962*, Newcastle-upon-Tyne.
Pentelow, F. T. K., 'Biological Aspects', *Proceedings of the Society for Water Treatment and Examination*, Vol. 9, Part I, 1960.
— 'River Boards in Britain', *Nature*, June 7, 1958.
— 'A Survey of the Problem of Trade-Waste Waters', Dept. of Civil Engineering, King's College, Newcastle-upon-Tyne, n.d.
— *River Purification*, London, Edward Arnold, 1953.
'Pollution of the Humber', Ministry of Agriculture and Fisheries, *Fishery Investigations*, Series I, Vol. V, No. 4, 1951.
Report of Committee on Salmon and Freshwater Fisheries, H.M.S.O., London, May 1961. Cmnd. 1350.
River Boards Association, *Year Book 1963*, London.
Salmon and Trout Magazine, No. 149, January 1957, 'The London Conference, 1956'.
Southgate, B. A., 'Pollution of Surface Water Supplies', *Treatment of Sewage and Industrial Wastes*, Proceedings of the Society for Water Treatment and Examination, Vol. 9, Part I, 1960.
— 'Progress in the Control of River Pollution, 1948–65', Salmon and Trout Association, 1965.
Taverner, Eric and others, *Salmon Fishing*, London, Seeley Service, n.d.
Turing, R. H., Four Pollution Reports Prepared on Behalf of the British Field Sports Society, London, 1949.
— *River Pollution*, London, Edward Arnold, 1952.
Wye River Board, *Annual Report*, *1964*, Hereford.

Chapter 8

Brown, P. Hume, *A Short History of Scotland*, new edition by Henry W. Meikle, Edinburgh, Oliver and Boyd, 1961.
Calcott, Ian, *The Art of Salmon Fishing*, Edinburgh, Oliver and Boyd, 1963.
Calderwood, W. L., *The Life of the Salmon*, London, Arnold, 1907.
Campbell, R. H., *Scotland since 1707: The Rise of an Industrial Society*, 1965.

Day, J. Wentworth, *The Angler's Pocket Book*, London, Evans Bros., 1961.

Ellangowan, *Outdoor Sports in Scotland*, London, W. H. Allen and Co., 1890, 2nd edn.

Fisheries of Scotland, Report for 1964, Dept. of Agriculture and Fisheries, Edinburgh, H.M.S.O., 1965. Cmnd. 2644.

Franck, Richard, *Northern Memoirs*, London, Constable, 1821.

Gathorne-Hardy, A. E., *The Salmon*, London, Longmans, Green, 1898.

Glasgow, ed. J. Cunnison and J. B. S. Gilfillan, Glasgow, Collins, 1958.

'Grey Seals and Fisheries', Nature Conservancy, London, H.M.S.O., 1963.

Grimble, Augustus, *The Salmon Rivers of Scotland*, London, Kegan Paul, 1913.

Gwynn, Stephen, *River to River: A Fisherman's Pilgrimage*, London, Country Life, 1937.

Hamilton, Henry, *An Economic History of Scotland in the 18th Century*, Oxford, Clarendon Press, 1963.

Hansen, Paul M., 'Preliminary Report on Recaptures in Subarea 1 of Salmon Tagged in Rivers in America and Europe', Intern. Comm. for the Northwest Atlantic Fisheries, Research Document No. 69, 1965.

Lamond, Henry, *Loch Lomond: A Study in Angling Conditions*, Glasgow, Jackson, Wylie and Co., 1931.

Laurence, David W., 'The Recovery of a Scottish Salmon River', *Salmon and Trout Magazine*, September 1965.

Lucas, John, 'Salmon on a Shoe String', *Scottish Field*, August 1965.

Mackenzie, Hugh, *The City of Aberdeen*, Edinburgh, Oliver and Boyd, 1953.

Menzies, W. J. M., *The Salmon: Its Life Story*, Edinburgh, Blackwood, 1925.

— *The Stock of Salmon*, London, Edward Arnold, 1949.

Menzies, W. J. M. and Pentelow, F. T. K., 'Fisheries and the Development of Hydro-electric Power in Scotland', I.C.E.S., Salmon and Trout Committee, 1965.

North of Scotland Hydro-Electric Board, *Reports and Accounts*, 1962–1965, Edinburgh, H.M.S.O.

Parnell, Richard, *The Natural History of the Fishes of the Firth of Forth and Tributaries*, Edinburgh, Neill and Co., 1833.

Pryde, George S., *Scotland from 1703 to the Present Day*, London, Nelson, 1962.

Rae, Gordon, and Brown, Charles E., *A Geography of Scotland*, London, Bell and Sons, 1959.

Rae, L. B. and Shearer, W. M., 'Seal Damage to Salmon Fisheries', Dept. of Agriculture and Fisheries, Edinburgh, H.M.S.O., January 1965.

Russel, Alex., *The Salmon*, Edinburgh, Edmonston and Douglas, 1864.

Scottish Salmon and Trout Fisheries, First Report by the Committee appointed by the Secretary of State for Scotland, Edinburgh, H.M.S.O., July 1963, Cmnd. 2096.

Scrope, William, *Days and Nights of Salmon Fishing in the Tweed*, London, Arnold, 1898.

Stamp, L. Dudley, *A Regional Geography*, Part V, *Europe and the Mediterranean*, London, Longmans, 1961.

Stewart, Leslie, 'The Impact of the Water Resources Act 1963 on Fisheries', London, Salmon and Trout Association.

Stoddard, Thomas Tod, *Art of Angling*, 2nd ed., Edinburgh, Chambers, 1836.

Turing, H. D., *Pollution*, Report No. 4, Rivers in Scotland, British Field Sports Society, February 1949.

— *River Pollution*, London, Arnold, 1952.

Warner, Rev. Richard, *A Tour through the Northern Counties of England and the Border of Scotland*, London, G. and J. Robinson, 1802.

West Highland Survey, ed. F. Fraser Darling, Oxford University Press, 1956.

Wood, Ian, *My Way with Salmon*, London, Allen and Unwin, 1957.

Young, Archibald, *Salmon Fisheries*, London, Stanford, 1877.

Chapter 9

Demangeon, A., *The British Isles*, tr. E. D. Laborde, London, Heinemann, 1949, 2nd ed.

Department of Lands, *Report on the Sea and Inland Fisheries* for 1960, 1961, 1962, 1963, Dublin, Stationery Office.

Electricity Supply Board, *Annual Reports*, 1963–1965, Dublin.

Fisheries (Consolidation) Act, 1959, Dublin, Stationery Office, Department of Lands, Fisheries Division.

Foyle Fisheries Commission, *Annual Reports* for years ended 30 September 1961, 1962, 1963, 1964, Londonderry.

Freeman, T. W., *Pre-Famine Ireland*, Manchester University Press, 1957.

Gibbings, Robert, *Lovely is the Lee*, New York, Dutton, 1945.

Green, Alice Stopford, *The Making of Ireland and its Undoing, 1200–1600*, London, Macmillan, 1909.

Grimble, Augustus, *The Salmon Rivers of Ireland*, 2 vols., London, Kegan Paul, 1903.

Gwynn, Stephen, *From River to River*, London, Country Life, 1937.

Hansen, Paul M., 'Report on Recaptures in Greenland Waters of Salmon

Tagged in Rivers in America and Europe', I.C.E.S., 1965, Salmon and Trout Committee.

Harris, J. R., 'The Salmon Disease', *Trout and Salmon*, February, 1967.

Illustrations of Irish History and Topography, Mainly in the Seventeenth Century, ed. C. Litton Falkiner, London, Longmans, 1904.

Inland Fisheries, Bulletin Number 2, 1965, Dublin, Department of Agriculture and Fisheries.

Irish Fisheries Investigations, Dublin, Department of Agriculture and Fisheries, Series A, No. 1, 1965.

Landreth, Helen, *Dear Dark Head, an Intimate Story of Ireland*, New York, McGraw-Hill, 1936.

MacLysaght, Edward, *English Life in the Seventeenth Century*, Cork University Press, 2nd ed., 1950.

Maxwell, Constantia, *Country and Town in Ireland under the Four Georges*, Dundalk, Dundalgen Press, 1949.

McGrath, C. J., 'Dams as Barriers or Deterrents to the Migration of Fish', International Union for the Conservation of Nature, Technical Meeting, 1959, Vol. IV.

— 'Inland Fisheries and the Engineer', *Transactions of the Institution of Civil Engineers of Ireland*, Vol. 82, 1956.

Murphy, A. M. and Dodge, J. C. I., 'The Hydraulic Fish Lift at Leixlip', Bulletin, Institution of Civil Engineers of Ireland, April 1951.

O'Brien, George, *The Economic History of Ireland in the 17th Century*, Dublin, Maunsel, 1919.

Robertson, N. K., *Thrifty Salmon Fishing*, London, Herbert Jenkins, n.d.

Salmon and Sea Trout Fishing in Ireland, compiled by the Inland Fisheries Trust for the Irish Tourist Board, 1964 edition.

de Tocqueville, Alexis, *Journeys to England and Ireland*, ed. J. P. Mayer, New Haven, Yale University Press, 1958.

Went, Arthur E. J., *The Irish Salmon and Salmon Fisheries*, London, Edward Arnold, 1955.

— 'Irish Salmon—A Review of Investigations up to 1963', *Scientific Proceedings of the Royal Dublin Society*, Series 4, Vol. I, No. 15, 1964.

— 'The Pursuit of Salmon in Ireland', *Proceedings of the Royal Irish Academy*, Vol. 63, Section C, No. 6, 1964.

— 'The Irish Drift Net Fishery for Salmon', *Journal of the Department of Agriculture* (Ireland), Vol. III (1956).

— 'Fisheries of the River Liffey', *Journal of the Royal Society of Antiquaries of Ireland*, Vol. LXXXIII, Part II, 1953 and Vol. LXXXIV, Part I, 1954.

— 'Fisheries of the Munster Blackwater', *Journal of the Royal Society of Antiquaries of Ireland*, Vol. XC, Part II, 1960, and Vol. XCI, Part I, 1961.

Went, Arthur E. J., 'The Fisheries of the River Lee', *Journal of the Cork Historical and Archaeological Society*, Vol. LXV (1960).

— 'Irish Fishery Weirs—II. The Duncannon Weir', *Journal of the Royal Society of Antiquaries of Ireland*, Vol. LXXVIII, Part I, July 1948.

— 'Historical Notes on the Fisheries of the River Suir', *Journal of the Royal Society of Antiquaries of Ireland*, Vol. LXXXVI, Part II, 1956.

— 'Notes on the Irish Salmon Industry', *Journal of the Department of Agriculture*, Vol. III (1951).

— 'Inland Fisheries', in *A View of Ireland*, published for the British Association for the Advancement of Science, Dublin, 1957.

— 'A Short History of the Fisheries of the River Nore', *Journal of the Royal Society of Antiquaries of Ireland*, Vol. LXXXV, Part I, 1955.

— 'Notes upon some Fixed Engines for the Capture of Salmon, Used in Ireland since 1800', *Journal of the Royal Society of Antiquaries of Ireland*, Vol. XCIII, Part II, 1963.

— 'Historical Notes on Some of the Fisheries of Co. Louth', *County Louth Archaeological Journal.*

— 'Historical Notes on the Fisheries of Some Tidal Tributaries of the River Shannon', *North Munster Antiquarian Society Journal*, Vol. VIII, No. 3, 1960.

Young, Archibald, *Salmon Fisheries*, London, Edward Stanford, 1877.

Chapter 10

'Aroostook River Salmon Restoration and Fisheries Management', Maine Dept. Inland Fisheries, Fishery Research Bulletin, No. 4, 1956.

Bean, Tarleton H., *The Food and Game Fishes of New York*, New York Forest, Fish and Game Commission, 1903.

Bigelow, Henry B. and Shroeder, William C., *Fishes of the Gulf of Maine*, U.S. Dept. of the Interior, Fishery Bulletin 74, 1953.

Cheney, A. N., 'Salmon in the Hudson River', *Bulletin of the U.S. Fish Commission for 1886*, Washington Government Printing Office, 1887.

Coolidge, Philip T., *History of the Maine Woods*, Bangor, Maine, 1963.

Earle, Alice Morse, *Home Life in Colonial Days*, New York, Macmillan, 1899.

Farb, Peter, *The Land and Wildlife of North America*, Life Nature Library, New York, 1964.

Follett, Richard, ' "Salmo Salar" of the St. Lawrence River', *Transactions of the American Fisheries Society*, Vol. 62, 1932.

Frank Forester's Fish and Fishery of the United States and British Provinces of North America, London, Richard Bentley, 1849.

Goode, George Brown, *The Fisheries and Fishery Industries in the United States*, Vol. I, Washington, Government Printing Office, 1887.

Goodspeed, Charles E., *Angling in America*, Houghton Mifflin, Boston, 1939.

Hansen, Paul M., 'Report on Recaptures in Greenland Waters of Salmon Tagged in Rivers in America and Europe', I.C.E.S., Salmon and Trout Committee, 1965.

Huntsman, A. G., 'Why Did Ontario Salmon Disappear?' *Transactions of Royal Society of Canada*, May 1944, Series III, Vol. XXXVIII.

Huth, Hans, *Nature and the American*, Berkeley, Calif., University of California Press, 1957.

Jones, Gwyn, *The Norse Atlantic Saga*, London, Oxford University Press, 1964.

Kendall, William C., *New England Salmons*, Memoirs of Boston Society of Natural History, Vol. 9, No. 1, 1935.

'Maine Salmon Survey' conducted for the Boone and Crockett Club by Wildlife Management Institute, Washington, D.C., 1959.

McCrimmon, Hugh R., 'Reintroduction of Atlantic Salmon into Tributary Streams of Lake Ontario', *Transactions of the American Fisheries Society*, Vol. 78, 1948.

Meister, Alfred L., '*Salmo Salar*'s Future in Maine', *Atlantic Salmon Journal*, Fall, 1965.

— 'Atlantic Salmon Fishing: A Look Back', *Maine Fish and Game*, Spring, 1964.

Morison, Samuel Eliot, *The Oxford History of the American People*, New York, Oxford University Press, 1965.

Norris, Thad., *The American Angler's Guide*, Philadelphia, 1864.

Report of the Commissioner of Fish and Fisheries for 1872–1873, Washington, Government Printing Office, 1874:

Charles G. Atkins, 'Local History of Salmon and Salmon Fishing in New England Rivers'.

E. M. Stilwell, 'Obstructions in the Rivers of Maine'.

M. C. Edmunds, 'Obstructions in the Tributaries of Lake Champlain'.

Rostlund, Erhard, *Freshwater Fish and Fishing in Native North America*, University of California Publications in Geography, Vol. 9, 1952.

Scott, Genio, *Fishing in American Waters*, New York, American News Co., 1875.

Simpson, Elizabeth, *Mexico, Mother of Towns*, Buffalo, N.Y., S. W. Clement Co., 1949.

Thoreau, Henry D., *A Week on the Concord and Merrimack Rivers*, Boston, Houghton Mifflin, 1893.

Travels of Timothy Dwight in New England and New York, London, 1823.

Walden, Howard T., 2nd, *Familiar Freshwater Fishes of North America*, New York, Harper and Row, 1964.

Wells, Henry P., *The American Salmon Fisherman*, New York, Harper and Bros., 1886.

Wolf, P., 'Salmon Which Disappeared', *Atlantic Salmon Journal*, January 1963.

Chapter 11

Alderdice, D. F. and Worthington, M. E., 'Toxicity of a DDT Spray to Young Salmon', *Canadian Fish Culturist*, No. 24, February 1959.

Berg, Leo S., *Freshwater Fishes of the U.S.S.R. and Adjacent Countries*, Vol. I, 4th ed., Washington National Science Foundation, 1962.

Blair, A. A., 'Atlantic Salmon Tagged in East Coast Newfoundland Waters at Bonavista', *Journal Fisheries Research Board of Canada*, 13 (2), March 1965.

— 'Salmon Tagging at Francis Harbour Bight, Labrador', *Journal Fisheries Research Board Canada*, 14 (2), 1957.

Carter, Wilfred M., 'Quebec's Salmon Rivers', *Atlantic Salmon Journal*, Winter, 1964–65.

Chambers, E. T. D., *Game Fishes of Quebec*, Commission of Conservation, Ottawa, 1911.

Creighton, Donald, *A History of Canada*, Boston, Houghton Mifflin, 1958.

Easterbrook, W. T. and Aitken, Hugh G. J., *Canadian Economic History*, Toronto, Macmillan, 1963.

Elson, P. F. and Kerswill, C. J., 'Studies on Canadian Atlantic Salmon', *Transactions North American Wildlife Conference*, Wildlife Management Institute, 1955.

— 'Forest Spraying and Salmon Angling', *Atlantic Salmon Journal*, October 1964.

Grasberg, Eugene, *Economic Benefits of the Atlantic Salmon in the Province of New Brunswick*, Fredericton, N.B., 1956.

Greenaway, Bill, 'The Rape of a Salmon River', *Atlantic Salmon Journal*, August 1963.

Grenfell, Wilfred *et al.*, *Labrador: The Country and the People*, New York, Macmillan, 1909.

— *The Romance of Labrador*, New York, Macmillan, 1934.

Griswold, F. Gray, *The Life History of the Salmon*, New York, Dutton, Inc., 1931.

Hansen, Paul M., 'Report on Recaptures in Greenland Waters of Salmon Tagged in Rivers in America and Europe', I.C.E.S., Salmon and Trout Committee, 1965.

Huntsman, A. G., *The Maritime Salmon of Canada*, Biological Board of Canada, Bull. XXI, Ottawa, 1931.

Bibliography

Huntsman, A. G., *Return of Salmon from the Sea*, Biological Board of Canada, Bull. LI, Ottawa, 1936.

— 'Why Did Ontario Salmon Disappear?' *Royal Society of Canada Transactions*, May 1944, Series III, Vol. XXXVIII.

Innis, Harold A., *The Cod Fisheries*, New Haven, Yale University Press, 1940.

Keenleyside, Miles H., 'Effects of Spruce Budworm Control on Salmon and other Fishes in New Brunswick', *Canadian Fish Culturist*, No. 24, February 1959.

Kerswill, C. J., 'Regulation of the Atlantic Salmon Fisheries', *Canadian Fish Culturist*, No. 22, May 1958.

Lounsbury, *The British Fishery at Newfoundland, 1634–1763*, New Haven, Yale University Press, 1934.

MacEachern, N. E. J. and MacDonald, J. R., 'The Salmon Fishery in Nova Scotia', *Canadian Fish Culturist*, No. 31, October 1962.

Maheux, Georges, *Atlantic Salmon in the Economy of the Province of Quebec*, Quebec, Les Presses Universitaires Laval, 1956.

Marcotte, Alexandre, 'The Future of Quebec's Fifty Salmon Rivers', *Atlantic Salmon Journal*, June 1962.

Menzies, W. J. M., *A Report on the Present Position of the Atlantic Salmon Fisheries of Canada*, Atlantic Salmon Association, Montreal, October 1951.

Morse, Norman H., *Economic Value of the Atlantic Salmon Fishery in Nova Scotia*, Wolfville, N.S., Acadia Univ. Institute, September 1965.

Murray, A. R., 'Survival and Utilization of Atlantic Salmon of the Little Codroy River, Newfoundland', Progress Reports of Atlantic Coast Stations, Fisheries Research Board, Canada, No. 70, September 1958.

Newfoundland Department of Fisheries, *Report for the Year 1902*.

Norris, Thad., *The American Angler's Guide*, Philadelphia, 1864.

Northern Quebec and Labrador Journals and Correspondence, 1819–1835, ed. K. G. Davies, London, Hudson's Bay Record Society, 1963.

Rudd, Robert L., *Pesticides and the Living Landscape*, Madison, University of Wisconsin Press, 1964.

Sanderson, Ivan T., *The Continent We Live On*, New York, Random House, 1961.

Scott, Genio, *Fishing in American Waters*, New York, American News Co., 1875.

Stevens, Isaac B., 'The Pinware River of Newfoundland', *Atlantic Salmon Journal*, March 1964.

Thomas, L. O., *Natural Resources and Development, Province of New Brunswick*, Ottawa, 1930.

Wooding, F. H., *Canada's Atlantic Salmon*, Dept. of Fisheries, Ottawa, 1956.

Chapter 12

Greenland, published by the Royal Danish Ministry for Foreign Affairs, Copenhagen, n.d.

Nielsen, Jørgen, 'Contributions to the Biology of the Salmonidae in Greenland', I–IV, Copenhagen, Bianco Lunos Bogtrykkeri, 1961.

Parliamentary Debates (*Hansard*), House of Lords, Monday, July 5, 1965.

'Reports on Greenland Salmon Fisheries', American Embassy, Copenhagen, October 11, 1965, and January 10, 1966. Unclassified.

Stefansson, Vilhjalmur, *Greenland*, New York, Doubleday, 1947.

Williams, Geoffrey, *Changing Greenland*, New York, Library Publishers, 1954.

Chapter 13

Brooks, Joseph W., Jr., *A World of Fishing*, New York, D. Van Nostrand, 1964.

Fitter, Richard, *Iceland for the Naturalist*, Icelandic Air Lines.

Fridriksson, Arni, 'Salmon Investigations in the Years 1937–1939', Reykjavik, 1940.

Gjerset, Knut, *History of Iceland*, New York, Macmillan, 1925.

Gudjonsson, Thor, *Salmon and Trout Fishing in Iceland*, Icelandic Air Lines.

O'Dell, Andrew C., *The Scandinavian World*, London, Longmans, Green, 1957.

Saemundsson, Bjarni, *Fiskarnir* (*Pisces Islandiae*), Reykjavik, 1926.

Stefansson, Vilhjalmur, *Iceland*, New York, Doubleday, 1947.

Stewart, Major-General R. N., *Rivers of Iceland*, Reykjavik, Iceland Tourist Bureau, 1950.

— *Salmon and Trout: Their Habits and Haunts*, Edinburgh, W. and R. Chambers, 1963.

Thorlaksson, Gudmundur, *A Brief Geography of Iceland*, Icelandic Air Lines.

Conversion of pounds avoirdupois to kilograms

lb.	0	1	2	3	4	5	6	7	8	9
0	0·0	0·454	0·907	1·361	1·814	2·268	2·722	3·175	3·629	4·082
10	4·536	4·990	5·443	5·897	6·350	6·804	7·257	7·711	8·165	8·618
20	9·072	9·525	9·979	10·433	10·886	11·340	11·793	12·247	12·701	13·154
30	13·608	14·061	14·515	14·969	15·422	15·876	16·329	16·783	17·236	17·690
40	18·144	18·597	19·051	19·505	19·958	20·412	20·865	21·319	21·772	22·226
50	22·680	23·133	23·587	24·040	24·494	24·948	25·401	25·855	26·308	26·762
60	27·215	27·669	28·123	28·576	29·030	29·484	29·937	30·391	30·844	31·298
70	31·752	32·205	32·659	33·112	33·566	34·019	34·473	34·927	35·380	35·834
80	36·287	36·741	37·195	37·648	38·102	38·555	39·009	39·462	39·916	40·370
90	40·823	41·277	41·730	42·184	42·638	43·091	43·545	43·998	44·452	44·906
100	45·359	45·813	46·266	46·720	47·174	47·627	48·081	48·534	48·988	49·442
110	49·895	50·345	50·802	51·256	51·710	52·163	52·617	53·070	53·524	53·978
120	54·431	54·884	55·338	55·792	56·245	56·699	57·153	57·606	58·060	58·513
130	58·967	59·420	59·874	60·328	60·781	61·235	61·689	62·142	62·596	63·049
140	63·503	63·956	64·410	64·864	65·317	65·771	66·224	66·678	67·132	67·585
150	68·039	68·492	68·946	69·400	69·853	70·307	70·760	71·214	71·668	72·121

Conversion of kilograms to pounds avoirdupois

Kg.	0	1	2	3	4	5	6	7	8	9
0	0·0	2·205	4·409	6·614	8·818	11·023	13·228	15·432	17·637	19·842
10	22·046	24·251	26·455	28·660	30·865	33·069	35·274	37·479	39·683	41·888
20	44·092	46·297	48·502	50·706	52·911	55·116	57·320	59·525	61·729	63·934
30	66·139	68·343	70·548	72·752	74·957	77·162	79·366	81·571	83·776	85·980
40	88·185	90·389	92·594	94·799	97·003	99·208	101·413	103·617	105·822	108·026
50	110·231	112·436	114·640	116·845	119·050	121·254	123·459	125·663	127·868	130·073
60	132·277	134·482	136·687	138·891	141·096	143·300	145·505	147·710	149·914	152·119
70	154·324	156·528	158·733	160·937	163·142	165·347	167·551	169·756	171·961	174·165
80	176·370	178·574	180·779	182·984	185·188	187·393	189·598	191·802	194·007	196·211
90	198·416	200·621	202·825	205·030	207·235	209·439	211·644	213·848	216·053	218·258
100	220·462	222·667	224·871	227·076	229·281	231·485	233·690	235·895	238·099	240·304
110	242·508	244·713	246·918	249·122	251·327	253·532	255·736	257·941	260·145	262·350
120	264·555	266·759	268·964	271·169	273·373	275·578	277·782	279·987	282·192	284·396
130	286·601	288·806	291·010	293·215	295·419	297·624	299·829	302·033	304·238	306·443
140	308·647	310·852	313·056	315·261	317·466	319·670	321·875	324·079	326·284	328·489
150	330·693	332·898	335·103	337·307	339·512	341·716	343·921	346·126	348·330	350·535

Index

Index

Index